Basic Concepts
of Mathematics

Basic Concepts
of Mathematics

GEORGE C. BUSH

PHILLIP E. OBREANU

Queen's University, Kingston, Ontario

Holt, Rinehart and Winston

New York—Chicago—San Francisco—Toronto—London

Preface

The flood during the last few years of elementary college mathematics texts with titles containing the words "basic," "fundamental," "modern," or "abstract" is a clear indication of the shift in emphasis in the undergraduate program in mathematics. These books serve various purposes and require various backgrounds. Since there is such a variety of content despite the similarity of titles, it is in order to give some explanation of the content of the present work.

The material presented has been developed from a course that was originally designed for first-year students in mathematics or physics who had taken "college" algebra, two-dimensional analytic geometry, and plane trigonometry in their last year of high school and that was then broadened to include a much greater variety of students. The course has also been taught in the summer school to a class consisting largely of teachers who were seeking a higher professional classification.

The purpose of the book is to lay a suitable foundation for later mathematics courses. Accordingly we have dealt with the basic concepts of a number of branches of mathematics rather than developing any one of them in great detail. While the scope is broad, the language of sets, relations, and functions provides a unifying thread.

We have departed from the current trend to start such a study with the propositional calculus and truth tables. We have chosen instead to give an informal discussion of the logical arguments used in mathematics. We believe that this is more meaningful and more important to the student at this level.

Although we introduce the concept of the quotient set, we do not make extensive use of it since experience has shown that this is a difficult idea for the student to handle. For this reason we do not discuss quotient groups or quotient rings. We also choose to introduce real numbers as infinite decimals, a procedure that has intuitive advantages for the student, although it may seem cumbersome to the expert.

The concept of a vector is introduced geometrically. We chose this approach rather than using ordered triples because it has more intuitive appeal, especially in the application of vectors to problems in geometry, even while we recognized the disadvantages from an axiomatic point of view since we cannot assume that the student has a proper axiomatic basis even for two-dimensional geometry.

In Part Four, we have emphasized the conceptual rather than the computational aspects of the calculus. This emphasis is in keeping with the rest of the material; a mathematics major would receive a course concentrating on the calculus and would need only a brief indication of the set theoretical background of the subject. Thus, Part Four is not an attempt to duplicate a calculus text.

In several places, particularly in examples, we have depended rather heavily on the reader's intuition. We have chosen this rather than a more rigorous presentation when we felt that it would aid the student's understanding of the material.

The book could be covered entirely in three semesters, or it offers a variety of two semester courses. We have used the material of Parts One. Two, and Three since our students were taking a concurrent calculus course, The first seven chapters are prerequisite to the later chapters (although they could be abbreviated). After Chapter 7 it is possible to begin at Chapters 8, 10, or 12. Some of the results in Parts Three and Four are stated in the language of groups and rings, but these require only the definition of these structures.

A variety of exercises is included. In many of these the emphasis is on the proof and so no short answer can be given. Answers to about one half of the exercises that have short answers are given under the heading "Selected Answers to Exercises."

We are indebted to a number of people for their help in writing this book. Professors E. Hewitt and B. W. Jones read the manuscript in detail and offered valuable criticisms. To them we owe our special thanks. Our colleagues who have taught from earlier versions of the work and our students who have studied from it have pointed out various places where improvements could be made; Mrs. E. M. Wight has patiently typed the various versions of the manuscript. Finally, we express our gratitude to our wives who have for many months tolerated our preoccupation with the preparation of this material.

Kingston, Canada
February, 1965

G.C.B.
P.E.O.

Contents

PART TWO: Number Systems and Algebraic Systems

Basic Concepts
of Mathematics

Introduction
The Language of
Mathematics

As an introduction to our study of mathematics, we shall attempt an elementary analysis of the processes of mathematical reasoning. We shall do this by considering examples from high school mathematics and especially from geometry. Our study is far from complete. The whole problem of analyzing mathematical arguments belongs to the realm of mathematical (or symbolic) logic.

There are two different approaches in teaching mathematics. One, the traditional approach that is usually taught in high schools, attempts to start from definitions of the basic objects studied. The other, more modern, approach accepts certain objects as undefined elements, makes no attempt to define them, and uses them as the basis of a body of theorems and definitions. The second approach is more or less the one used in this book.

These two approaches are well illustrated in the study of Euclidean geometry. Euclid himself, followed by the authors of many high school texts up to the present, defined point and line as follows:

"A point is that which has no parts."   (1)

"A line is length without breadth."   (2)

The student who encounters these definitions might well ask for definitions of part, length, and breadth. Such a quest for ultimate definition is endless.

The purpose of such definitions is to help the student to an intuitive grasp of the subject. He is encouraged to draw from the real objects around him some abstract concept. This is a valid and useful approach. Intuition is required to understand mathematical facts and to discover new ones.

The more modern approach to mathematics starts from undefined terms and thus avoids two pitfalls. The first is the endless regression from one definition to another, the second is the so-called vicious circle in which two words are defined in terms of each other. It uses intuition and abstrac-

3

tion from real objects only as motivation and excludes them from the formal statement of theorems. In keeping with this modern approach, we shall make no attempt to define such entities as line, point, or set. We consider such terms *primitive concepts* and give certain statements called *axioms* or *postulates* that express relations among these concepts. One example of such an axion, chosen from Euclidean geometry, is

> "There is exactly one line which passes through two distinct points." (3)

There has been until quite recently a traditional distinction between axioms and postulates. According to this tradition, which grew out of the teaching of Euclid's *Elements*, an axiom was a "self-evident truth" without which thought would be impossible. A postulate was not considered self-evident but was believed to be a fundamental truth about the subject matter being studied, a truth that was beyond question.

By the nineteenth century leading mathematicians abandoned this distinction. They realized that the essence of mathematics is not the pursuit of an absolute truth; in fact the idea of truth based on overwhelming evidence is quite foreign to mathematics. In the new view a mathematical theory is concerned only with proofs of the validity of statements of the form: "If P holds, then Q holds." In constructing such a system we start from a few propositions which we call axioms, but we are no longer concerned about whether these axioms express some truth that is beyond all possible doubt. We shall sometimes state that "A is true," but we interpret this to mean only that A comes at the end of a chain of arguments of the type "If P holds, then Q holds," a chain that begins with one or more of our axioms. This view frees us from the need for a priori evidence for the truth of the axioms. It is no longer claimed that axioms represent the behavior of the physical world.

The present view of axioms has come about as the result of study in various branches of mathematics. The concern about the *parallel postulate* of Euclid (the fifth postulate in the *Elements*) is typical of these studies. In the form given by the Scottish mathematician J. Playfair (1748–1819), this postulate is:

> "Through a given point outside a given line one and only one line can be drawn parallel to the given line." (4)

To the followers of Euclid this postulate seemed less "self-evident" than the others he had stated, and they attempted to find a proof for it. This search for a proof ended when the Russian mathematician N. I. Lobatschefski (1793–1856) constructed a geometry in which the parallel postulate does not hold. This new geometry is one of the class of geometries referred to as *non-Euclidean*. Other geometries of this class have been constructed and provide a model of the physical world that for some purposes is more convenient than the geometry of Euclid.

We shall not spend more time on the history of the axiomatic method, which now permeates all of mathematics. The more familiar we become with the method, the less we feel the need for explicit definitions of the primitive concepts and the more we realize that all we need to know about them is contained in the system of axioms. This book does not completely adopt the axiomatic approach, but Chapters 8 and 9 come very close to it.

We introduce new objects in any mathematical system by means of statements that we call *definitions*. In these definitions we use words that we assume to be already known. Examples of such definitions are the following from geometry.

"The line A is said to be parallel to the line B if A and B have no common point." (5)

"By a segment ab we mean the set of all points of the line passing through a and b and which are between a and b." (6)

The next example is drawn from arithmetic.

"An integer p is called a prime number if its only positive divisors are 1 and p." (7)

If we look at definition (6), we see that it contains undefined words such as "point," "line," and "between." If we are prepared to assume a knowledge of these words as our undefined concepts which have been introduced in the axioms, then (6) is a satisfactory definition of a segment.

Similarly, (7) is a satisfactory definition of a prime number only if we understand the meaning of "integer," "positive," and "divisor."

A definition may be thought of as a description of how to construct a certain new object from known objects and relations. A definition may also be considered to describe a certain object and to assign a name to it. It is natural to ask whether the construction can be carried out or whether an object with the specified properties exists.

We have already seen that, in a certain system where the parallel postulate does not hold, the construction required for definition (5) could not be carried out, because in this system there are no parallel lines.

We shall not pursue the nature of the definition further but shall emphasize that it is possible to give a definition of an object that does not exist. We must be careful to avoid such a mistake. Failure to recognize this point can lead to the development of a theory that is vacuous, in that there are no objects to which it applies.

Perhaps the chief characteristic of mathematics is the fact that, after a list of axioms and definitions have been accepted, there follows a body of other statements called *theorems*. In order for a statement to be a theorem, a *proof* is required. Our confidence in the statement rests upon the proof, not upon the fact that the statement has been discovered to be true whenever it has been tested. Our confidence in the fact that $x^2 + y^2 = z^2$, where x, y, z are the lengths of sides of a right triangle, rests upon the proof of the theorem of Pythagoras, not upon the number of right triangles for which we have measured the sides. In the absence of a proof we may have strong evidence for our belief in a certain statement but we cannot state that it is true. Many theorems have been discovered by observing their truth in special cases, but until a proof is provided they remain only statements that may be true or false. It is the proof alone that elevates them to the rank of theorems.

No one can give an easy means by which to discover or prove theorems. Euclid said long ago to the King of Egypt that there is no royal road to geometry. This is still true, not only of geometry but of all branches of mathematics. Anyone who wants to discover and prove theorems must have as his tools intuition, imagination, and mathematical skill. He must also be prepared for hard work. The same could be said for an athlete—there is no easy way to success. In athletics there are certain rules of good form that are essential. These do not make a good athlete, but their absence can be ruinous. Similarly, in mathematics good form and a sound grasp of fundamentals do not guarantee success, but their absence may cause failure.

With these things in mind we shall examine some of the essential principles of logic that a mathematician or a student of mathematics must have at his command.

I.1 Implication

Many mathematical statements that we shall encounter are of the form "If . . . , then . . . ," where each set of dots represents a statement. For example:

If a and b are two distinct points, *then* there is exactly one line passing through a and b.

If a triangle has two equal angles, *then* it also has two equal sides.

If a prime number p divides the product of two integers, *then* p divides at least one of the integers.

In each case we have started with two statements, say A and B, and have combined them into a new statement: "If A then B." This new statement is called an *implication*. We sometimes say "A implies B" and use the notation $A \Rightarrow B$. This same relationship can be expressed as "A is a sufficient condition for B" or "B is a necessary condition for A." For example:

It is sufficient that a triangle have two equal angles in order that the triangle have two equal sides.

It is necessary that a triangle have two equal sides if the triangle has two equal angles.

The distinction between necessary and sufficient conditions must be clearly understood. We give a nonmathematical example to emphasize that this is a logical, not a mathematical concept.

Since every horse is a quadruped but not every quadruped is a horse, we say that being a quadruped is a necessary condition for being a horse, but it is not a sufficient condition.

We shall use the words "proposition" or "statement" without attempting to define them. For our purposes these are primitive or undefined terms. We expect that the reader will have an adequate intuitive grasp of this concept.

Many statements we shall consider have the form ". . . has the property . . . ," where the first blank is to be filled with the name of some object and the second with a description of some property. We shall also encounter statements such as "Every . . . has the property . . . " and "There exists a . . . which has the property . . . ." We shall not enter into a discussion of truth and falsehood but merely point out that, as the student already knows, these propositions may be either true or false depending on what is written in the blanks.

The composition of two propositions, which we call implication $A \Rightarrow B$, is a new proposition that states that, whenever A is true, then B is also true. Therefore if we know that the proposition $A \Rightarrow B$ is true and the proposition A is true, then the proposition B is also true. Such reasoning is perhaps the most important type in mathematical proofs. It is referred to as the *rule of detachment* or *modus ponendo ponens*. This phrase can be translated approximately as "the rule of establishing by establishing," an appropriate name because, by establishing A, we establish B, provided of course that we have established "If A, then B."

The implication $A \Rightarrow B$ is true if, whenever A is true, then B is also true. It does not put any restriction on the truth or falsehood of B in the case when A is false. We sometimes express this by saying that a false statement implies any statement. Students frequently have difficulty at this point. We shall give two examples in an attempt to clarify the idea. The first is nonmathematical, the second mathematical.

Suppose that a person says, "If an event A takes place, then I shall perform the act B." If A does not take place we have no basis for charging the person with breaking a promise whether or not he performs B.

Consider the implication, "If 5 divides 27 then this polygon is regular." This is a true statement because in every case for which 5 divides 27 (which is never) the polygon is regular. There is no case in which A is true and therefore there is nothing to check about the truth or falsehood of B when A is true.

I.2 Converse of an implication

Consider an implication $A \Rightarrow B$. By the *converse* of this we mean the proposition $B \Rightarrow A$. For example, we have the implication: "If $\triangle DEF$ is equilateral, then $\triangle DEF$ is equiangular."

The converse of this is, "If $\triangle DEF$ is equiangular, then $\triangle DEF$ is equilateral."

In this example the implication and the converse are both true. In such a case we say that the two statements are *equivalent*. We also express this as "A if and only if B," "A is a necessary and sufficient condition for B," "B is a necessary and sufficient condition for A," "$A \Leftrightarrow B$," or "A iff B."

The converse of a true implication is not always true. For example, the implication "If an animal is a horse, then it is a quadruped" (which we usually express as "every horse is a quadruped") is true, but the converse, "If an animal is a quadruped then it is a horse," is false.

In a definition we frequently write "if" to mean "if and only if." For example, "A triangle is called equilateral if all its sides are equal." Such departure from our careful terminology is very common and causes no confusion if we remember that a definition by its very nature must state that two propositions are equivalent.

I.3 Conjunction

Let A, B be two propositions. By their *conjunction* we mean the statement "A and B." The conjunction "A and B" is a true proposition if both A and B are true propositions.

For example, let A be the proposition: "Triangle T is isosceles" and let B be: "Triangle T is right-angled." Then "A and B" is true if the triangle T is *both* isosceles (A) *and* right-angled (B).

Most mathematical proofs consist of a chain of implications or repeated applications of the rule of detachment. Such proofs depend on the transitive property of the implication, that is,

$$\text{If } A \Rightarrow B \text{ and } B \Rightarrow C, \text{ then } A \Rightarrow C.$$

We shall not prove this, but the following argument should make the result plausible. We want C to be true whenever A is true. From $A \Rightarrow B$ we see that, if A is true, then B is true. From $B \Rightarrow C$ we see that, if B is true, then C is true. Thus, if A is true, then C is true, that is, $A \Rightarrow C$.

I.4 Disjunction

Let A, B be two propositions. We use the expression "A or B" to mean "either A or B or both," or "at least one of A or B." This is not the only use of the word "or" in English. It corresponds to the Latin word "vel." We might call this the *inclusive* use of "or," that is, "one or the other or both." By the *exclusive* use we would mean "one or the other, but not both." In this book we mean the inclusive use unless the contrary is specified.

We call the new proposition "*A* or *B*" the *disjunction* of *A* and *B*. The disjunction "*A* or *B*" is true if *at least* one of the propositions *A* or *B* is true.

I.5 Negation

By the negation of the proposition *A* we mean a proposition, sometimes written "not *A*," that is false if *A* is true and true if *A* is false.

We shall use examples to clarify how the negation of the different types of propositions that we encounter is formed.

We have mentioned that we are concerned with propositions of the forms "Every . . . has the property . . . ," "There exists a . . . such that . . . ," and "If . . . , then . . . ."

What is the negation of the statement "Every lock has a key"? Many people would answer "No lock has a key." This is not the correct answer. By our definition of negation it must be a statement that is false if the original is true and true if the original is false. Consider the situation in which every lock except one has a key. Both statements are false in this case.

The negation of this statement is "Not every lock has a key." This statement is equivalent to "There is at least one lock that does not have a key."

This point is frequently misunderstood. We give several further examples to clarify it.

Consider the statement: "For each student there is a group of courses sufficient for graduation." The negation is, "There is a student for whom there is no group of courses sufficient for his graduation."

Consider the statement: "For each line and each point outside the line, there is exactly one line through the point and parallel to the given line." The negation is: "There is a line and a point outside it such that there is not exactly one line through the point and parallel to the given line." This means that we can find a point and a line for which either there is no parallel or there is more than one parallel.

These examples suggest the following rules:

1. To negate "Every *A* is such that *B*," we write "There is an *A* for which not *B*."

2. To negate "There is an *A* for which *B*," we write "For all *A*, not *B*" or "There is no *A* for which *B*."

Consider the conjunction, "Mary is sick and John is away." The negation of this is, "Either Mary is not sick or John is not away." This is an example of the rule that states that the negation of the conjunction "*A* and *B*" is "not *A* or not *B*."

Consider the disjunction: "Bill is wealthy or Tom is dishonest." The negation is, "Bill is not wealthy and Tom is not dishonest." This illustrates the rule that the negation of the disjunction "*A* or *B*" is "not *A* and not *B*."

What do we mean by the negation of $A \Rightarrow B$? We want a statement that will be true when $A \Rightarrow B$ is false. But if $A \Rightarrow B$ is false, then A is true and B is false. Consider the statement: "A and not B" or "A and the negation of B." It is clear that this is true when $A \Rightarrow B$ is false and it is false when $A \Rightarrow B$ is true. Thus we have the rule

To negate "$A \Rightarrow B$," write "A and not B."

For example, the negation of "If 9 is not a prime number, then it is the product of prime numbers" is "The number 9 is not a prime number and it is not the product of primes."

I.6 Principle of contradiction

Suppose that in a certain system of propositions, where propositions may be either true or false, the proposition A and the negation of A are both true. Such a system is called *contradictory*.

One problem of modern mathematics is to prove that each system of propositions with which we deal, and in particular each system of axioms, is free from contradiction. This is often a difficult problem and goes far beyond the scope of this book. We simply point out that one way in which it can be solved is by constructing an object in whose existence we have reason to believe and by showing that it satisfies all the conditions in our axioms, that is, that all the propositions in the system of axioms are true for this object. Such an object is called a *model* or a *realization* of the axiomatic system. Since this realization is found in another mathematical system whose consistency we trust, we see that all we can say is that the axiom system we are studying is consistent if the system in which our realization is found is consistent. What we have obtained is simply a relative proof of noncontradiction.

I.7 Law of the excluded middle

The *law of the excluded middle* or *tertium non datur* rests upon our confidence that, if statement A is meaningful in our system, then either A is true or the negation of A is true. It denies that there is some middle ground between true and false. Some mathematicians (of the school known as "intuitionists") object to this assertion and refuse to use this law. Without it, many widely accepted proofs are invalid. We shall use this law freely. Hence we have many theorems that those who reject the law do not have. This illustrates the fact that the system of mathematics which we develop depends *both upon the axioms from which we start and also upon the system of logic which we use*.

The law of the excluded middle is essential to the method known as *indirect proof* or *reductio ad absurdum.* Suppose we wish to prove a proposition T. If we cannot find a direct proof we may consider the consequences of the supposition that T is false. If one of these consequences is the negation of a known result in our system, then the supposition that T is false cannot be correct if our system is consistent. In view of the law of the excluded middle this means that T is true.

We shall clarify this type of proof by giving as an example an indirect proof of a famous theorem of Euclid.

THEOREM

There are infinitely many prime numbers.

Proof

Let us *assume* that the theorem is false.

We suppose that there is only a finite number of primes, which we denote by $p_1, p_2, \cdots, p_n$. Then any other number can be written as a product of these primes. Consider $a = p_1 p_2 \cdots p_n + 1$. This is larger than any prime and hence is a product of primes. Suppose p_j is one of these primes. Then p_j should divide a, but if we attempt this division we have a remainder of 1. This is a contradiction. Therefore our *assumption* is false and hence the theorem must be true. •

We shall consider some of these topics in logic again in the context of set theory.

EXERCISES

Put statements I.1 to I.9 in the form: "If A, then B."

I.1. We shall go on a picnic if the weather is fair.

I.2. Unless you study you cannot succeed.

I.3. Double your money refunded if you are not satisfied.

I.4. Once bitten, twice shy.

I.5. We shall fight for our freedom if necessary.

I.6. We shall fight for our freedom only if it is necessary.

I.7. A rectangle all of whose sides are equal is a square.

I.8. No even integer other than 2 is a prime number.

I.9. An isosceles triangle has two equal angles.

In I.10 to I.13, accept as true the implication $A \Rightarrow B$. What can you conclude if the statement C is also true?

I.10. If a student is not diligent he cannot pass. C: John is a diligent student.

I.11. If train travel is cheaper than driving I go by train. C: I drove my own car on the trip west.

I.12. If a person is not careful about his diet he cannot expect good health. *C*: Mary is careless about her diet.

I.13. If the weather is bad I drive to work. *C*: I drove to work this morning.

Give the converse of statements I.14 through I.18.

I.14. Whenever we have a picnic it rains.

I.15. Any friend of Jane's is a friend of mine.

I.16. All mice are afraid of cats.

I.17. Students who do well in a subject enjoy the subject.

I.18. All members of the House of Commons are elected to their position.

Give the negation of propositions I.19 to I.29.

I.19. If Tom works hard, then he gets good marks.

I.20. Whenever John and Joe meet, there is a fight.

I.21. There are some people who find genuine satisfaction in their wealth.

I.22. Both John and Mary were present.

I.23. Some students find this course difficult.

I.24. If I need money, then I shall write.

I.25. Bill is a Canadian and John is an American.

I.26. Either he is a good student or he is lucky on exams.

I.27. For every man there is exactly one woman to whom he can be happily married.

I.28. One or the other of us is wrong.

I.29. There is one and only one way to solve the problem.

In I.30 to I.32, tell whether the statements $A \Leftrightarrow B$, $A \Rightarrow B$, or $B \Rightarrow A$ are true.

I.30. A: X is a rectangle with equal sides.
B: X is a rhombus with a right angle.

I.31. A: E is an ellipse.
B: E is represented by a second degree equation in x and y.

I.32. A: P is a parabola.
B: P is represented by the equation $y = ax^2 + bx + c$.

I.33. The implication (not B) $\Rightarrow$ (not A) is called the *contrapositive of* $A \Rightarrow B$. Show that an implication and its contrapositive are equivalent.

Give the contrapositive of statements I.34 to I.36.

I.34. All citizens are loyal to their country.

I.35. If you attend all the meetings you will be given a prize.

I.36. If you do your work now you will not be rushed later.

I.37. If an implication is true, which of the following must also be true?
    (a) the contrapositive,
    (b) the converse,
    (c) the negation.

Part One

THE THEORY OF SETS

1
The Algebra of Sets

1.1 Introduction

It is very difficult to say at what stage in a person's development he begins to abstract a common characteristic of different objects he has observed. This process of abstraction produces what we call a "concept." It is a characteristic of human thought to grasp a concept that is associated with a particular collection of individual objects. This mental process of forming concepts is the underlying idea of set theory, and we might say that the pre-history of set theory goes back to the beginning of these thought processes.

The true history of set theory, that is, the recognition of its importance and its first formulation, dates back to G. Cantor (1845–1918), who developed the main part of this discipline. His work on set theory started about 1870 as a by-product of his study of the part of analysis that is concerned with trigonometric series. It quickly became an independent discipline and was recognized by mathematicians as a means of studying the foundations of all known mathematics. The theory of sets brought clarity, precision, and simplicity to many difficult mathematical theories.

By the end of the nineteenth century the importance of the new theory was recognized, but then came the difficulties with the so-called "paradoxes" (or contradictions) of set theory. The beginning of the twentieth century saw a concentrated effort by many mathematicians to eliminate these paradoxes and establish a firm set-theoretical basis for mathematics. This "paradox crisis" did not destroy the study of set theory but motivated a search for a satisfactory organization of set theory that would provide the basis for the presentation of all mathematical theories.

To eliminate these paradoxes, an *axiomatic approach* to set theory was developed. Such a study is beyond the scope of an elementary course. We shall use the "naïve" or "informal" approach to the subject. We shall assume that the reader has an intuitive idea of what a set is and shall make no attempt to define such primitive terms as *set, element,* and *is a member of.* Rather, we shall assume that these are the simplest objects from which we can construct a mathematical theory. We shall give examples to suggest what we mean by these terms.

Our position with respect to basic definitions is similar to the situation in geometry. Euclid tried to define primitive concepts such as point and line, but these definitions were not valid, since they used undefined terms that did not appear later in the theory. Cantor attempted to define a set approximately as: "A set is any collection of definite, distinguishable objects of our intuition or of our mind which we conceive as a whole." Such a definition is open to the same criticism as those of Euclid and cannot be accepted in a mathematical theory. Although we do not accept this as a definition, it is useful to suggest to the reader what we mean by a set. This definition thus plays a role in the theory of sets similar to that of Euclid's definitions in geometry.

1.2   Description of and notation for a set

We shall assume that the thought process which lumps various objects together under a common heading, characteristic, or concept gives us an adequate intuitive knowledge of what is meant by a set. We refer to the objects lumped together in this way as elements (or individuals), and we say that the *elements belong to* or *are members of the set.* We can illustrate this idea by a more physical process. Suppose we select some objects (elements, individuals) and put them together. This collection of objects is a new object, analogous to our idea of a set.

For example, consider all the persons in the classroom. We say that they form the set of persons in the room. We can completely describe this set by a list of names of the persons in the room. From this list we could easily obtain an answer to the question: "Is (the individual whose name is) x an element of the set of all persons in the classroom?"

We give several additional examples of sets:

The set of natural numbers 1,2,3, $\cdots$
The set of all nonnegative integers divisible by 3: 0, 3, 6, 9, $\cdots$
The set of all the books in a particular library at a particular time
The set of all words listed in *The Oxford English Dictionary* which are spelled with fewer than ten letters

We shall generally denote elements by small letters a, b, $\cdots$, x, y, z and sets by capital letters. We shall use the notation $a \in A$ to mean, "a is an element of A" or, equivalently, "a belongs to A." The symbol $\in$ stands for the *fundamental relation of set theory,* the *membership relation.* This is a relation between an element and a set. We write $a \notin A$ to mean "the element a does not belong to A."

Since it is possible to think of a set as a single object, it is also possible to think of a set whose elements are themselves sets. Instead of speaking about a set of sets we prefer the phrase *class of sets* (for reasons of linguistic style). The idea of a set whose elements are themselves sets is encountered many times in mathematics.

One way to describe a set is to list all its members. This is not possible for all sets. For a set with an infinite number of elements it is clearly impossible; for a set with a large but finite number of elements it is impracticable and, in some cases, impossible.

Certain conventions of notation are useful in describing sets. As an example of a set that is given by listing all its members, consider the set of the first four positive integers. This set is denoted by

$$A = \{1,2,3,4\}.$$

Sometimes, instead of listing all the elements of the set, we modify this notation by writing a row of three dots to indicate omitted elements. This is permissible only where no confusion of meaning can arise. For example,

$$A = \{1,2, \cdots ,100\}$$

means that A is the set of all the positive integers from 1 to 100. Similarly,

$$B = \{1,2, \cdots ,m\}$$

is the set of all positive integers from 1 to some integer m that is not specified otherwise. By

$$N = \{1,2,3,4,5, \cdots \},$$

we mean that N is the set of all positive integers. We shall *reserve the letter N for the set of all positive integers.*

There are some cases in which we cannot conveniently write out all the elements, nor can we introduce a row of dots without ambiguity about the elements they represent. In such a situation we shall consider that a set is defined by giving a property or condition which is satisfied by all elements of the set and by no other objects. As an example, consider all the people in your class with blond hair. This defines a set. Of course this set could also have been defined by listing all its elements. But now consider the set of all North Americans with blond hair who have lived or will live during the twentieth century. At present we cannot give a list of the elements of this set. In the year 2000 such a list would be possible if adequate records were available, but it would be of prohibitive length. We allow such a set, even though we cannot list its elements. We can denote it:

$B = \{x|x$ is a blond North American alive at
some time during the twentieth century$\}$.

We read this: "B is the set of all x such that x is a blond North American alive at some time during the twentieth century."

When we allow sets defined in terms of a property of its elements, we may have sets with an infinite number of elements. We may also have sets for which it is very difficult to determine whether a certain object is an element of the set. As one example, consider the set of prime numbers. The calculations involved in determining whether a number is a prime may be very lengthy. In the following example, the test for membership is even more difficult.

Let A be the set of algebraic numbers, that is,

$A = \{x | x$ is a root of a polynomial equation with integer coefficients$\}$.

The question of whether $\pi \in A$ or $\pi \notin A$ remained unsolved until 1882, when the German mathematician, Lindemann, proved that $\pi \notin A$.

Our belief in the law of the excluded middle[1] (see Section I.7) leads us to believe that the question of membership has an answer.

1.3 Equality of sets

We have seen that in some cases a set can be described either by giving a list of its elements or by giving a property satisfied by all its elements and by no other objects. It can also happen that a set can be described by two different conditions. In view of this fact we must define what we mean by equal sets.

Sets A and B are called equal if each $a \in A$ is an element of B and each $b \in B$ is an element of A.

As usual we write $A = B$ to indicate equality of sets. We write $A \neq B$ if the sets A and B are not equal.

Consider the sets

$$A = \{a | a \text{ is an equilateral triangle}\},$$
$$B = \{b | b \text{ is a triangle with all angles equal}\}.$$

We can prove in geometry that every $a \in A$ is a member of B and every $b \in B$ is a member of A. That is, $A = B$.

We should recognize that stating that two sets are equal is the same thing as stating that their defining conditions are equivalent. The proof of such a statement may require a great deal of skill and ingenuity. For example, consider the sets

$A = \{1,2\}$,
$B = \{n | n$ is a positive integer and $x^n + y^n = z^n$ for some integers x, y, $z\}$.

It is not known whether sets A and B are equal.[2]

---

[1] This law was formulated by the ancient philosophers as an extrapolation of their experience with certain finite sets. A further study of this subject belongs to the foundations of mathematics or logic.

[2] The proposition that $A = B$ is known as "Fermat's last theorem." P. Fermat, a famous French mathematician of the seventeenth century, asserted that for an integer $n > 2$, there are no positive integers x, y, z such that $x^n + y^n = z^n$. Three centuries later, despite much work by many excellent mathematicians, this statement has been neither proved nor disproved.

1.4   The inclusion relation

Consider two sets A, B such that for each $a \in A$ it is also true that $a \in B$. In this case we say that A is *included* in or *contained* in B and that A is a *subset* of B. We denote this property by the notation $A \subset B$. If the relation $A \subset B$ does not hold, we write $A \not\subset B$.

It is clear that $A = B$ is equivalent to $A \subset B$ and $B \subset A$. If $A \subset B$ and $A \neq B$, we say that A is a *proper subset* of B.

There is a close analogy between the inclusion relation ($\subset$) of set theory and the inequality relation ($\leq$) for numbers. We first observe that $A \subset A$ for all sets A, and also that $x \leq x$ for all numbers x. This property is called *reflexivity*.

If for three sets A, B, C we have $A \subset B$ and $B \subset C$, then $A \subset C$. Analogously, for three numbers x, y, z, if $x \leq y$ and $y \leq z$, then $x \leq z$. This property is called *transitivity*. We saw this use of the word "transitive" in connection with implication in Section I.3.

Finally, if $A \subset B$ and $B \subset A$, then $A = B$. Analogously, if $x \leq y$ and $y \leq x$, then $x = y$. This property is called *antisymmetry*.

The analogy is not complete, however. For numbers we have the *trichotomy* property; that is, if $x \not\leq y$ (x is not less than or equal to y), then $y \leq x$. This is not true for sets. We can easily construct sets for which $A \not\subset B$ and $B \not\subset A$. For example, consider the sets A, B, C, D represented by the interiors of the circles of Figure 1.1. Then $A \not\subset B$, $B \not\subset A$ and $C \not\subset D$, $D \not\subset C$.

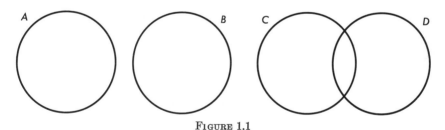

FIGURE 1.1

These two new relations, equality ($=$) and inclusion ($\subset$), have been defined in terms of the membership relation ($\in$). The membership relation is not reflexive, because $A \in A$ need not be true. Neither is it transitive, because $a \in A$ and $A \in B$ do not imply $a \in B$.

The essential ideas of inclusion between sets are extensively used in high school mathematics. Consider the problem of proving that "P is a sufficient condition for Q" or "Q is a necessary condition for P." This could be stated: "If x has the property P (or satisfies the condition P), then it has the property Q." To put this into set-theoretical terms let

$$A = \{a | a \text{ has the property } P\},$$
$$B = \{b | b \text{ has the property } Q\}.$$

Then our statement is equivalent to $A \subset B$. Thus we·have been using the notions of set theory throughout our study of mathematics, perhaps without realizing that we have been doing so.

Let A be a given set. Let P be some property such that the question, "Does x satisfy P?", is meaningful for all $x \in A$. Then we may associate with the property P the set of all elements of A for which P is satisfied, that is, the set

$$B = \{x | x \in A, x \text{ satisfies } P\}.$$

Let us consider the set of all elements of A that do not satisfy P, that is, the set of all elements of A that are not elements of B. We denote this set by $\complement_A B$.

$$\complement_A B = \{x | x \in A, x \notin B\}.$$

$\complement_A B$ is called *the complement of B relative to A*. For example, let A be the set of all triangles and let B be the set of all equilateral triangles. Then $\complement_A B$ is the set of all triangles that are not equilateral.

If A is the set of all the elements we are considering in a certain problem, we refer to $\complement_A B$ simply as the complement of B and denote it by $\complement B$. Other common notations for complements are $A - B$, $A \backslash B$, $\tilde{B}$, B'.

It may happen that there are no elements of A that satisfy property P. In this case we say that P defines the empty set, denoted by $\varnothing$, that is, the set containing no elements. For example, if Fermat's conjecture is true (see footnote 2), then

$$\varnothing = \{n | n \in N, n > 2, \text{ and there exist integers such that } x^n + y^n = z^n\}.$$

The empty set $\varnothing$ is a subset of all sets A. To see this, we recall that $B \subset A$ if and only if the implication "If $x \in B$, then $x \in A$" is true. In the present case, $B = \varnothing$, and hence the proposition $x \in \varnothing$ is always false. Thus the implication is true and $\varnothing \subset A$. (When a condition is satisfied by all elements of a certain type simply because there are no elements of this type, we say that the condition is satisfied *vacuously*.)

1.5   The power set

Consider the set $A = \{0,1,2\}$. From this we can form various subsets. We can also form the set consisting of all the subsets of A. We call this the power set of A and denote it by $\wp(A)$. Thus

$$\wp(A) = \{\varnothing, \{0\}, \{1\}, \{0,1\}, \{0,2\}, \{1,2\}, \{0,1,2\}\}.$$

We can define the power set of any set in this way as the set of all subsets of the given set. We note that we can deal with the power set of an infinite set.

We must distinguish between 1, an element of A, and $\{1\}$, the subset consisting of the single element 1. We have the relation $1 \in \{1\}$, but we cannot write $1 = \{1\}$ or $1 \subset \{1\}$. We must also distinguish between the empty set $\varnothing$ (that is, the set with no elements) and $\{0\}$ (the set consisting of the single element 0). Furthermore, we must distinguish between $\varnothing$, the empty set, and $\{\varnothing\}$, the class of sets consisting of only the empty set.

If A is a finite set with n elements, then $\mathcal{P}(A)$ is a finite set with 2^n elements. We shall not prove this formula here. It can be verified for the example considered above. The power set is one way of constructing a new set from a known set. Since $2^n > n$ for $n = 0,1,2, \cdots$, the power set of a finite set is larger (that is, it has more elements) than the original set.

1.6   Operations on sets

Before considering the operations that can be performed on sets, it is convenient to introduce a diagrammatic representation for sets. We do this as an aid to our intuition; it is not a necessary part of set theory. This representation may suggest properties of sets, but the diagrams never constitute a proof. The proof that $A = B$ is always of the form: For each $a \in A$ we prove $a \in B$, and for each $b \in B$ we prove $b \in A$. The diagram may motivate the abstract proof but cannot replace it.

We represent sets by regions of the plane. The relative positions of these regions represent various properties of the sets. We refer to this representation as a *Venn diagram*.[3]

If $A \subset B$, we represent this in a Venn diagram by drawing the region representing A inside the region representing B (see Figure 1.2).

[3] They are named for a British logician of the nineteenth century, although Euler used the device earlier.

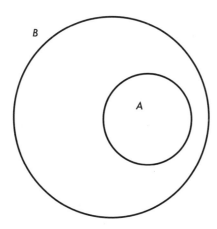

FIGURE 1.2

By the *union* of sets A and B we mean the set of all elements that belong to A or to B or to both. This union is written $A \cup B$ (read "A union B" or "A cup B"). It is represented by the shaded region in Figure 1.3. It is easy

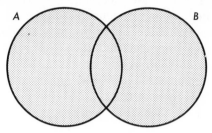

FIGURE 1.3

to see how the idea of union can be extended to any finite class of sets, for example, $A_1 \cup A_2 \cup \cdots \cup A_n$. The same idea can be extended to an infinite class. Let $\mathcal{C}$ be any class of sets. Let A be any set of $\mathcal{C}$. We define the union of all the sets in the class $\mathcal{C}$ as

$$\bigcup_{A \in \mathcal{C}} A = \{x | x \in A \text{ for at least one } A \in \mathcal{C}\}.$$

As an example consider the infinite class of sets

$$\mathcal{C} = \{A_j | j \in N\},$$

where

$$A_j = \{x | x = i/j; i, j \in N; 0 < i < j\}.$$

Then

$$\bigcup_{A_j \in \mathcal{C}} A_j = \{x | x \text{ a rational number}, 0 < x < 1\}.$$

By the *intersection* of sets A and B, we mean the set of all elements belonging to both A and B. We write this $A \cap B$ (read "A intersection B" or "A cap B"). It is represented by the shaded area of Figure 1.4.

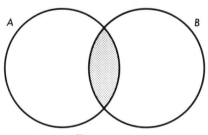

FIGURE 1.4

Let $\mathcal{C}$ be any class of sets and let A represent any one of these sets. Then, by the intersection of all the sets of the class $\mathcal{C}$, we mean

$$\bigcap_{A \in \mathcal{C}} A = \{x | x \in A \text{ for all } A \in \mathcal{C}\}.$$

Consider the example

$$\mathcal{C} = \{B_n | n \in N\},$$

where

$$B_n = \{b | b \text{ is a point } (x,y) \text{ such that } (x - n)^2 + y^2 = n^2\}.$$

That is, B_n is the set of points on the circle with center $(n,0)$ and radius n. Each circle passes through $(0,0)$. For $k \neq n$, B_k and B_n have no other points in common. Consequently,

$$\bigcap_{B_n \in \mathcal{C}} B_n = \{(0,0)\}.$$

We say that the sets A and B are *disjoint* if $A \cap B = \varnothing$, that is, if they have no points in common (see Figure 1.5). Let $\mathcal{C}$ be a class of sets such that,

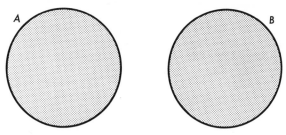

FIGURE 1.5

for any $A \in \mathcal{C}$, $B \in \mathcal{C}$, with $A \neq B$, $A \cap B = \varnothing$. Then the sets of $\mathcal{C}$ are said to be *mutually* or *pairwise disjoint*.

We have already referred (Section 1.4) to the complement of a subset. If $B \subset A$, then

$$\mathbf{C}_A B = \{x | x \in A, x \notin B\}.$$

This is represented by the shaded region of Figure 1.6.

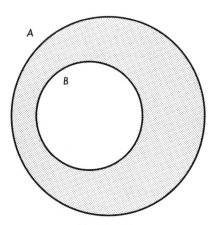

FIGURE 1.6

A similar idea can be applied even when $B \not\subset A$. We define the *difference* between two sets as

$$A - B = \{x | x \in A, x \notin B\}.$$

This is represented by the shaded area of Figure 1.7.

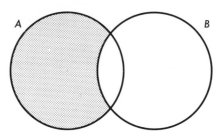

FIGURE 1.7

To make these notions clearer, consider the following examples. Complements are taken relative to the set $E = \{1,2,3, \cdots ,10\}$.

$$\{1,2,3\} \cap \{2,3,5\} = \{2,3\}$$
$$\{1,2\} \cup \{2,3\} = \{1,2,3\}$$
$$\complement \{1,3,5,7,9\} = \{2,4,6,8,10\}$$
$$\{2,4,8\} \cap \{3,5,7\} = \varnothing$$
$$\{1,3,5\} \cap \{3,6,9\} = \{3\}$$
$$\{2,5,6,8\} - \{6,8,10\} = \{2,5\}$$
$$\{1,3,5\} - \{2,4,6\} = \{1,3,5\}.$$

1.7   The algebra of sets

A problem may involve a combination of the various set operations we have defined. It would be possible to analyze each such problem in terms of a Venn diagram and then give an abstract proof of the result. It is simpler, however, to develop certain laws, similar to the laws of arithmetic, relating these operations. These laws are grouped together in several classes to assist our memory.

Laws of Identities

$$A \cup \varnothing = A$$
$$A \cap \varnothing = \varnothing.$$

Commutative Laws

$$A \cup B = B \cup A$$
$$A \cap B = B \cap A.$$

Associative Laws

$$(A \cup B) \cup C = A \cup (B \cup C)$$
$$(A \cap B) \cap C = A \cap (B \cap C).$$

Distributive Laws

$$A \cap (B \cup C) = (A \cap B) \cup (A \cap C)$$
$$A \cup (B \cap C) = (A \cup B) \cap (A \cup C).$$

Laws of Differences

$$A - \varnothing = A$$
$$\varnothing - A = \varnothing$$
$$A - A = \varnothing.$$

If we replace $\cap$ by multiplication and $\cup$ by addition, we see that these laws, except for the second distributive law and the second law of differences, are similar to the laws of arithmetic. There are also rules of set operations that have no analogues in arithmetic.

Laws of Inclusion

$$A \subset A \cup B, \quad B \subset A \cup B$$
$$A \cap B \subset A, \quad A \cap B \subset B.$$

Laws of Idempotents

$$A \cup A = A$$
$$A \cap A = A.$$

Laws of Complements

If $A \subset B$ and we take complements with respect to B, then

$$A \cup \complement A = B,$$
$$A \cap \complement A = \varnothing,$$
$$\complement (\complement A) = A.$$

De Morgan's Laws

If $A \subset C$, $B \subset C$ and we take complements with respect to C, then

$$\complement (A \cup B) = \complement A \cap \complement B,$$
$$\complement (A \cap B) = \complement A \cup \complement B.$$

Despite the analogy between union and addition, we cannot conclude from $A - B = C$ that $A = B \cup C$. To see this we need only consider the example $A = \{1,3,5,7\}$, $B = \{2,3,4,5\}$. Then $C = A - B = \{1,7\}$ and $B \cup C = \{1,2,3,4,5,7\} \neq A$.

The various laws we have stated should all be accompanied by the statement "for all sets A, B, C, etc." We are not asserting that there are some sets for which the statement is true, but that it is true for all sets.

All the laws can be illustrated by Venn diagrams, but we emphasize that such illustrations are not proofs. We do not accept an argument based on a Venn diagram as a proof that a statement is true for all sets, because the Venn diagram represents only one geometric example and does not exhaust all possible sets. A Venn diagram may, however, provide a proof of a statement of the form: "There are sets for which the following statement is true," since the proof requires only that we exhibit sets having the required property. Therefore a Venn diagram may also disprove a statement concerning all sets, since to disprove such a statement it is sufficient to find a set for which the statement is false.

For example, suppose it is claimed that, for all sets A and B, the sets $A \cup B$ and $A \cap B$ are equal. To prove this claim false it is sufficient to show that there exist sets A and B such that $A \cup B \neq A \cap B$. Such sets are shown in Figure 1.7.

We shall analyze the Venn diagram and give abstract proofs for two of the laws. Other proofs will be called for in the exercises.

EXAMPLE 1.1

A Distributive Law

A Venn diagram representing the distributive law $A \cup (B \cap C) = (A \cup B) \cap (A \cup C)$ is given in Figure 1.8.

A is represented by regions 1,2,4, and 5.
B is represented by regions 2,3,5, and 6.

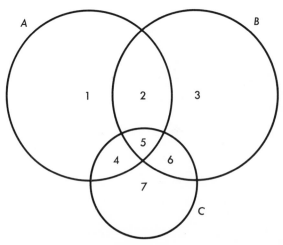

FIGURE 1.8

C is represented by regions 4,5,6, and 7.

$B \cap C$ is represented by regions 5 and 6.

$A \cup (B \cap C)$ is represented by regions 1,2,4,5, and 6.

$A \cup B$ is represented by regions 1,2,3,4,5, and 6.

$A \cup C$ is represented by regions 1,2,4,5,6, and 7.

$(A \cup B) \cap (A \cup C)$ is represented by regions 1,2,4,5, and 6.

We thus see that $A \cup (B \cap C)$ and $(A \cup B) \cap (A \cup C)$ are represented by the same regions, and hence this distributive law is plausible.

To prove the identity $A \cup (B \cap C) = (A \cup B) \cap (A \cup C)$ we must show (1) that every element of $A \cup (B \cap C)$ is an element of $(A \cup B) \cap (A \cup C)$ and (2) that every element of $(A \cup B) \cap (A \cup C)$ is an element of $A \cup (B \cap C)$.

(1) Suppose $x \in A \cup (B \cap C)$. Then either $x \in A$ or $x \in (B \cap C)$. If $x \in A$, then $x \in A \cup B$ and $x \in A \cup C$; hence $x \in (A \cup B) \cap (A \cup C)$. If $x \in B \cap C$, then $x \in B$ and $x \in C$. Therefore $x \in A \cup B$ and $x \in A \cup C$; hence $x \in (A \cup B) \cap (A \cup C)$. Thus in every case $x \in (A \cup B) \cap (A \cup C)$; hence $A \cup (B \cap C) \subset (A \cup B) \cap (A \cup C)$.

(2) Suppose $y \in (A \cup B) \cap (A \cup C)$. Then $y \in A \cup B$ and $y \in A \cup C$. If $y \in A$, then $y \in A \cup (B \cap C)$. If $y \notin A$, then $y \in B$ and $y \in C$; hence $y \in B \cap C$ and again $y \in A \cup (B \cap C)$. Thus in every case $y \in A \cup (B \cap C)$; hence $(A \cup B) \cap (A \cup C) \subset A \cup (B \cap C)$.

These two inclusions together prove that $A \cup (B \cap C) = (A \cup B) \cap (A \cup C)$.

EXAMPLE 1.2

One of De Morgan's Laws

A Venn diagram illustrating De Morgan's first law is given in Figure 1.9.

A is represented by regions 2 and 3.

B is represented by regions 3 and 4.

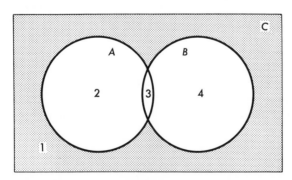

FIGURE 1.9

$A \cup B$ is represented by regions 2, 3, and 4.

$\mathbf{C}\,(A \cup B)$ is represented by region 1.

$\mathbf{C}\,A$ is represented by regions 1 and 4.

$\mathbf{C}\,B$ is represented by regions 1 and 2.

$\mathbf{C}\,A \cap \mathbf{C}\,B$ is represented by region 1.

This shows that $\mathbf{C}\,(A \cup B)$ and $\mathbf{C}\,A \cap \mathbf{C}\,B$ are represented by the same region and hence De Morgan's law, $\mathbf{C}\,(A \cup B) = \mathbf{C}\,A \cap \mathbf{C}\,B$, is plausible. The proof of the law follows.

Let x be any element of $\mathbf{C}\,(A \cup B)$. Then $x \in C$ and $x \notin A \cup B$; that is, $x \notin A$ and $x \notin B$, or equivalently, $x \in \mathbf{C}\,A$ and $x \in \mathbf{C}\,B$. Hence $x \in \mathbf{C}\,A \cap \mathbf{C}\,B$, and therefore $\mathbf{C}\,(A \cup B) \subset \mathbf{C}\,A \cap \mathbf{C}\,B$.

Let x be any element of $\mathbf{C}\,A \cap \mathbf{C}\,B$. Then $x \in \mathbf{C}\,A$ and $x \in \mathbf{C}\,B$. Therefore $x \in C$, $x \notin A$, and $x \notin B$; that is, $x \in C$ and $x \notin (A \cup B)$, or equivalently, $x \in \mathbf{C}\,(A \cup B)$, and hence $\mathbf{C}\,A \cap \mathbf{C}\,B \subset \mathbf{C}\,(A \cup B)$. These two inclusions show that $\mathbf{C}\,(A \cup B) = \mathbf{C}\,A \cap \mathbf{C}\,B$.

Theorem 1.1 shows the relations among the inclusion relation, union, and intersection.

THEOREM 1.1

The following statements are equivalent:

1. $A \subset B$.
2. $A \cup B = B$.
3. $A \cap B = A$.

Proof

A standard method of proof for such a theorem is to prove that $(1) \Rightarrow (2)$, $(2) \Rightarrow (3)$, and $(3) \Rightarrow (1)$. It is then clear that, if any one of the statements is true, then the other two are also true.[4]

$(1) \Rightarrow (2)$

We assume $A \subset B$; that is, for each $x \in A$ we also have $x \in B$. Let y be any element of $A \cup B$. Then $y \in A$ or $y \in B$. But $y \in A \Rightarrow y \in B$, and hence $A \cup B \subset B$. We know that it is always true that $B \subset A \cup B$. Therefore $A \cup B = B$.

---

[4] To see that this proves the equivalence of the statements we consider (1) and (2). We have a direct proof that $(1) \Rightarrow (2)$. Also $(2) \Rightarrow (3)$ and $(3) \Rightarrow (1)$. Therefore by the transitivity of implication we have $(2) \Rightarrow (1)$. Thus $(1) \Leftrightarrow (2)$.

$(2) \Rightarrow (3)$

We assume that $A \cup B = B$. Then $A \cap B = A \cap (A \cup B) = (A \cap A) \cup (A \cap B) = A \cup (A \cap B)$. Therefore $A \subset A \cap B$. Since it is always true that $A \cap B \subset A$, we have $A \cap B = A$.

$(3) \Rightarrow (1)$

We assume that $A \cap B = A$. Let x be any element of A. Then $x \in A \cap B$, and hence $x \in B$. Therefore $A \subset B$.

This completes the proof. •

The following examples will illustrate the use of the laws listed at the beginning of this section. Let C be a set containing both A and B. All complements are with respect to C. Then we can write

$$(A - B) \cap (B - A) = \left(A \cap \complement B\right) \cap \left(B \cap \complement A\right)$$
$$= \left(A \cap \complement A\right) \cap \left(B \cap \complement B\right)$$
$$= \varnothing \cap \varnothing = \varnothing.$$

Also

$$(A - B) \cup (B - A) = \left(A \cap \complement B\right) \cup \left(B \cap \complement A\right)$$
$$= \left\{\left(A \cap \complement B\right) \cup B\right\} \cap \left\{\left(A \cap \complement B\right) \cup \complement A\right\}$$
$$= (A \cup B) \cap \left(\complement B \cup B\right) \cap \left(A \cup \complement A\right)$$
$$\cap \left(\complement B \cup \complement A\right)$$
$$= (A \cup B) \cap C \cap C \cap \complement (A \cap B)$$
$$= (A \cup B) \cap \complement (A \cap B)$$
$$= (A \cup B) - (A \cap B).$$

1.8 Everyday language and set theory

There is a close connection between the algebra of sets and the logic that we met in the Introduction. This connection sometimes enables us to use our knowledge of set theory to analyze logical statements.

Consider the statements A: "x is an equilateral triangle" and B: "x is a triangle with at least two sides equal." Then $A \Rightarrow B$. Let T_A be the set of all triangles for which A is true, that is, the set of all equilateral triangles. Let T_B be the set of all triangles for which B is true, that is, the set of all triangles with at least two sides equal. Then $T_A \subset T_B$. This example illustrates the close connection between $\Rightarrow$ and $\subset$.

The statement, "Bill is tall and handsome," can be represented as follows. Let T be the set of all tall persons, H be the set of all handsome persons, and b represent Bill. Then $b \in T \cap H$.

To negate this statement we want $b \notin T \cap H$, that is, $b \in \complement (T \cap H)$, where the complement is taken with respect to the set of all people. By de Morgan's law we have $b \in \complement\, T \cup \complement\, H$, and from this we see that the negation of "Bill is tall and handsome" is "Bill is either not tall or not handsome." Since we use "or" in the inclusive sense, this includes the possibility that Bill is neither tall nor handsome.

The statement, "He is either an army officer or a civil servant," can be represented as $x \in A \cup C$, where x is the person under discussion, A is the set of army officers, and C is the set of civil servants. Since "or" is used in the inclusive sense, we need not consider whether $A \cap C = \varnothing$. For the negation we have $x \notin A \cup C$, that is, $x \in \complement (A \cup C) = \complement\, A \cap \complement\, C$. In words this is, "He is neither an army officer nor a civil servant."

We sometimes encounter a statement such as "He is tall and handsome or wealthy." Such a statement is ambiguous. If T is the set of tall people, H the set of handsome people, W the set of wealthy people, and x the individual under consideration, then one interpretation is represented by $x \in (T \cap H) \cup W$, the other by $x \in T \cap (H \cup W)$. Although it is not the usual linguistic use of parentheses, they are sometimes borrowed from set theory to clarify meaning: "He is (tall and handsome) or wealthy" and "He is tall and (handsome or wealthy)." Linguistic style would require the rewriting of the sentences as "Either he is tall and handsome, or he is wealthy" and "Either he is tall or he is handsome and wealthy."

The reader is warned against a mechanical translation of "and" into $\cap$ and "or" into $\cup$. The English language admits many ambiguities; the meaning and not the words must be translated. This should become clear from the following examples.

"Peter is slow but dependable" can be represented as $p \in S \cap D$, where p represents Peter, S is the set of those persons who are slow, and D is the set of those persons who are dependable.

"Britons and Americans are English-speaking people" in set-theoretical form is $B \cup A \subset E$, where B is the set of all Britons, A the set of all Americans, and E the set of persons who speak English.

"There are some wealthy Germans" or "Some Germans are wealthy" in set-theoretical language is $G \cap W \neq \varnothing$, where G is the set of Germans and W is the set of wealthy persons.

"All farmers are poor" or simply "Farmers are poor" is represented by $F \subset P$, where F is the set of all farmers and P is the set of poor persons.

"Some farmers are not poor" or "Not all farmers are poor" can be translated as $F \cap \complement\, P \neq \varnothing$.

1.9 Cartesian products

The student is already familiar from analytic geometry with the idea of denoting any point P in the plane by an *ordered pair* of numbers (x,y), where

x is called the *first coordinate (abscissa)* and y is called the *second coordinate (ordinate)* of the point. In this way we construct a new set, which we call the (Euclidean) plane, consisting of the set of all ordered pairs (x,y), where x and y are real numbers representing distances measured along two axes (see Figure 1.10). We know that if $x \neq y$, then (x,y) and (y,x) are two different points.

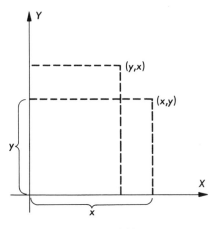

FIGURE 1.10

In many of our examples we shall use the set of real numbers, for which we reserve the symbol R. We cannot give a satisfactory definition of a real number at this point (see Chapter 6) and shall count on the reader's intuition to make the examples clear. We shall refer to the Euclidean plane as $R \times R$. This construction of the plane from two straight lines appears to be due to the French mathematician and philosopher R. Descartes (1596–1650). By this device he reduced the study of plane figures to the study of two copies of a straight line, that is, to the study of a problem stated in terms of real numbers.

The special case studied by Descartes is generalized in set theory to associate with each ordered pair[5] of sets (A,B) a new set denoted by $A \times B$. This new set is called the Cartesian product of A and B in honor of Descartes, whose Latinized name was Cartesius. The Cartesian product of sets A and B is the set of all ordered pairs (a,b), where $a \in A$, $b \in B$; that is,

$$A \times B = \{p \mid p = (a,b),\ a \in A,\ b \in B\}.$$

---

[5] Our approach is open to the charge that, by using "ordered" pairs here and introducing order later, we are guilty of unsound and circular reasoning. In defense we point out that we are giving a very informal presentation of set theory and that the reader's intuitive understanding of ordered pair should suffice to prevent confusion. The logical difficulty can be avoided by a more rigorous presentation.

We point out that if $A \neq B$, then $A \times B \neq B \times A$. As an example, consider

$$A = \{1,2,3\} \qquad B = \{5,7\}$$
$$A \times B = \{(1,5),(1,7),(2,5),(2,7),(3,5),(3,7)\}$$
$$B \times A = \{(5,1),(7,1),(5,2),(7,2),(5,3),(7,3)\}.$$

These sets are not equal; the ordered pair $(1,5)$, for example, is not in $B \times A$. The ordered pairs (a,b) and (a',b') are equal if and only if $a = a'$ and $b = b'$.

If $(a,b) \in A \times B$, we call a the *first coordinate* (or *first projection*) of (a,b) and b the *second coordinate* (or *second projection*) of (a,b).

If the Cartesian product has two equal factors, that is, has the form $A \times A$, then the subset consisting of all elements with equal coordinates is called the *diagonal* and is denoted by Δ_A; that is,

$$\Delta_A = \{p | p = (a,a),\ a \in A\}.$$

EXAMPLE 1.3

For $A = \{x | 0 \leq x \leq 1,\ x \text{ a real number}\}$, the Cartesian product $A \times A$ has the form shown in Figure 1.11a. The diagonal Δ_A is shown in Figure 1.11b.

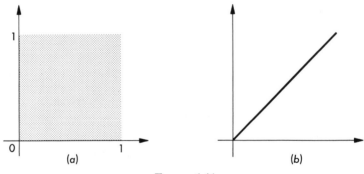

(a) $\qquad\qquad\qquad\qquad\qquad$ (b)

FIGURE 1.11

If C and D are subsets of R, then $C \times D$ is a subset of $R \times R$ and in many cases can be drawn as a subset of the plane. Even when C and D are abstract sets, it is frequently helpful to represent them as segments of R, in which case $C \times D$ is a rectangle in the plane. This representation has many of the same advantages as a Venn diagram, but it also has the same limitations and can at best illustrate proofs. The use of such a diagram will be seen in Example 1.4.

EXAMPLE 1.4

Prove that, for all sets A and B,

$$\complement_{A \times A}[(A - B) \times (A - B)] = [(A \cap B) \times A] \cup [A \times (A \cap B)].$$

We represent A and B by overlapping segments of R as in Figure 1.12. The area shaded with dots represents $(A - B) \times (A - B)$, and the area shaded with lines represents the complement with respect to $A \times A$. It will

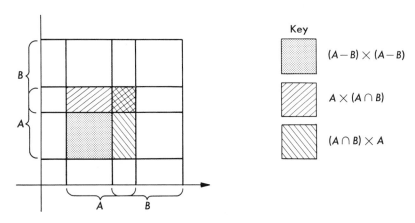

FIGURE 1.12

also be seen from the key to the diagram that the area shaded with lines represents $[(A \cap B) \times A] \cup [A \times (A \cap B)]$. This diagram is not a proof, but it suggests the statement of the theorem and also the method of proof. We now *prove* the above identity.

Pick $(x,y) \in \complement_{A \times A} [(A - B) \times (A - B)]$. Then $(x,y) \in A \times A$ but $(x,y) \notin (A - B) \times (A - B)$. Therefore $x \in A$, $y \in A$, and either $x \notin A - B$ or $y \notin A - B$. If $x \notin A - B$, then $x \in A \cap B$ since $x \in A$. Therefore $(x,y) \in (A \cap B) \times A$. Similarly if $y \notin A - B$, we see that $(x,y) \in A \times (A \cap B)$. In either case $(x,y) \in [(A \cap B) \times A] \cup [A \times (A \cap B)]$. Thus we have shown that $\complement_{A \times A} [(A - B) \times (A - B)] \subset [(A \cap B) \times A] \cup [A \times (A \cap B)]$.

Now pick $(x,y) \in [(A \cap B) \times A] \cup [A \times (A \cap B)]$. Then either $(x,y) \in (A \cap B) \times A$ or $(x,y) \in A \times (A \cap B)$. In the first case, we have $x \in A \cap B$ and $y \in A$. Thus $(x,y) \in A \times A$ but $(x,y) \notin (A - B) \times (A - B)$. The second case is similar. Therefore $(x,y) \in \complement_{A \times A} [(A - B) \times (A - B)]$ and we have shown that $[(A \cap B) \times A] \cup [A \times (A \cap B)] \subset \complement_{A \times A} [(A - B) \times (A - B)]$. These two inclusions prove the asserted equality.

We shall also have occasion to refer to the Cartesian product of more than two sets. For sets A_1, A_2, A_3 the Cartesian product, denoted by $A_1 \times A_2 \times A_3$, is the set of all ordered triples (a_{1j}, a_{2j}, a_{3j}) with $a_{ij} \in A_i$. Similarly, $A_1 \times A_2 \times \cdots \times A_n$ is the set of n-tuples $(a_{1j}, a_{2j}, \cdots, a_{nj})$.

The study of subsets of Cartesian products is of great importance in set theory, and in fact throughout mathematics. It is the subject of the next chapter.

EXERCISES

1.1. Sketch in the xy plane the following sets:

$$A = \{p|p = (x,y), \ x^2 + y^2 < 1 \text{ and } x^2 < y^2\}$$
$$B = \{p|p = (x,y), \ x + y > 1 \text{ or } x - y < 1\}$$
$$C = \{p|p = (x,y), \ x^2 - y \neq 0 \text{ and } x^2 + y^2 = 1\}$$
$$D = \{p|p = (x,y), \ (x^2 + y^2)^2 < 1\}$$

1.2. Indicate by shading the region of the xy plane representing the following sets:

$$A = \{p|p = (x,y) \text{ and if } x^2 + y^2 = 0, \text{ then } \sin x = \tan y\}$$
$$B = \{p|p = (x,y) \text{ and if } x = y, \text{ then } \sin x = \tan y\}$$

1.3. Prove that if $A = \{x|x \text{ is a real number and } \sin^2 x + \cos^2 x = 2\}$ and $B = \{x|x \text{ is a real number and } |x| > 2\}$, then $A \subset B$.

1.4. What is the relation between the following sets A and B?

$$A = \{x|x \text{ is a real number, } x^2 + x + 1 > 0\}.$$
$$B = \{x|x \text{ is a real number, } (x^2 + x + 1)^2 > 0\}.$$

1.5. Which of the following relations holds?

$$\{1,2,3\} \in \{\{1,2\},3,4\}.$$
$$\{1,2,3\} \subset \{\{1,2\},\{3,4\},5\}.$$
$$\{1,2\} \subset \{\{1,2\},1,2\}.$$

Give reasons for each answer.

1.6. Give an example of two sets A and B such that $A \in B$ and $A \subset B$.

1.7. Let $E = \{a,b,c\}$, where a, b, c are three different objects. Find $\mathcal{P}(E)$.

1.8. Let $A = \{\{1,2\},1,2\}$. Find $\mathcal{P}(A)$.

1.9. If $E \subset F$, prove that $\mathcal{P}(E) \subset \mathcal{P}(F)$.

1.10. Are the following true for all sets A and B?

(a) $\mathcal{P}(A \cap B) = \mathcal{P}(A) \cap \mathcal{P}(B)$.
(b) $\mathcal{P}(A \cup B) = \mathcal{P}(A) \cup \mathcal{P}(B)$.

Give reasons for your answers.

1.11. Let A be the set of all four-sided polygons, B the set of all equiangular polygons, C the set of all equilateral polygons, and D the set of all polygons with at least one right angle. What polygons are included in the sets: $A \cap B$, $A \cap C$, $B \cap C$, $A \cap C \cap D$?

1.12. Let $X = \{\{1,2,3\},3,4,5\}$, $Y = \{1,2,3,5,7\}$, and $Z = \{1,2,3\}$. List the elements in the following sets: $X \cap Y$, $X \cup Z$, $X - Z$.

1.13. Let E be a set and A, B, C, D subsets of E. Let $\complement$ denote the complement with respect to E. Express $\complement((A \cup B) \cap (C \cup D))$ and $\complement((A \cap B) \cup (C \cap D))$ in terms of $\complement A$, $\complement B$, $\complement C$, and $\complement D$.

1.14. If E is a set, A, B, C are subsets of E, and $\complement$ denotes the complement with respect to E, which of the following statements are true? Give reasons for your answers.

(a) $\complement\,(A \cup B \cup C) = \complement\,A \cap \complement\,B \cap \complement\,C.$

(b) $A \cup B \cup C = E.$

(c) $(A \cap B \cap C) - E = \varnothing.$

1.15. Let $A = \{\{1,2\},\{1,2,3\},2,3\}$ and $B = \{\{1,2\},1,2,3,\{2,3\}\}$. Which of the following statements are true and which are false? Give reasons for your answers.

(a) $\{2\} \subset A \cap B.$

(b) $\{1,2\} \subset A.$

(c) $\{1,2\} \subset B.$

(d) $\{1,2\} \in A.$

(e) $\{1,2\} \in B.$

(f) $\{1,2,3\} \subset A \cup B.$

(g) $\{1,2,3\} \in A \cup B.$

(h) $\{\{1,2\},2\} = A \cap B.$

(i) $A - B$ has only one element.

(j) $\mathcal{P}(A) \cap B = \varnothing.$

1.16. Let $A = \{1,2\}$, $B = \{3,4\}$, $C = \{1,2,\{3,4\}\}$. Which of the following are true? Give reasons for your answers.

(a) $A \subset C.$

(b) $B \subset C.$

(c) $A \cup B \subset C.$

(d) $B \in C.$

1.17. Which of the following assertions can be proved by using a Venn diagram? Give reasons for your answers.

(a) $A \cap B \subset A$ for all sets A, B.

(b) There exist sets A, B, C such that $(A \cup B) \cap C \neq A \cup (B \cap C).$

(c) $A \subset A \cup B$ for all sets A, B.

1.18. Let $A = \{1,2,3\}$, $B = \{2,3,4\}$, $C = \{3,4,5\}$. List the elements in the following sets, and represent (a), (b), (c), and (d) by Venn diagrams:

(a) $A \cap B$, (b) $\complement_{A \cup C}\, B$, (c) $B - (A \cap C)$,

(d) $A \cup B \cup C$, (e) $\mathcal{P}(A)$, (f) $\mathcal{P}(B) \cap \mathcal{P}(C).$

1.19. Prove the following laws:

(a) $A \cap (B \cup C) = (A \cap B) \cup (A \cap C).$

(b) $\complement\,A \cap A = \varnothing.$

(c) $\complement_B\, A \cup A = B.$

(d) $\complement\,(\complement\,A) = A.$

(e) $\complement\,(A \cap B) = (\complement\,A) \cup (\complement\,B).$

1.20. Draw and analyze the Venn diagram for each part of Exercise 1.19.

1.21. Given that $A_1 \subset A_2 \subset A_3$ and $B_3 \subset B_2 \subset B_1$, prove that $(A_1 \cap B_1) \cup (A_2 \cap B_2) \cup (A_3 \cap B_3) = A_3 \cap B_1 \cap (A_1 \cup B_2) \cap (A_2 \cup B_3).$

1.22. Given that $(E_1 \cup E_2 \cup E_3 \cup \cdots \cup E_n \cup \cdots) \cap (E_2 \cup \cdots \cup E_n \cup \ldots) \cap \cdots = E$ and $(E_1 \cap E_2 \cap \cdots \cap E_n \cap \cdots) \cup (E_2 \cap \cdots \cap E_n \cap \cdots) \cup \cdots = F$, prove that $E_1 \cap E_2 \cap \cdots \cap E_n \cap \cdots \subset F \subset E \subset E_1 \cup E_2 \cup \cdots \cup E_n \cup \cdots.$

1.23. Let $E_{2n} = \,]-\dfrac{1}{2n},\ \dfrac{2n-1}{2n}\,[\,\cup\,\{2\}$, $E_{2n-1} = \,]-\dfrac{1}{2n-1},\ \dfrac{2n-2}{2n-1}\,[\,\cup\,\{3\}$, where $]a,b[= \{x \mid x \in R,\ a < x < b\}$. Show that in this case the three inclusions in Exercise 1.22 are all proper.

1.24. Express in set theoretical form the truth of the statements in the answers to the following exercises from the Introduction: I.1, I.5, I.6, I.7, I.8, I.9, I.10, I.13.

1.25. Give set-theoretical expressions for each of the following:

   (a) Peter is neither clever nor handsome.
   (b) There are some men who have both brains and brawn.
   (c) Peggy is beautiful but dumb.
   (d) No one can be lazy and successful.
   (e) John is either brave or foolhardy.

1.26. Put the following statement in the form "If . . . , then . . . ." Give the negation, converse, and contrapositive. Give a set-theoretical expression and a Venn diagram for each of these four statements, using five sets in each expression: "Early to bed and early to rise makes a man healthy, wealthy, and wise."

1.27. Write the following statement in the form "If A, then B," give the converse and negation, and interpret each by means of a Venn diagram: "All artists and musicians are poor but happy."

1.28. Express the following argument in the notation of set theory: "John is a man. All men are mortal. Therefore John is mortal."

1.29. Use set theory to show the fallacy in the following argument: "Aristotle is a Greek. Greek is a nationality. Therefore Aristotle is a nationality."

1.30. Prove the following:

   (a) $(A \cup B) \times (C \cup D) = (A \times C) \cup (A \times D) \cup (B \times C) \cup (B \times D)$.
   (b) $(A \cap B) \times (C \cap D) = (A \times C) \cap (B \times D)$.

1.31. If $A \subset E$ and $B \subset F$, express $\complement_{E \times F} (A \times B)$ in terms of $A, B, \complement A, \complement B$. State explicitly the sets with respect to which complements are taken.

1.32. Let $S = \{a,b\}$, $T = \{e,f\}$, $V = \{0,1,2\}$. List the ordered pairs in (a) $S \times V$, (b) $T \times V$, (c) $(S \cup T) \times V$, (d) $(S \cap T) \times V$.

1.33. Is it true that $\mathcal{P}(A \times B) = \mathcal{P}(A) \times \mathcal{P}(B)$ for all sets A and B?

1.34. Prove that $(B - A) \times (A - B) = [(B - A) \times (A \cup B)] \cap [(A \cup B) \times (A - B)]$.

1.35. Prove that $\complement_{A \times B} [((A \cap B) \times B) \cup (A \times (A \cap B))] = (A - B) \times (B - A)$.

1.36. Prove that

$$\complement_{(A \cup B) \times (A \cup B)} [((A \cap B) \times (A \cup B)) \cup ((A \cup B) \times (A \cap B))]$$
$$= [(A - B) \times (A - B)] \cup [(A - B) \times (B - A)] \cup [(B - A) \times (A - B)]$$
$$\cup [(B - A) \times (B - A)].$$

2
Equivalence
Relations

2.1   Relations

The idea of relation is found throughout mathematics and in fact throughout
our experience. We describe the relation between Orville and Wilbur Wright
by saying that they are brothers. If we want to emphasize the fact that this
is a relation we might say, "Orville and Wilbur Wright are in the brotherhood
relation." As further examples consider: "Between two equilateral triangles,
there is a similarity relation," or more usually, "Two equilateral triangles
are similar"; "John and Paul are in the friendship relation," or "John and
Paul are friends"; and "Between the coordinates x, y of a point on a circle
with center $(0,0)$ and radius 1 there is the relation $x^2 + y^2 = 1$." We shall
apply the language and technique of the theory of sets to clarify the mathematical concept of relation.

Consider the relation "x is the husband of y." This is a relation ("is the
husband of") between elements of the set of all men M and the set of all
women W. For a given pair (a,b) with $a \in M$ and $b \in W$, a and b are related
in this way; that is, a is the husband of b; or they are not. If we had a list of
all the pairs (a,b) such that a is the husband of b, we would have complete
knowledge about this marriage relation between elements in the sets M and
W. Such a list of pairs (a,b) is a subset of the Cartesian product $M \times W$.
Thus the marital status of mankind could be completely described by listing
the elements of a certain subset of $M \times W$. If we had such a list for the
relation "is the husband of," we could easily prepare the list for the associated relation "is the wife of."[1] This list would describe a subset of $W \times M$.

Let us consider now the relation between two real numbers x and y
determined by $x^2 + y^2 = 1$. This relation is associated with a circle with
center at $(0,0)$ and radius 1. The circle is also called the *locus* or *graph* of

---

[1] The second relation is called the *inverse* or *opposite* of the first.

points whose coordinates satisfy $x^2 + y^2 = 1$. The set of points on the circle C is a subset of $R \times R$ (which is the plane). This circle defines the relation. That is, the relation $x^2 + y^2 = 1$ holds for x and y if and only if the point $P = (x,y)$, an element of $R \times R$, is on the circle.

Consider now the concept of relation in general. We shall write $x \rho y$ to mean "x and y are in the relation ρ" and $x \not\rho y$ to mean "x and y are not in the relation ρ." If we wish to speak about several relations at once, we shall denote them by $\rho_1, \rho_2, \cdots$ or by $\rho, \rho^*, \bar{\rho}, \cdots$. The symbol ρ can be replaced by a symbol representing a particular relation, for example, $\in, <, \subset, =$, etc.

The order in which x and y appear in the notation $x \rho y$ is important. We require that x be an element of the domain and y an element of the co-domain. For example, we have considered the relation "is the husband of" with domain M and codomain W. Since Mary is not an element of M and Henry is not an element of W, we cannot say "Mary is the husband of Henry." Even if the domain and codomain are the same set, the order is still important, since we may have $x \rho y$ but $y \not\rho x$. Consider the relation "is a parent of" with the set of all human beings as domain and codomain. Then if Jack is a parent of Mary it cannot be true that Mary is a parent of Jack.

We associate with the relation ρ a subset G_ρ of $A \times B$ defined by

$$G_\rho = \{(x,y) | x \in A, y \in B \text{ and } x \rho y\}.$$

We call this subset of $A \times B$ the *graph of the relation*. The set A is called the *domain* of the relation and B is called the *codomain*. We see that, to completely define a relation ρ, we must give a triple of sets (A, B, G_ρ), where A is the domain, B the codomain, and $G_\rho \subset A \times B$ is the graph of ρ. If two relations differ in any of these three respects, we shall consider them different relations.

In our example "x is the husband of y" we have chosen x from the set of all men M and y from the set of all women W. In this case M is the domain, W the codomain, and the graph is the set of ordered pairs (x,y), where x is the husband of y. We could have chosen a similar relation where the domain is M_1, the set of all married men, and the codomain is W_1, the set of all married women. We shall consider these two different relations, although some authors do not insist on this distinction. We shall consider this point again in Section 3.2 in connection with functions.

The relations we have discussed have the property that they involve *two* individuals, chosen from sets. Such a relation is called a *binary* relation. It is easy to construct relations that are not binary, that is, those that involve more than two individuals; for example, "p is a point between q and r," "x is the son of y and z" (y the father, z the mother), or "$x + y = z$." We shall study only binary relations, especially those types that occur most frequently in mathematics—*equivalence relations*, *order relations*, and *functions* (or *functional relations*).

2.2 Equivalence relations

The statements, "triangle t_1 is congruent to triangle t_2" and "triangle t_1 is similar to triangle t_2," are familiar from elementary geometry. Each refers to a binary relation having as both domain and codomain the set T of all triangles. If C is the graph of the congruence relation and S the graph of the similarity relation, then $C \subset T \times T$ and $S \subset T \times T$. Since two triangles are similar whenever they are congruent, we see that $C \subset S$. We also know that $C \neq S$.

There are three important properties of both the congruence and similarity relations. We state these for congruence and leave the reader to formulate them for similarity.

1. Every triangle is congruent to itself.
2. If t_1 is congruent to t_2, then t_2 is congruent to t_1.
3. If t_1 is congruent to t_2 and t_2 is congruent to t_3, then t_1 is congruent to t_3.

We express these by saying that the congruence relation is (1) *reflexive,* (2) *symmetric,* and (3) *transitive.* These three properties are also satisfied by the equality relation between numbers and the equality relation between sets.

Relations with these three properties occur in almost all branches of mathematics. They are important enough for us to study them in detail.

DEFINITION

A binary relation ρ having as domain and codomain the same set A is called an *equivalence relation* if it satisfies the following conditions:

1. $x \rho x$ for all $x \in A$ (reflexivity).
2. If $x \rho y$, then $y \rho x$ (symmetry).
3. If $x \rho y$ and $y \rho z$, then $x \rho z$ (transitivity).

We say x is *equivalent* to y (under an equivalence relation ρ) if $x \rho y$.

If ρ is an equivalence relation defined for the elements of a set A (we sometimes say simply that ρ is an equivalence relation on A) and a is any element of A, then we may define a subset

$$C_a = \{x | x \in A \text{ and } a \rho x\}$$

of all elements x of A that are equivalent to a. This subset is called the *equivalence class of a with respect to the relation ρ.*

THEOREM   2.1

If ρ is an equivalence relation on a set A and if we have $a \in A$ and $b \in A$, then $C_a = C_b$ if and only if $a \rho b$.

Proof

1. We assume that $a \rho b$ and want to prove that $C_a = C_b$. If $x \in C_a$, then $a \rho x$ by the definition of C_a, $x \rho a$ by the symmetric property, $x \rho b$ by the transitive property, and $b \rho x$ by the symmetric property. Therefore $x \in C_b$ and hence $C_a \subset C_b$. Similarly, $C_b \subset C_a$ and therefore $C_a = C_b$.

2. We assume that $C_a = C_b$ and want to prove that $a \rho b$. By the reflexive property we have $b \in C_b$ and therefore $b \in C_a$. Then $a \rho b$ by the definition of C_a. •

In the first part of this proof we used the symmetric and transitive properties but not the reflexive property. In the second part we used only the reflexive property.

THEOREM   2.2

If ρ is an equivalence relation defined on a set A and C_a, C_b are any two equivalence classes, then C_a and C_b are either equal or disjoint, that is,

$$C_a = C_b \quad \text{or} \quad C_a \cap C_b = \varnothing.$$

Also we have

$$A = \bigcup_{a \in A} C_a.$$

Proof

We want to prove that we cannot have $C_a \cap C_b \neq \varnothing$ if $C_a \neq C_b$. Suppose $C_a \cap C_b \neq \varnothing$. Then there is an element $x \in C_a \cap C_b$ and hence $a \rho x$ and $b \rho x$. By symmetry $x \rho b$ and by transitivity $a \rho b$. By Theorem 2.1 $C_a = C_b$, and the first part of the theorem is proved.

We now want to prove

$$A = \bigcup_{a \in A} C_a.$$

For each $a \in A$ we have $C_a \subset A$ and hence $\bigcup_{a \in A} C_a \subset A$. Also for each $a \in A$ we have $a \in C_a$ by the reflexive property. Thus $A \subset \bigcup_{a \in A} C_a$ and hence $A = \bigcup_{a \in A} C_a$. •

DEFINITION

If $\mathfrak{D}$ is a class of pairwise, disjoint, nonempty subsets of a set A (that is, if B, B' are distinct elements of $\mathfrak{D}$, then $B \cap B' = \varnothing$), and if A is the union of all the sets in $\mathfrak{D}$,

$$A = \bigcup_{B \in \mathfrak{D}} B,$$

we call the class $\mathfrak{D}$ a *partition* of the set A.

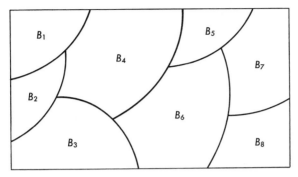

FIGURE 2.1

This definition is illustrated by Figure 2.1. The rectangle represents the set A. The sets $B_1, B_2, \cdots, B_8$ are subsets. The diagram indicates that these subsets are disjoint and that together they include all of A. The class of subsets $\mathfrak{D} = \{B_1, B_2, \cdots, B_8\}$ is a partition of A.

Theorem 2.2 shows that any equivalence relation can be associated with (or defines) a certain partition of the set A (the domain and codomain of the relation). The partition is the class of all the equivalence classes for the equivalence relation ρ.

We shall illustrate this point by a nonmathematical example. Let S be the set of students who wrote a certain examination in which grades of A, B, C, D, and F were given. We shall consider a pair of students related if they received the same grade. It is left to the reader to show that this is an equivalence relation. The equivalence classes are S_A, S_B, S_C, S_D, and S_F, where S_A is the set of all students who received an A grade, and so on. Since each student in S is in exactly one of these subsets, we see that they are disjoint and their union is S. The subsets are nonempty, provided each grade was given to at least one student. Thus $\{S_A, S_B, S_C, S_D, S_F\}$ is a partition of S.

We shall now prove the converse of Theorem 2.2, that is, every partition of a set A defines an equivalence relation. The equivalence classes for this relation are simply the disjoint subsets of A which constitute the partition $\mathfrak{D}$. We state this precisely in the following theorem.

THEOREM 2.3

Each partition of a set A by a class $\mathfrak{D}$ of its subsets defines an equivalence relation ρ; the equivalence classes for ρ are the elements of $\mathfrak{D}$.

Proof

If $\mathfrak{D}$ is a class of subsets that forms a partition of A, then

$$A = \bigcup_{B \in \mathfrak{D}} B.$$

We define a binary relation ρ between elements of A by: $x \rho y$ if and only if there is a $B \in \mathfrak{D}$ such that $x \in B$ and $y \in B$. We now prove that ρ is an equivalence relation.

For each $x \in A$ there is a $B \in \mathfrak{D}$ such that $x \in B$. Then $x \rho x$ and so ρ is reflexive.

If $x \in A$ and $y \in A$ are such that $x \rho y$, then by the definition of ρ there is some $B \in \mathfrak{D}$ such that $x \in B$ and $y \in B$. But it is then clear that $y \in B$ and $x \in B$. Hence $y \rho x$, and so ρ is symmetric.

If $x \rho y$ and $y \rho z$, then there are sets B, B' in $\mathfrak{D}$ such that $x \in B$, $y \in B$, $y \in B'$, $z \in B'$. Since $\mathfrak{D}$ forms a partition we have either $B = B'$ or $B \cap B' = \varnothing$. But $y \in B \cap B'$. Therefore $B = B'$, and hence $x \in B$, $z \in B$, and $x \rho z$. Thus ρ is transitive.

This completes the proof that ρ is an equivalence relation. The definition of ρ shows that the elements of $\mathfrak{D}$ are the equivalence classes. •

Theorems 2.2 and 2.3 show that the same situation can be described either in terms of an equivalence relation or in terms of a partition. We can also observe this in a nonmathematical context. Consider a set of people in a large room. We want to divide the people into four smaller groups and have one group meet in each corner. This could be done in two ways. We could describe in some way the people we want in each corner. Then two people would be equivalent if they satisfied the same description. In this way we could *use an equivalence relation to obtain a partition* into four subsets. On the other hand, we could describe the partition directly by dividing the room into quarters and calling each one a "corner." We would then have the people separated into a partition of four subsets according to the corner they occupied. Two people who occupied the same corner would be said to be related. This relation is an equivalence relation and so, in our second method, we have *used a partition to obtain an equivalence relation*.

The graph of the equivalence relation defined by a partition has the following property.

THEOREM   2.4

If ρ is the equivalence relation associated with a partition $\mathfrak{D}$ of A as above and G_ρ is the graph of ρ, then

$$G_\rho = \bigcup_{B \in \mathfrak{D}} B \times B.$$

Proof

If $x \rho y$, there is a $B \in \mathfrak{D}$ such that $x \in B$ and $y \in B$. Then $(x,y) \in B \times B \subset \bigcup_{B \in \mathfrak{D}} B \times B$ and hence $G_\rho \subset \bigcup_{B \in \mathfrak{D}} B \times B$.

Conversely, if $(x,y) \in \bigcup_{B \in \mathfrak{D}} B \times B$, then there is a $B \in \mathfrak{D}$ such that $(x,y) \in B \times B$. But this means $x \in B$, $y \in B$, and hence $x \rho y$. Thus

$\cup_{B\in\mathfrak{D}} B \times B \subset G_\rho$. These two inclusions together show that $G_\rho = \cup_{B\in\mathfrak{D}} B \times B$. •

Theorem 2.4 is illustrated in Figure 2.2, where A is represented by a line segment, the subsets $B_1, B_2, \cdots$ are represented by nonoverlapping subintervals, and the shaded area represents G_ρ.

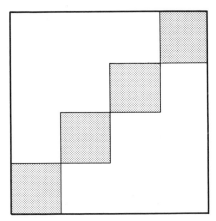

FIGURE 2.2

Equivalence relations are often used to construct from a given set of objects a new set consisting of new objects. Many mathematical structures that we wish to study are constructed in just this way. Some of these ideas have already been encountered in high school mathematics, although there the set-theoretical aspect may not have been emphasized.

Consider any set A for whose elements we have an equivalence relation ρ. Each equivalence class $C_a(C_a \subset A)$ is a new object, and from these new objects we can form a new set. We denote this set of equivalence classes by A/ρ and call it the *quotient set of A with respect to (or modulo) the equivalence relation ρ.*

Any subset B of A that contains one and only one element from each equivalence class with respect to the relation ρ is called a *set of representatives* of the relation.

2.3 Some examples

We have a twofold purpose in our choice of the examples that follow. We want the reader to realize that he has already handled the ideas of equivalence, even if they were not stated explicitly, in both mathematical and nonmathematical contexts. We also want to clarify the ideas that have been discussed in general form. We emphasize the importance of the equivalence relation in mathematics and point out that many concepts are introduced as quotient sets of some set by an equivalence relation.

EXAMPLE   2.1

Let A be the set of all the residents of the cities of a particular country. Define a relation ρ as follows: "$x \, \rho \, y$ if and only if x and y are residents of the same city." We leave the reader to verify that ρ is an equivalence relation, assuming that no one can be a resident of two different cities. An equivalence class modulo ρ is the set of residents of some city. The quotient set A/ρ is a new set, each of whose elements consists of all residents of some city. We can denote an element of A/ρ by the name of the city without causing confusion.

There are various ways of choosing a set of representatives, for example,[2]

$$B = \{x | x \text{ is the mayor of a city}\}.$$

To choose another set of representatives for the relation suppose that each city holds a beauty contest in which only residents can compete[3] and in which the winner receives the title "Miss City." Then as a set of representatives we might choose

$$B_1 = \{y | y \text{ is a "Miss City"}\}.$$

The reader will be able to give several other sets of representatives.

EXAMPLE   2.2

In some cases we can draw a diagram to represent the graph of the relation. This example and the one that follows illustrate two ways in which this can be done.

We write $[x]$ to represent the "largest integer in x," that is, the integer n such that $n \leq x < n + 1$. For example $[5\frac{1}{2}] = 5, [\pi] = 3, [-1.25] = -2$.

We define a relation for the set R of real numbers by: "$x \, \rho \, y$ if and only if $[x] = [y]$." We leave to the reader the proof that ρ is an equivalence relation.

The equivalence class of x modulo ρ is

$$C_x = \{y | y \in R, [x] \leq y < [x] + 1\}.$$

For example, $C_{3.28} = \{y | y \in R, 3 \leq y < 4\}$.

The graph G_ρ of this relation is seen in Figure 2.3. R is represented by a straight line and $R \times R$ as the plane. The elements of G_ρ are represented by points inside the squares or on the boundaries represented by solid lines.

---

[2] We are assuming here that each city has exactly one mayor and that he is a resident of the city.

[3] We assume that every city has eligible contestants. If there were a city inhabited only by men this would not give a set of representatives.

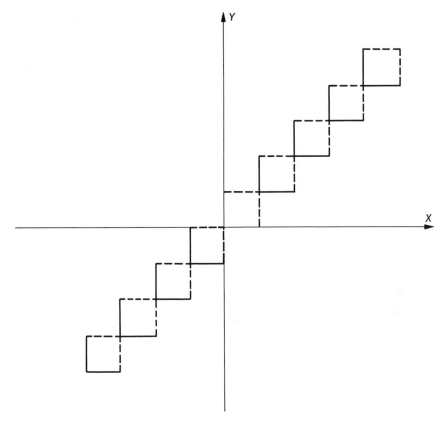

FIGURE 2.3

This example and the diagram illustrate Theorem 2.4;

$$B_n = \{x | n \le x < n + 1\}$$

and $B_n \times B_n$ is one of the squares in the diagram.

EXAMPLE 2.3

Consider the set $E = \{a,b,c\}$ and its power set $\mathcal{P}(E)$. We shall define a relation with domain and codomain both $\mathcal{P}(E)$. If $A \in \mathcal{P}(E)$ and $B \in \mathcal{P}(E)$, then $A \rho B$ if and only if A and B contain the same number of elements. We show this relation in Figure 2.4.

The large square represents $\mathcal{P}(E) \times \mathcal{P}(E)$ and each small square represents an ordered pair. For example, the square in the (vertical) column labeled $\{a\}$ and the (horizontal) row $\{b,c\}$ represents the ordered pair $(\{a\},\{b,c\})$. The shaded squares represent elements of G_a.

We shall leave as an exercise the proof that ρ is an equivalence relation and the description of the equivalence classes.

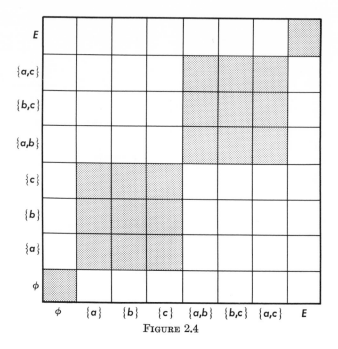

FIGURE 2.4

EXAMPLE 2.4

The following example of equivalence classes was known in arithmetic before the general study of equivalence relations was undertaken.

Let Z be the set of all integers; that is,

$$Z = \{\cdots, -3, -2, -1, 0, 1, 2, 3, \cdots\}.$$

We define a relation with Z as domain and codomain as follows: Choose a positive integer n. Define the relation ρ by: $x \rho y$ if and only if $x - y$ is divisible by n. We follow tradition and write $x \equiv y(\mathrm{mod}\ n)$ instead of $x \rho y$, and read this "x is congruent to y modulo n."

As examples of such a relation observe $80 \equiv 3(\mathrm{mod}\ 7)$, $-6 \equiv 8(\mathrm{mod}\ 7)$, $-12 \equiv 4(\mathrm{mod}\ 8)$, $14 \not\equiv 3(\mathrm{mod}\ 9)$.

We want to prove that congruence modulo n is an equivalence relation for integers. For all x, $x \equiv x(\mathrm{mod}\ n)$, since $x - x = 0$ is divisible by n. Therefore congruence is reflexive. If $x \equiv y(\mathrm{mod}\ n)$, then $x - y = kn$, and hence $y - x = -kn$. But this shows that $y \equiv x(\mathrm{mod}\ n)$. Thus congruence is symmetric.

Suppose $x \equiv y(\mathrm{mod}\ n)$ and $y \equiv z(\mathrm{mod}\ n)$. Then $x - y = k_1 n$ and $y - z = k_2 n$. Therefore $x - z = (x - y) + (y - z) = k_1 n + k_2 n = (k_1 + k_2)n$. Therefore $x \equiv z(\mathrm{mod}\ n)$, and so congruence is transitive.

In studying the equivalence classes of the congruence relation, we consider the example in which $n = 3$. What is the equivalence class containing

0, that is, what integers are congruent to 0 modulo 3? If $x \equiv 0 \pmod 3$, then $x - 0 = 3k$ for some $k \in Z$. Also $3k \equiv 0 \pmod 3$ for all $k \in Z$. Thus we have the equivalence class

$$C_0 = \{x | x = 3k, \; k \in Z\} = \{\cdots, -6, -3, 0, 3, 6, \cdots\}.$$

If $x \equiv 1 \pmod 3$, then $x - 1 = 3k$ for some $k \in Z$, that is, $x = 3k + 1$. Similarly, if $x \equiv 2 \pmod 3$, then $x = 3k + 2$ for some $k \in Z$. This gives the equivalence classes

$$C_1 = \{x | x = 3k + 1, \; k \in Z\} = \{\cdots, -5, -2, 1, 4, 7, \cdots\}.$$
$$C_2 = \{x | x = 3k + 2, \; k \in Z\} = \{\cdots, -4, -1, 2, 5, 8, \cdots\}.$$

We observe that $C_0 \cup C_1 \cup C_2 = Z$; therefore we have all the equivalence classes. We denote the quotient set $\{C_0, C_1, C_2\}$ by $Z/(3)$.

The graph $G_{(3)}$ of the congruence relation modulo 3 is represented in Figure 2.5. The elements of $Z \times Z$ are the points in the plane with integer

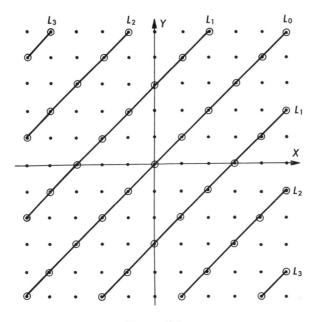

FIGURE 2.5

coordinates. These are denoted in the figure by $\cdot$ or $\odot$. The elements of $G_{(3)}$ are the points (x, y) such that $x \equiv y \pmod 3$. These are denoted by $\odot$. We observe that the elements of $G_{(3)}$ can be gathered together in sets $L_k = \{p | p = (x, y), \; x \in Z, \; y \in Z, \; y = 3k + x\}$; that is,

$$G_{(3)} = \bigcup_{k \in Z} L_k.$$

The sets L_k consist of points with integer coordinates on a line parallel to the diagonal $x = y$ and at a vertical distance of $3k$ from the diagonal.

We shall now turn to the general case of equivalence classes with respect to congruence modulo n. Consider $a \in N \cup \{0\}$, $a < n$. We want to find the class of all elements equivalent to a with respect to congruence modulo n. If x is an integer such that $x \equiv a(\bmod n)$, then $x - a = kn$, where $k \in Z$, and hence $x = a + kn$. Therefore the class of elements equivalent to a is included in the set $\{x | x = a + kn,\ k \in Z\}$. But also every $x = a + kn$ satisfies $x \equiv a(\bmod n)$. If we denote by C_a the equivalence class of $a \in Z$ modulo n, we have

$$C_a = \{x | x = a + kn,\ k \in Z\}.$$

Let y be any integer. If y is divided by n it leaves a remainder r; that is, $y = kn + r$, $0 \le r < n$. We use the expressions: "The remainder is 0" and "There is no remainder" interchangeably to mean that n divides y. Then $y \in C_r$ and

$$Z = \bigcup_{0 \le r < n} C_r.$$

The quotient set of Z with respect to congruence modulo n is denoted by $Z/(n)$. Thus we have $Z/(n) = \{C_0, C_1, \cdots, C_{n-1}\}$, where

$$C_0 = \{x | x = 0 + kn,\ k \in Z\},$$
$$C_1 = \{x | x = 1 + kn,\ k \in Z\},$$
$$\cdots$$
$$C_{n-1} = \{x | x = (n - 1) + kn,\ k \in Z\}.$$

There are, of course, many sets of representatives for $Z/(n)$; the most frequently used is $\{0, 1, 2, \cdots, n - 1\}$, that is, the set of all possible remainders when an integer is divided by n.

EXAMPLE   2.5

We can give an example similar to Example 2.4 but with R, the set of real numbers, as domain and codomain. Choose a positive integer n. For $x \in R$, $y \in R$ we define: $x \, \rho \, y$ if and only if $x - y$ is an integer divisible by n. We again write $x \equiv y(\bmod n)$. The reader can show that this is an equivalence relation by copying the proof from Example 2.4. The graph $G_{(n)}$ again consists of lines parallel to the diagonal $y = x$ and with vertical spacing n, but now it contains all the points on these lines, not just those with integer coefficients. The diagram for $G_{(1)}$ is shown in Figure 2.6.

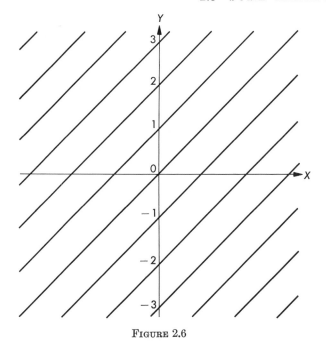

FIGURE 2.6

EXAMPLE 2.6

Consider the set L of all straight lines in the plane. We define a relation ρ between elements of L as follows: $l_1 \rho l_2$ if and only if l_1 is either identical with or parallel to l_2.

We can easily verify that ρ is an equivalence relation. For each $l \in L$, it is clear that $l \rho l$ and hence ρ is reflexive. It is also clear that if $l_1 \rho l_2$, then $l_2 \rho l_1$ and ρ is symmetric. Suppose $l_1 \rho l_2$ and $l_2 \rho l_3$. We want to show $l_1 \rho l_3$. If $l_1 \neq l_3$ but l_1 and l_3 meet in a point p, then l_1, l_3 are both parallels to l_2 passing through p. This is impossible by Euclid's parallel postulate, and hence l_1, l_3 are parallel. Thus $l_1 \rho l_3$ and ρ is transitive.

An equivalence class with respect to ρ consists of all lines with a certain direction as indicated by the slope. We can designate such a class by its direction. As a set of representatives of the equivalence classes we choose the lines passing through the origin. Each such line except the horizontal one cuts the semicircle of Figure 2.7 at one point. If we consider the points a and a' as one, that is, if we "identify" them,[4] we can then associate the set of directions in the plane with the points on a semicircle whose end points are considered as one.

[4] This identification or matching process is in fact an application of another equivalence relation. We consider a and a' equivalent, but all other points on the semicircle are equivalent only to themselves. The semicircle with its end points identified is the quotient set of this equivalence.

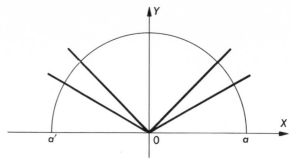

FIGURE 2.7

The same idea could be carried out in three-dimensional space instead of on the plane. The quotient set in the plane is called the projective line; the quotient set in space is called the projective plane. We shall not make further use of these ideas. Their study is known as projective geometry.

EXAMPLE 2.7

We here anticipate some of the material on rational numbers given in Chapter 6. There we shall be concerned with properties of the rational numbers; here we are primarily interested in the equivalence relation used to define them.

Consider the set of all numbers a/b, where a, b are integers and $b \neq 0$. The notation a/b could be replaced by (a,b), where $a \in Z$ and $b \in Z_0$; that is, $(a,b) \in Z \times Z_0$, where $Z_0 = \complement_Z \{0\}$. We ordinarily say that a/b and c/d are equal if and only if $ad = bc$. This defines a relation ρ whose domain and codomain are $Z \times Z_0$: we define $(a,b) \rho (c,d)$ if and only if $ad = bc$.

We want to show that ρ is an equivalence relation. It is clear that $(a,b) \rho (a,b)$, since $ab = ba$. Therefore ρ is reflexive. If $(a,b) \rho (c,d)$ then $ad = bc$. But then $(c,d) \rho (a,b)$, and so ρ is symmetric. Finally, if $(a,b) \rho (c,d)$ and $(c,d) \rho (e,f)$, then $ad = bc$ and $cf = de$. Since $ad = bc$, we have $adf = bcf$. But $cf = de$ and therefore $adf = bde$. But $d \neq 0$, since $(c,d) \in Z \times Z_0$. Therefore $af = be$ and $(a,b) \rho (e,f)$. Thus ρ is transitive.

We can now recognize a rational number as an equivalence class of the relation ρ. Any pair (a,b) (or a/b) in the equivalence class can be chosen as a representative of the class, but we frequently choose the one "in lowest terms," or the *irreducible* fraction, that is, the fraction a/b, where a, b have no factors in common except 1.

This approach emphasizes the difference between a fraction and a rational number. A rational number is an equivalence class of fractions, and each fraction is a representative of some rational number.

We shall denote the set of rational numbers by Q.

EXERCISES

2.1. Let R be the set of real numbers. A relation ρ is defined by $0 \leq x - y < 1$. On the xy plane shade the graph of ρ.

2.2. In the xy plane represent the points with integer coordinates by dots and represent by $\odot$ the graph of the relation "x divides y," where x and y are integers.

2.3. Consider the set $A = \{\{1,2,3\},\{1,2\},1,2,3\}$. Give the graph (as a list of ordered pairs) for the following relations:

(a) $x \in y$, where $x \in A$ and $y \in A$.
(b) $x \subset y$, where $x \in A$ and $y \in A$.

2.4. Let R be the set of real numbers. We define a relation on R as: $x \rho y$ if and only if $x^2 = y^2$. Draw the graph of this relation. Is it an equivalence relation?

2.5. Let R be the set of real numbers. We define a relation on R as follows: $x \rho y$ if and only if $|x - y| < 1$. Shade on the xy plane the graph of ρ. Show that ρ is reflexive and symmetric. Is ρ transitive?

2.6. Let R be the set of real numbers. For $x \in R$, $y \in R$ we define $x \rho y$ if and only if $0 < |x - y| < 1$. Is this relation reflexive? Is it symmetric? Is it transitive?

2.7. Let $A = \{1,2,3,4,5\}$. Which of the following sets of subsets are partitions?

(a) $\{\{1\},\{1,2\},\{3,4\},\{5\}\}$.
(b) $\{\{1,2\},\{4,5\}\}$.
(c) $\{\{1,2\},\{3,4\},\{5\}\}$.

2.8. Prove that the similarity relation for triangles is an equivalence relation.

2.9. Let M be a set of men. If $x \in M$ and $y \in M$, we say that $x \rho y$ if and only if x is older than y. Determine whether this relation is reflexive, symmetric, or transitive.

2.10. Let S be the set of all students who wrote a certain examination in which grades of A, B, C, D, and F were given. A pair of students are said to be related if they received the same grade. Prove that this is an equivalence relation.

2.11. Prove that the relation ρ in Example 2.1 is an equivalence relation.

2.12. Prove that the relation ρ in Example 2.2 is an equivalence relation.

2.13. Prove that the relation ρ in Example 2.3 is an equivalence relation. What are the equivalence classes?

2.14. For $x \in R$, $y \in R$ the relation $x \equiv y \pmod{0}$ is defined as in Example 2.5. Draw the graph of this relation.

2.15. Let E be any set and $M \in \mathcal{P}(E)$, $M \neq \varnothing$. We define $A \rho B$ for $A \in \mathcal{P}(E)$, $B \in \mathcal{P}(E)$ to mean that $M \subset A \cap B$. Is ρ reflexive? Is it symmetric? Is it transitive?

2.16. Consider the plane $R \times R$. We define $(a,b) \rho (c,d)$ if and only if $a + d = b + c$. Prove that this is an equivalence relation. What is the equivalence class containing $(0,0)$? Indicate this equivalence class by a diagram. Describe the other equivalence classes.

2.17. Let $S = \{1,2,3,4\}$. Set B is a subset of $S \times S$. The pairs $(1,2)$ and $(2,3)$ are elements of B, and B is the graph of an equivalence relation with S as domain and codomain. List all the elements of the smallest set B that has all these properties.

2.18. Which of the following is a set of representatives of $Z/(5)$?

(a) $\{0,2,4,6,8\}$.
(b) $\{1,2,3,4\}$.
(c) $\{0,1,-1,4,-4\}$.

2.19. Two integers are said to be related if either divides the other. Is this relation reflexive? Is it symmetric? Is it transitive? Give reasons for your answers.

2.20. Let S be the set of students in a given university. A pair of students are said to be related if they take at least one course together. Is this relation symmetric? Is it transitive?

2.21. Is the relation "Line l_1 is related to line l_2 if and only if $l_1 \perp l_2$" reflexive? Is it symmetric? Is it transitive?

2.22. Let ρ_1 and ρ_2 be equivalence relations with a set A as domain and codomain. Let G_{ρ_1} and G_{ρ_2} be their respective graphs. Then $G_{\rho_1} \cap G_{\rho_2} \subset A \times A$. Is $G_{\rho_1} \cap G_{\rho_2}$ the graph of an equivalence relation with A as domain and codomain? Give reasons for your answer.

2.23. Let A be the set of all human beings. For $x \in A$ and $y \in A$ we define $x \rho y$ to mean x and y have a common ancestor not more than five generations back. Is ρ an equivalence relation?

2.24. Let L be the set of all straight lines in the plane. We define a relation ρ as follows: If $a \in L$ and $b \in L$, then $a \rho b$ if and only if either $a \perp b$ or there exists $c \in L$ such that $a \perp c$ and $c \perp b$. Prove that ρ is an equivalence relation.

2.25. Let ρ be any relation on a set A, that is, $G_\rho \subset A \times A$. We define a relation ρ^* as follows: $x \rho^* y$ if and only if there is a finite sequence $x_1, x_2, \cdots, x_n$ of elements of A such that $x \rho x_1, x_1 \rho x_2, \cdots, x_n \rho y$. Prove that ρ^* is a transitive relation.

2.26. Let ρ be the relation on the integers defined by: $x \rho y$ if and only if $y = x + 1$. Prove that ρ^* is the relation $x < y$, where ρ^* is as in Exercise 2.25.

2.27. Let ρ be a relation with domain A and codomain B. We define the relation ρ_* between elements of A as: $x \rho_* x'$ if and only if, for every $y \in B$ such that $x \rho y$, $x' \rho y$ also. Prove that ρ_* is reflexive and transitive.

2.28. Let E be any set and $\mathcal{P}(E)$ its power set. If $A \in \mathcal{P}(E)$ and $B \in \mathcal{P}(E)$, we say $A \rho B$ if and only if $A \cap B \neq \varnothing$. Is this relation reflexive? Is it symmetric? Is it transitive?

2.29. Let E be any set and $\mathcal{P}(E)$ its power set. We define a relation ρ: If $A \in \mathcal{P}(E)$ and $B \in \mathcal{P}(E)$, then $A \rho B$ if and only if $A = B$ or there is a set $C \in \mathcal{P}(E)$ such that $A \cap C \neq \varnothing$ and $C \cap B \neq \varnothing$. Prove that ρ is an equivalence relation. Describe the equivalence classes.

2.30. Let E be any set and let C be a given subset. If A and B are subsets, we say $A \rho B$ if $(A - B) \cup (B - A) \subset C$. Prove that ρ is an equivalence relation. What is the equivalence class of E, of $\varnothing$, of C?

2.31. For a relation ρ with $G_\rho \subset A \times B$, where A is the domain and B the codomain of ρ, we can define the sets $G_\rho(x) = \{y | (x,y) \in G_\rho\}$ for each $x \in A$ and $G_\rho^{-1}(y) = \{x | (x,y) \in G_\rho\}$ for each $y \in B$. Consider the relation ρ with $A = Q_+$, the set of positive rational numbers, $B = N$, the set of natural numbers, defined as: $x \rho y$ if and only if $x = p/q$ and $p + q = y$, with $p \in N$ and $q \in N$. Describe the sets $G_\rho(\frac{1}{2})$, $G_\rho^{-1}(10)$.

2.32. Let ρ be any relation with domain A and codomain B and let $G_\rho(x)$, $G_\rho^{-1}(y)$ be defined as in Exercise 2.31. We define the following relations:

    (a) $x \bar{\rho} x'$ if and only if $G_\rho(x) \subset G_\rho(x')$; domain $\bar{\rho}$ = codomain $\bar{\rho} = A$.
    (b) $x \hat{\rho} x'$ if and only if $G_\rho(x) = G_\rho(x')$; domain $\hat{\rho}$ = codomain $\hat{\rho} = A$.
    (c) $y \hat{\rho} y'$ if and only if $G_\rho^{-1}(y) \subset G_\rho^{-1}(y')$; domain $\hat{\rho}$ = codomain $\hat{\rho} = B$.
    (d) $y \check{\rho} y'$ if and only if $G_\rho^{-1}(y) = G_\rho^{-1}(y')$; domain $\check{\rho}$ = codomain $\check{\rho} = B$.

Which of these relations are transitive? Which are reflexive? Which are symmetric? Give reasons for your answers.

2.33. If any of the relations defined in Exercise 2.32 are equivalence relations, describe the equivalence classes.

2.34. Are any of the relations defined in Exercise 2.32 equal to ρ_* of Exercise 2.27? Give reasons for your answer.

2.35. If ρ is an equivalence relation on a set A, prove that the relations $\bar{\rho}$, $\tilde{\rho}$, $\hat{\rho}$, $\check{\rho}$ of Exercise 2.32 are all equal to ρ.

2.36. If $x \rho y$ is defined by $x^2 - y^2 = 1$, where $x \in R$, $y \in R$, R the real numbers, draw the graphs of the relations $\bar{\rho}$, $\tilde{\rho}$, $\hat{\rho}$, $\check{\rho}$ of Exercise 2.32.

2.37. Describe the set $G_\rho(x)$ as defined in Exercise 2.31 in the following cases

(a) $A = \{a,b,c,d\}$, $B = \{\{a\},\{b,c\},\{b,c,d\},\{d\}\}$, $x \rho y$ if and only if $x \in y$. List the elements in $G_\rho(d)$.

(b) $A = \{\varnothing,\{\varnothing\},\{\varnothing,\{\varnothing\}\},\{1\}\}$, $B = \{\{\varnothing,1,2\},\{\{1\},\varnothing\}\}$, $x \rho y$ if and only if $x \subset y$. List the elements in $G_\rho(\{\varnothing\})$.

(c) $A = B = R$ (the set of real numbers), $x \rho y$ if and only if $x^2 + y^2 = 1$. List the elements in $G_\rho(\frac{1}{2})$, $G_\rho(2)$.

(d) $A = B = Z$ (the set of all integers), $x \rho y$ if and only if $x \equiv y(\text{mod } 5)$. List the elements in $G_\rho(5)$.

2.38. Use $G_\rho(x)$ as defined in Exercise 2.31 to define a new relation ρ_1, with A as domain and codomain, as follows: $x \rho_1 x'$ if and only if $G_\rho(x) = G_\rho(x')$. Prove that ρ_1 is an equivalence relation.

2.39. Describe the equivalence classes with respect to the relation ρ_1 defined in Exercise 2.38 in each of the special cases in Exercise 2.37.

2.40. With ρ_1 defined as in Exercise 2.38, show that, if $B = A$ and ρ is an equivalence relation, then ρ_1 is the same relation as ρ.

2.41. If $x \rho y$ is the relation $x^2 - y^2 = 1$ and $x \rho' y$ the relation $x^2 + y^2 = 1$, where $x \in R$, $y \in R$, draw the graph of the relation $x \sigma y$ defined as follows: $x \sigma y$ if and only if there exists a $z \in R$ such that $x \rho z$ and $z \rho y$. Also draw the graph of the relation $x \tau y$ defined by $x \tau y$ if and only if there is a $z \in R$ such that $x \rho' z$ and $z \rho' y$. Are σ and τ the same relation?

2.42. The three properties reflexivity, symmetry, and transitivity are independent of each other. By this we mean that a relation may have none of them, any one of them, any two of them, or all three. Give examples of these eight cases. You may either make up your own examples or choose appropriate ones from the exercises and examples of this chapter.

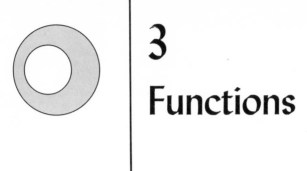

3

Functions

3.1 Introduction

The word "function" is in general use at the high school level in mathematics, physics, and some other fields, but the approach is frequently by way of examples and vague descriptions; a precise definition of a function is not always given. We shall try to give a clear and precise definition of the concept of a function, and to help the reader to see how this concept includes what he has already been taught to refer to as a function and how it extends to many other situations. We shall also give some attention to the historical development of the idea of function to show the simplicity and clarity afforded by set theory.

3.2 Definition

We shall start with one of the techniques used in high school for the study of functions, and shall consider the function given as $y = x^2 + 2x$. For this function we construct a table of values

x	-2	-1	0	1	2
y	0	-1	0	3	8

and draw a graph as in Figure 3.1.

The table of values consists of various columns, each consisting of two numbers, the first representing some value of x and the second representing the corresponding value of y determined by $y = x^2 + 2x$. These numbers could be considered ordered pairs (x,y) instead of columns consisting of two numbers. We know that each such pair can be represented by a point in the plane. The parabola in Figure 3.1 consists of all points $(x, x^2 + 2x)$ in the plane. These points are obtained by allowing x to assume all real values. The parabola thus represents the same list of ordered pairs as the complete table of values.

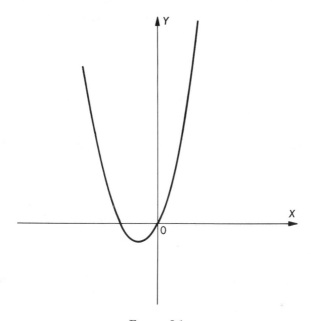

FIGURE 3.1

Since the table of values and the graph both represent sets of ordered pairs, we may say that this collection of ordered pairs is essential to the description of the function. That is, our function can be described by saying that, for each real number x, there is exactly one ordered pair (x, y) that is in the graph of the function, and this pair satisfies the equation $y = x^2 + 2x$. This suggests that we are dealing with a relation whose graph is

$$G = \{p | p = (x, y), y = x^2 + 2x\}.$$

What are the domain and codomain of this graph? The set from which the values of x are to be chosen is not explicitly stated. This is one of the ways in which this approach is vague. We have chosen to select x from the set of real numbers R, a choice that is supported by the usual use of this approach in elementary books. The set in which the values of y are found is not explicitly stated either. Here the choice is even less obvious than before. We shall again choose R, the set of real numbers, but also point out that we could have chosen the set of complex numbers or some subset of R such as $\{x | x \in R, x \geq -1\}$.

If we make this choice of the set R in each case we see that in fact we have a relation with R as both domain and codomain and graph

$$G = \{p|p = (x,y), x \in R, y = x^2 + 2x\}.$$

This relation has an important property not possessed by all relations. For each real number x there is one and only one pair (x,y) in the graph; that is, if (x,y) and (x,y_1) are in the graph G, then $y = y_1$.

In this example there obviously are real numbers y for which there is no $x \in R$ such that $(x,y) \in G$. We say that f is a function from R *into* R, the word *into* being chosen to convey the idea that not all the codomain is actually used in selecting the second coordinates in the graph of the function. We shall return to this idea later.

The function $y = \log x$ is known to the student as a table of values consisting of pairs of numbers $(x, \log x)$ where x is a positive real number. The set

$$G_{\log} = \{p|p = (x, \log x), x \in R, x > 0\}$$

is called the *graph of the function* $y = \log x$. This graph describes a relation whose domain is the set R_+ of positive real numbers and for which we have chosen as codomain the set R of all real numbers. That is, $G_{\log} \subset R_+ \times R$. For each positive real number x there is in $G_{\log}$ one and only one pair $(x, \log x)$.

As a nonmathematical example of a function, consider a statistical table giving the wheat production in bushels for each country of the world in a certain year. This table is in fact a list of ordered pairs (country x, wheat production in bushels of country x). Such a table is the graph of a relation whose domain is the set of all countries in the world and whose codomain can be chosen as the set of nonnegative integers. If we make the reasonable assumption that, for each country, there is only one number giving its wheat production, we see that the graph has the following property: For each x in the domain there is one and only one pair in the graph such that x is its first coordinate.

We can now offer a definition of a function that will include the essential features of these examples.

DEFINITION

A *function f* with *domain A* and *codomain B* is a relation with this domain and codomain and such that *for each $x \in A$ there is one and only one $y \in B$ for which xfy.*

For the purpose of this definition we have expressed the function in the usual notation for relations. In Section 3.3 we shall consider some of the other notations that are more common for functions.

The set $G_f = \{p|p = (x,y), x \in A, y \in B, xfy\}$, a subset of $A \times B$, is called the *graph* of the function. The condition that is needed to make a relation a function can be stated in terms of the graph as follows: For each $x \in A$ there is one and only one $y \in B$ such that $(x,y) \in G_f$.

If domain A and codomain B of a function are both subsets of the real numbers, the graph can be represented as a set of points in the plane. For many of the functions encountered in mathematics this set of points forms a "curve" in the plane. As an example, consider Figure 3.2.

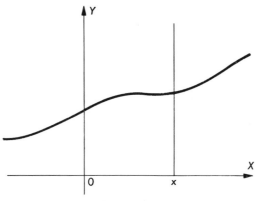

FIGURE 3.2

In this case we can describe the condition that the relation represented by the graph be a function in the following geometric form. Choose any $x \in A$ and draw through this x on the x axis a line parallel to the y axis. *For the relation to be a function, this line must intersect the graph in exactly one point.*

According to this definition of a function, the relation defined by $x \rho y$ if and only if $x = y^2$, with $x \in R_+$, the set of positive real numbers, and $y \in R$, is not a function, since to each element of the domain there are related *two* elements of the codomain. If, however, we consider the relations ρ_1 and ρ_2, where $x \rho_1 y$ if and only if $x = y^2$, $y \geq 0$ and $x \rho_2 y$ if and only if $x = y^2$, $y \leq 0$, we see that both these relations are functions. We often write $y = + \sqrt{x}$, if $x \rho_1 y$, and $y = - \sqrt{x}$, if $x \rho_2 y$. When we wish to study the square root as a function, we shall study these two functions.[1] When there is no danger of confusion, we sometimes write $\sqrt{x}$ for $+ \sqrt{x}$.

A function, since it is a relation, is an ordered triple of sets (A,B,G), where A is the domain, B is the codomain, and G is the graph. For any relation and hence for a function, we have $G \subset A \times B$.

For a relation to be a function, the domain, codomain, and graph must satisfy certain conditions. Let $pr_1(G) = \{x | x \in A, (x,y) \in G \text{ for some } y \in B\}$. We call $pr_1(G)$ the *first projection* of G. For example, in the relation "is the

---

[1] Some authors require only that there be *at least* one y in the codomain for each x in the domain. They would refer to what we call a function as a *single-valued function*. These authors would call the relation ρ a two-valued (multivalued) function and use the notation $y = \pm \sqrt{x}$.

husband of" in Section 2.1, the first projection is the set of all married men. Let $G(x) = \{y | y \in B, (x,y) \in G\}$. For any relation, $pr_1(G) \subset A$, but we may or may not have $pr_1(G) = A$. Also $G(x)$ for a given $x \in A$ may be empty, may contain one element, or may contain several elements. The relation is a function if and only if (1) $pr_1(G) = A$, and (2) $G(x)$ contains exactly one element for each $x \in A$.

A relation that satisfies property 2 but not property 1 is sometimes called a *pseudofunction*. We shall not be concerned with such relations.

Since a function is an ordered triple of sets, two functions are equal if they have the same domain, the same codomain, and the same graph. Functions that differ in any of these respects are different functions.

Students sometimes find it difficult to accept the fact that two functions that differ only in codomain are in fact different functions. Some authors do not insist on this distinction, but we shall consider two functions different if they have different codomains even though they are the same in other respects. We shall not attempt to justify this distinction. It is of value in some advanced branches of mathematics but for many purposes is of no importance. In some cases we shall deliberately ignore this distinction.

A great deal of mathematics is concerned with studying functions. We shall develop some general ideas of functions that do not involve the specializations of the various branches of mathematics. We shall also try to help the reader to see how the various functions with which he is familiar can be fitted into this general framework.

3.3   Terminology and notation

There are various notations and terminologies in use to describe a function. In part this variety is due to tradition and in part to certain advantages in particular situations. We shall give a review of those in most common use.

It is desirable that the notation for a function indicate the domain and codomain. Such a notation for a function f with domain A and codomain B is

$$A \xrightarrow{f} B \qquad \text{or} \qquad f : A \to B.$$

We say that f is a function *from A into B* or that *f is defined on A and takes its values in B*. We recall that the words *in* and *into* are intended to convey the idea that some $y \in B$ may not be related to any $x \in A$ by the relation (or function) f.

The set A is referred to variously as the *domain*, the *domain of definition*, the *domain of the variable*, or the *domain of the independent variable*. The set B is called the *codomain* or the *set of values*. We shall use the terms *domain* and *codomain*. It is possible to study functions without using the term *variable*. We shall use it, but only to indicate an element chosen from the domain. A function whose domain is a subset of the real numbers is sometimes called a *function of a real variable*. A function whose codomain is a subset of the real numbers is called a *real-valued function*, a function *valued in the real numbers*, or simply a *real function*. Similarly, a function whose codomain is a subset of the complex numbers is called a *complex function*. A function whose domain and codomain are both subsets of the real numbers is called a *real-valued function of a real variable*.

If $f:A \to B$ is a function, the element $y \in B$ such that $(x,y) \in G_f$ is denoted $f(x)$ and is called the *value of f at x*.

We have already pointed out that we do not assume that for each $y \in B$ there is an $x \in A$ such that $y = f(x)$. The subset of B for which this is true, that is, the set $\{y | y \in B$, there exists $x \in A$ such that $y = f(x)\}$ is called the *range of the function f* or the *image of A under f*. This set is denoted by $f(A)$. We see that $f(A) \subset B$, but examples can easily be found in which $f(A) \neq B$; for example, consider the function $f:N \to N$, where $f(n) = 2n$ for $n \in N$. Then the codomain is the set of *all* positive integers; the range is the set of *even* positive integers.

Before we consider some of the other notations that are used to denote the value of a function at a point we shall define an n-tuple.

An *n-tuple* (or *finite sequence*) is a function whose domain is

$$\{1,2,3, \cdot \cdot \cdot ,n\},$$

and whose codomain may be any nonempty set.

The graph of the n-tuple

$$u:\{1,2,3, \cdot \cdot \cdot ,n\} \to A$$

is

$$\{(1,a),(2,b), \cdot \cdot \cdot ,(n,k)\}$$

where $u(1) = a$, $u(2) = b$, $\cdot \cdot \cdot u(n) = k$. If we change our notation to $a = u_1$, $b = u_2$, $\cdot \cdot \cdot$, $k = u_n$, we see that we need write only

$$(u_1,u_2, \cdot \cdot \cdot ,u_n)$$

to have complete information about the graph of the function. We call the symbol u_n the subscript notation for the value of the function.

We have defined a function in terms of an ordered pair. Therefore we cannot define an ordered pair in terms of a function. An ordered pair is, however, a special case of an n-tuple. This is often the most convenient way to think of an ordered pair, even though we cannot define it in this way. The ordered pair (a_1,a_2) is the function

$$f:\{1,2\} \to A,$$

where $f(1) = a_1 \in A$, $f(2) = a_2 \in A$.

The subscript notation is also used for an infinite sequence which we shall now define. A *sequence* (or *infinite sequence*) is a function whose domain is the set N of positive integers. The codomain, which may be any nonempty set, is frequently included in referring to the sequence; for example, "a sequence of rational numbers," "a sequence of complex numbers," "a sequence of circles." For the sequences

$$a:N \to B \qquad \text{and} \qquad u:N \to B$$

we frequently write a_n for $a(n)$ and u_i for $u(i)$.

It is important to distinguish between an n-tuple, which is a function, and its range, which is a set. Consider the n-tuples

$$u:\{1,2,3,4\} \to R,$$

where $u(n) = 1/n$, and

$$v:\{1,2,3,4\} \to R,$$

where $v(1) = \frac{1}{2}$, $v(2) = 1$, $v(3) = \frac{1}{4}$, $v(4) = \frac{1}{3}$. It is clear that these are different n-tuples (functions), but they have the same range $\{1,\frac{1}{2},\frac{1}{3},\frac{1}{4}\}$.

Distinct (infinite) sequences may also have the same range. Consider the sequences

$$f:N \to R \qquad \text{and} \qquad g:N \to R,$$

where

$$f_n = \frac{1}{n},$$

$$g_{2n} = \frac{1}{2n - 1},$$

$$g_{2n-1} = \frac{1}{2n}.$$

These are obviously different sequences, but they have the same range, $\{1/n \mid n \in N\}$.

We write f to represent the function and $f(x)$ to represent the element of the codomain related, by the function, to the element x in the domain. We have referred to $f(x)$ as the value of the function at x. Some authors write xf instead of $f(x)$ for the value of the function at x.

This discussion does not exhaust all possible notations, but it should be sufficient to enable the reader to apply his knowledge of functions even to cases where the notation is unfamiliar.

The terms *map* and *mapping* are used as synonyms for *function*. For $f:A \to B$, we say that f maps A into B. We may also say that f *transforms* A into a subset of B and refer to the function as a *transformation*. A function is sometimes called an *operator*, and for $f:A \to B$ we say that f *operates* on A or f is an operator defined on A with values in B. If we want to emphasize that a certain relation is also a function, we shall call it a *functional relation*.

The wide variety of language and notation used in dealing with the concept of function may seem confusing to the reader at first. But the fact that during the years mathematicians have invented such a variety of language should suggest that the concept is very important and occurs in many contexts. It also indicates that mathematics, a development of many human minds, has followed no fixed code or canon but has developed in many different directions and with many different purposes.

3.4 Examples of functions

The examples of this section are chosen with a twofold purpose. We want the reader to recognize that many concepts with which he is already familiar are functions, although they may not have been explicitly named as such. The realization that these are functions should enable the reader to obtain a clearer understanding of the aspects of these concepts that may not have been fully explained. Our second purpose is to convince the reader that a *function is not the same as a formula.*

EXAMPLE 3.1

The idea of distance is in general use in mathematics and in everyday life, but the reader has perhaps never recognized that distance is a function. If we say that the distance between points a and b is 10 miles, we have associated with the pair (a,b) a real number 10. If we perform this operation for all pairs of points in S, the three-dimensional space in which we live, we have in fact a function, called the distance (in any convenient units), whose domain is $S \times S$ [the set of pairs of points (a,b)] and whose codomain is $R_+ \cup \{0\}$, the set of nonnegative real numbers. If we alter the units, we have a different distance function. All these functions have nonnegative real values and are defined on $S \times S$. They must also satisfy certain conditions, as follows.

If $\delta: S \times S \to R_+ \cup \{0\}$ is a distance function, then

1. $\delta(a,b) = 0$ if and only if $a = b$.
2. $\delta(a,b) = \delta(b,a)$ (we call this property *symmetry*).
3. $\delta(a,c) \leq \delta(a,b) + \delta(b,c)$.

Property 3 is called the *triangle inequality*. It states the well-known geometric property that, for any triangle (abc), the sum of the distances $\delta(a,b)$, $\delta(b,c)$ is not less than the distance $\delta(a,c)$ (see Figure 3.3). We have $\delta(a,c) = \delta(a,b) + \delta(b,c)$ if and only if b is on the line segment joining a and c.

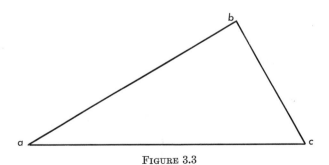

FIGURE 3.3

Mathematicians have generalized the concept of distance to include many other functions with codomain $R_+ \cup \{0\}$ and also to sets S other than our three-dimensional space. In all cases the distance function satisfies properties 1 to 3 above. In addition we require that the distance functions we use be related in certain ways to the geometric properties of the space.

EXAMPLE 3.2

The distance function we considered in Example 3.1 is closely related to the idea of the length of a line segment, and this in turn can be generalized to study the length of a polygonal line or a curve.

Let C be a set of curves.[2] When we speak of the length of $c \in C$, we mean a real number $l(c)$ (called the length of c) associated with c by some rule that constitutes a definition of the function $l : C \to R_+ \cup \{0\}$. We shall not attempt to define the length of a curve, but we shall describe some of its properties. The definition and hence the properties are dependent on some distance function $\delta : S \times S \to R_+ \cup \{0\}$.

1. By the segment $[a,b]$ we mean the set consisting of a, b, and all points that lie between a and b on the line defined by a and b. The segment is a very simple example of a curve, that is, $[a,b] \in C$. We require that

$$l([a,b]) = \delta(a,b),$$

where $\delta(a,b)$ is the distance between the points a and b.

2. If c is a polygonal line formed by the segments $[a_1,a_2]$, $[a_2,a_3]$, $\cdots$, $[a_{n-1},a_n]$, then

$$l(c) = l([a_1,a_2]) + \cdots + l([a_{n-1},a_n]).$$

3. We define two curves as congruent if one can be superimposed on the other.[3] We can visualize this by thinking of the curve c being represented by a rigid wire. If this model can be moved without distortion to coincide with curve c', then c and c' are congruent. One geometric property that we require our distance functions to have is that, whenever two *line segments* are congruent, their lengths are equal. It can then be shown that, if c and c' are congruent *curves*, then $l(c) = l(c')$.

---

[2] We shall not attempt the thorough study of curves that would be necessary to specify the exact nature of the set C. The concept of a curve and a discussion of rectifiable curves, that is, curves for which a length can be defined, can be found in advanced calculus texts. We shall assume that the reader's experience with such simple examples as polygonal lines and circles gives him an adequate intuitive understanding of this example.

[3] We recognize that this definition is not satisfactory for a precise study of geometry. We defend its use here on two grounds. It provides an adequate intuitive understanding for our purposes. The alternatives would require either an axiomatic study of geometry, a study of transformations in space, or the concept of a bijective function, which we have not yet introduced.

EXAMPLE 3.3

Area and volume are examples of functions. Let A be a set of plane figures such as triangles, closed polygons, circles, and many other figures.[4] Area is a function $a : A \to R_+ \cup \{0\}$ with the following properties:

1. $a(s) = a(s')$ if s is congruent to s'.
2. $a(\underset{1 < i < n}{\cup} s_i) = a(s_1) + \cdots + a(s_n)$, where $s_i \in A$ and $s_i \cap s_j = \varnothing$ for $i \neq j$.
3. $a(s) = 1$ where s is a square whose side has length 1.

Similarly, let B be a set of subsets of three-dimensional space such as cubes, spheres, pyramids, cones.[5] Volume is a real-valued function $v : B \to R_+ \cup \{0\}$ such that:

1. $v(b) = v(b')$, if b is congruent to b'.
2. $v(\overset{n}{\underset{i=1}{\cup}} b_i) = v(b_1) + \cdots + v(b_n)$, where $b_i \in B$ and $b_i \cap b_j = \varnothing$ for $i \neq j$.
3. $v(b) = 1$ if b is a cube with sides of length 1.

For both area and volume, property 3 relates these functions to the distance function.

EXAMPLE 3.4

When we draw the map of a country[6] we are in fact making use of a function whose domain is the set of points in the country and whose codomain is the set of points on the paper on which the map is drawn.

In some maps of the world a single point on the earth E may be represented by more than one point on the paper P. For example, in Mercator's projection, the same place appears on the right and left edges of the map. This violates the conditions for a function $E \to P$. We have, however, a function $m : P \to E$.

EXAMPLE 3.5

In this example we shall consider a sphere with one point removed and map it into a plane by means of a function called a *stereographic projection*.

[4] It is not possible at this level to give a characterization of the sets A or B.
[5] See previous footnote.
[6] This example should be intuitively clear to the reader even though we have not given a precise definition of what we mean by a country.

Let S be the surface of any sphere. Let P be a plane tangent to S at point s. Let n be the point on S diametrically opposite s (that is, n is the antipode of s). We shall now define a map $\sigma : A \to P$, where $A = \complement_S \{n\}$, that is, the surface of S without the point n.

Let x be any point of A. Then $\sigma(x)$ is the point of intersection of the plane P with the line through n and x (see Figure 3.4). We see that $\sigma(s) = s$.

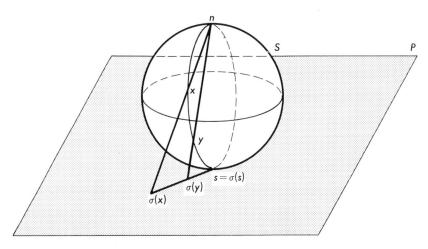

FIGURE 3.4

We can now see why n was excluded. The line through n and n is not determined.

From Figure 3.5 the reader can visualize the fact that any point in the "southern" hemisphere (shaded) maps into the interior of the shaded circle; any point on the "equator" maps into a point on the circle; and

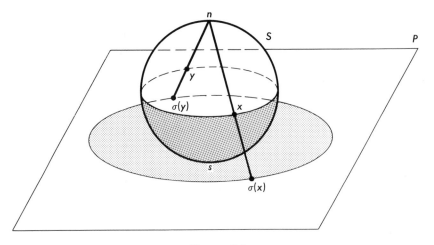

FIGURE 3.5

any point in the "northern" hemisphere maps into a point outside the shaded circle.

Any circle on S parallel to the equator is mapped by σ into a circle on P with center s. Any meridian circle on S passing through n and s is mapped by σ into a straight line in P passing through s (see Figure 3.6).

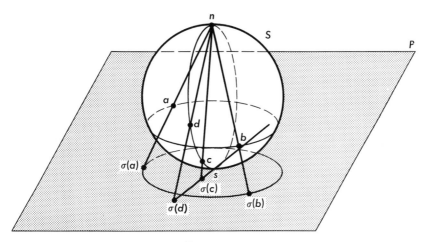

FIGURE 3.6

EXAMPLE 3.6

Addition and multiplication of numbers are also examples of functions. In performing addition we associate with the pair (a,b) of numbers a new number $a + b$, called the sum of a and b. If we are working with the real numbers, both addition and multiplication are functions whose domain is $R \times R$ and whose codomain is R.

EXAMPLE 3.7

The operations of set theory provide examples of functions similar to addition and multiplication. Let E be some set and let A, B be any subsets of E, that is, $A \in \mathcal{P}(E)$, $B \in \mathcal{P}(E)$ where $\mathcal{P}(E)$ is the power set of E, defined in Section 1.5. The union is a function

$$f : \mathcal{P}(E) \times \mathcal{P}(E) \to \mathcal{P}(E),$$

where $f(A,B) = A \cup B$. Similarly, for the intersection,

$$g : \mathcal{P}(E) \times \mathcal{P}(E) \to \mathcal{P}(E),$$

where $g(A,B) = A \cap B$. The complement can also be considered a function:

$$h:\mathcal{P}(E) \to \mathcal{P}(E),$$

where $h(A) = \complement_E A$.

If E contains only a finite number of elements, we can use the technique of Example 2.3 to draw the graph of h. In particular, Figure 3.7 shows the graph of h when $E = \{a,b,c\}$.

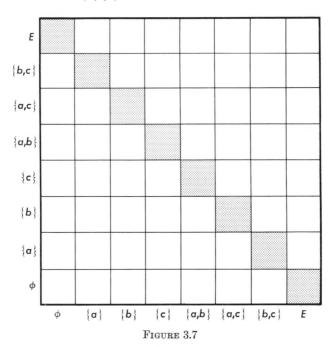

FIGURE 3.7

EXAMPLE   3.8

This example is based on Example 2.2. With any real number x we associate the integer $[x]$, the unique integer satisfying the condition $[x] \le x < [x] + 1$. These inequalities define a function with the set R of real numbers as domain and codomain, that is, $f:R \to R$ and $f(x) = [x]$. The graph G_f of this function is given in Figure 3.8. The graph is the union of the heavily drawn line segments, excluding the right end point but including the left.

The range of this function is the set Z of integers. We could also define a function $g:R \to Z$, where $g(x) = [x]$. We consider f and g different functions because they have different codomains, even though the domains and graphs are the same. This distinction is not insisted upon by some authors. It is consistent with our earlier statement that a function is determined by its domain, codomain, and graph. We consider two functions equal if and only if they have the same domain, the same codomain, and the same graph.

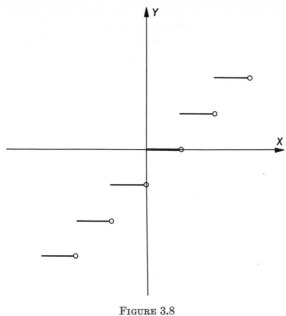

FIGURE 3.8

EXAMPLE 3.9

The reader has probably encountered in high school the concept of the absolute value of a real number; he may or may not have been given a precise definition for it. The absolute value is a function $f: R \rightarrow R$ whose graph is defined by

$$f(x) = x \qquad \text{if } x \geq 0,$$
$$= -x \qquad \text{if } x < 0.$$

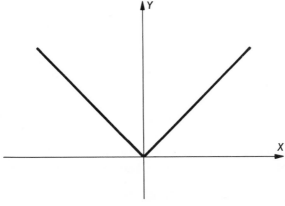

FIGURE 3.9

We usually write this $f(x) = |x|$. The reader will find that this definition includes his intuitive ideas of the absolute value.

The concept of absolute value appears several times later in this book. We shall not study it further at present, but simply present its graph in Figure 3.9.

EXAMPLE   3.10

The graph of a function is a set of ordered pairs that we may or may not be able to represent by a diagram. Even for a real-valued function of a real variable, it is not always possible to draw a reasonable facsimile of the graph, although we can describe the function and its graph. Consider the function $f:R \rightarrow R$, where

$$f(x) = 0 \quad \text{if } x \text{ is rational,}$$
$$= 1 \quad \text{if } x \text{ is irrational.}$$

This function is more easily defined than many functions with which the reader is familiar, such as $\sin x$, but its graph can hardly be drawn. We are able to sketch only a restricted class[7] of subsets of $R \times R$. The graph of this function is, of course,

$$G_f = \{p|p = (x,0), x \in Q\} \cup \{p|p = (x,1), x \in \complement_R Q\},$$

where Q, as usual, denotes the set of rational numbers.

We emphasize again that a function is not necessarily connected with an elementary formula. In very few of the examples we have considered has it been possible to represent the graph of the function by such a formula.

3.5   Some simple properties of functions

We have already pointed out that we speak of a function mapping A *into* B to emphasize that there may be $b \in B$ for which there is no $a \in A$ such that $f(a) = b$. This is illustrated in Figure 3.10. In this case $b \in B$ but $b \notin f(A)$; that is, there is no $a \in A$ such that $f(a) = b$. This diagram also illustrates the fact that there may be two or more points (a_1, a_2) with the same image with respect to f.

As an example consider $f:R \rightarrow R$, where $f(x) = x^2$. For any $y \in R$, $y < 0$, there is no $x \in A$ such that $f(x) = y$. Also $f(x) = f(-x)$ for all $x \in R$.

There are certain important properties which some functions possess and which are defined by restricting these properties that we have just seen may be true for some functions. We shall now consider these special properties.

---

[7] We are not concerned with a characterization of the sets that can be drawn but we point out that our limitations arise from the fact that drawing involves moving a pencil continuously with finite speed.

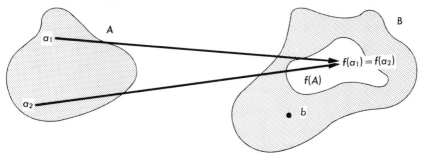

FIGURE 3.10

DEFINITION

A function $f:A \to B$ such that, for each $y \in B$, the equation $f(x) = y$ has *at least* one solution $x \in A$ is called a map of A *onto* B.

The map $f:R \to R$, where

$$f(x) = \tan x \qquad \text{if } x \neq \frac{k\pi}{2},$$

$$= 0 \qquad \text{if } x = \frac{k\pi}{2},$$

is a map of R *onto* R. A part of the graph of this function is represented in Figure 3.11 by the union of the curves and the dots on the x axis.

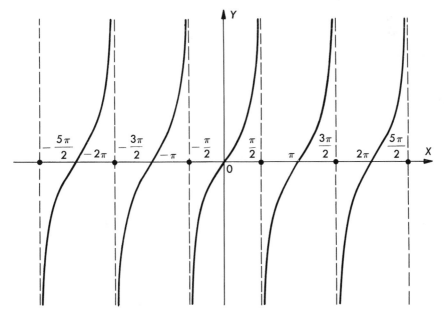

FIGURE 3.11

Another example is given by the *projection* of the plane on the y axis. This function is denoted by $pr_2 : R \times R$, where $pr_2((x,y)) = y$. The graph G_{pr_2} is a subset of $(R \times R) \times R$, that is, a subset of three-dimensional space. The reader who has had some experience with solid geometry, or who has good spatial intuition, will find Figure 3.12 helpful in visualizing G_{pr_2}. The

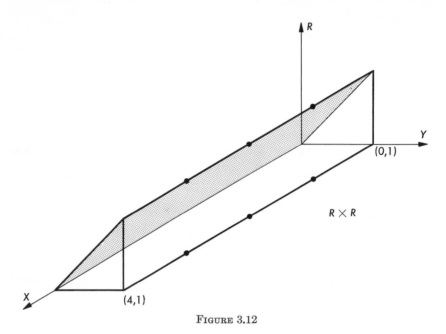

FIGURE 3.12

graph is represented by the shaded plane, which makes an angle of 45° with $R \times R$, the horizontal plane.

DEFINITION

A function $f: A \to B$ is called *injective*[8] if, for every $y \in B$, the equation $f(x) = y$ has *at most* one solution.

In other words, $f: A \to B$ is injective if $f(x_1) = f(x_2)$ implies that $x_1 = x_2$. For an injective map it is impossible for two different elements of the domain to be mapped into the same element of the codomain.

Let R_0 be the set of nonzero real numbers, that is,

$$R_0 = \{x | x \in R, x \neq 0\}.$$

Consider the function $f: R_0 \to R$, where $f(x) = 1/x$. If $1/x_1 = 1/x_2$, then $x_1 = x_2$, and the function is therefore injective. The function is not a map onto R because there is no $x \in R$ such that $1/x = 0$, that is, 0 is not in the range of f.

[8] Some authors use "one-to-one" for this concept.

DEFINITION

A map $f:A \to B$ is called a *bijective* map if it is both an injective map and a map onto B.

We can express this by saying that $f:A \to B$ is a bijective map if, for each $y \in B$, the equation $f(x) = y$ has *exactly one* solution $x \in A$.

The map $f:R \to R$, where $f(x) = x^3$, is a bijective map.

DEFINITION

A bijective map whose domain and codomain are the same set is called a *permutation.*[9]

Let $A = \{1,2,3,4,5\}$. Let f be the function $f:A \to A$ whose graph is

$$G_f = \{(1,3),(2,5),(3,1),(4,2),(5,4)\}.$$

This function is a permutation of A.

The function $f:R \to R$, where $f(x) = 2x + 1$, is a permutation of R, the set of real numbers.

Let A be any set and let $\mathcal{O}(A)$ be its power set. Define a function $f:\mathcal{O}(A) \to \mathcal{O}(A)$, where $f(X) = \mathbf{C}_A X$ for each $X \in \mathcal{O}(A)$. This function is onto $\mathcal{O}(A)$, since for each $Y \in \mathcal{O}(A)$ we can choose $X = \mathbf{C} Y$ and then $f(X) = f(\mathbf{C} Y) = \mathbf{C}(\mathbf{C} Y) = Y$. Also it is injective because, if $f(X) = f(X')$, then $\mathbf{C} X = \mathbf{C} X'$ and $X = \mathbf{C}(\mathbf{C} X) = \mathbf{C}(\mathbf{C} X') = X'$. Hence the function is a permutation.

In particular, if $A = \{a,b\}$ we have the graph

$$G_f = \{(\varnothing,A),(\{a\},\{b\}),(\{b\},\{a\}),(A,\varnothing)\}.$$

EXERCISES

3.1. The following relations have the set R as domain and codomain, x represents an element of the domain, y of the codomain. Which are functions?

    (a) $x \rho y$, if and only if $x^2 - y^2 = 0$.
    (b) $x \rho_1 y$, if and only if $x^3 - y^3 = 0$.
    (c) $x \rho_2 y$, if and only if $\sqrt{x} - y = 0$.

3.2. A relation ρ with R as domain and codomain is defined as follows: $x \rho y$, if and only if $y = 4x/(2x + 1)$. Is ρ a function?

3.3. A relation ρ with R as domain and codomain is defined as follows: "$x \rho y$ if and only if $x^4 + y^4 = 1$." Is ρ a function?

3.4. Let S be the set of students who wrote an examination in set theory for which grades of A, B, C, D, F were given. Let $M = \{A,B,C,D,F\}$. A relation with domain S and codomain M is defined as follows: "If $x \in S$ and $m \in M$, then $s \rho m$ if and only if s received the grade m." Is ρ a function?

[9] Some writers restrict the word "permutation" to functions with finite domain.

3.5. Which of the following relations with R as domain and codomain are functions? In each case x is an element from the domain, y from the codomain.

(a) $x \rho y$, if and only if $x^2 = y$.
(b) $x \rho_1 y$, if and only if $y^2 = x$.
(c) $x \rho_2 y$, if and only if $y^3 = x$.

3.6. Let A be a set of authors and B the set of all books. If $a \in A$ and $b \in B$, we say that $a \rho b$ if and only if a is the author of b. Is ρ a function?

3.7. Let M^* be the set of all married men, W^* the set of all married women. If $x \in M^*$ and $y \in W^*$, we say that $x \rho y$ if and only if x is the husband of y. Is this relation a function? State any assumptions you must make in order to give an answer.

3.8. Under what conditions can a relation with A as domain and codomain be both a functional relation and an equivalence relation?

3.9. (a) What is the largest subset $A \subset R$ such that $f:A \to R$ is a function with $f(x) = (x + 1)/(x - 2)$?

(b) Draw the graph of f.
(c) What is the range of f?
(d) Is f injective?
(e) Is f onto?

3.10. Which of the following functions are (1) onto, or (2) injective?

(a) $f:\mathcal{P}(E) \times \mathcal{P}(E) \to \mathcal{P}(E)$, where $f(A,B) = A \cup B$.
(b) $g:\mathcal{P}(E) \to \mathcal{P}(F)$, where $E \subset F$, $E \neq F$, and $g(A) = \mathbf{C}_F A$.
(c) $h:\mathcal{P}(E) \times \mathcal{P}(E) \to \mathcal{P}(E)$, where $h(A,B) = (A - B) \cup (B - A)$.
(d) $k:\mathcal{P}(E) \times \mathcal{P}(E) \to \mathcal{P}(E)$, where $k(A,B) = A \cap B$.

3.11. Consider the function $f:Z \to Z$, where Z is the set of all integers, $b \in Z$ is a fixed integer, and $f(n) = bn$. Is f injective? Is it onto?

3.12. Consider the function $f:R \to R$, where $f(x) = 5x^3 - 1$. Is f injective? Is it onto?

3.13. Is the function $f:R \to R$, where $f(x) = x^2 + 2x$, injective? Is it onto?

3.14. Let R_+ be the set of positive real numbers. Is the function $f:R_+ \to R$, where $f(x) = \log x$, injective? Is it onto?

3.15. Is the distance function of Example 3.1 injective?

3.16. (a) Is the map of a country $m:C \to P$ in Example 3.4 injective? Is it onto?

(b) Is the Mercator projection map of the world, $m:P \to E$, in Example 3.4 injective?

3.17. Is the stereographic projection of Example 3.5 injective? Is it onto?

3.18. If $f:R \to R$, where $f(x) = [x]$, is the function of Example 3.8, is f injective? Is it onto?

3.19. Is the absolute value function $f:R \to R$, where $f(x) = |x|$, of Example 3.9 injective? Is it onto?

3.20. Consider the function $f:R \to R$, where

$$f(x) = \tan x \quad \text{if } x \neq \frac{k\pi}{2},$$

$$0 \quad \text{if } x = \frac{k\pi}{2}.$$

Is f injective?

3.21. Give examples chosen from those in the text or others to show that injective and onto are independent concepts, that is, that a function may have any of the following combinations of properties:

      (a) neither injective nor onto,
      (b) injective but not onto,
      (c) onto but not injective,
      (d) injective and onto (bijective).

3.22. Let $A = \{1,2,3,4,5\}$ and let $f: A \to A$ be the function whose graph is

$$G_f = \{(1,3),(2,5),(3,1),(4,2),(5,4)\}.$$

Show that f is a permutation.

3.23. Prove that the function $f: R \to R$, where $f(x) = 2x + 1$, is a permutation.

3.24. Let $f: A \to B$, $g: A \to B$ be functions with graphs G_f and G_g, respectively· If $G_f \cap G_g$ is the graph of a function with domain A and codomain B, what can you conclude about the functions f and g?

3.6 The concept of cardinal number

If a person were asked by a curious child or by a critically minded adult to define the concept of number or what he meant by saying there were a certain number of objects, he would find it a difficult task. The problem troubled mathematicians until G. Cantor introduced set theory. Even today many dictionaries do not give a satisfactory definition of number.

We now have sufficient set theory at our disposal to analyze the meaning of such statements as, "I have seven books" or "There are the same number of boys and girls in the class."

Let us for the moment lay aside our knowledge of counting to consider more carefully what counting means. Without using our process of counting, we want to test the truth of the statement: "The number of boys in the class is the same as the number of girls." One way to do this would be to ask each boy to select a partner for a dance and to make his choice so that no two boys are trying to dance with the same girl. If when this is done each girl is the partner of some boy, and each boy has a partner, we say that the number of boys is the same as the number of girls.

This process of choice can be described in set-theoretical terms as a function. The choice that each boy b made in selecting a girl g as a partner defined a map $p: B \to G$ (where B is the set of all boys and G is the set of all girls). It is a function provided each boy has a partner. We asked the boys not to quarrel for the same girl, that is, $p(b) \neq p(b')$ if $b \neq b'$. This means that p is an injective map. We checked whether for each $g \in G$ there was some $b \in B$ such that $p(b) = g$. If this is true, then p is a bijective map. If the mapping is bijective we say that there are the same number of boys and girls or that the *sets B and G have the same number of elements.* If there is a girl g that has no boy dancing with her (that is, there is no $b \in B$ such that $p(b) = g$), then we say that there are fewer boys than girls or that *the number of elements of B is less than the number of elements of G.*

The reader should realize that what we have done here is essentially what he was taught to do when he learned to count. Counting is traditionally taught in terms of deciding whether a certain set has the same number of elements as a subset of the set of beads on an abacus or counting frame. If the abacus is not available, many children count on their fingers, that is, they set up a bijective correspondence or function between the elements of the set they want to count and a subset of the set of their fingers. The idea of a bijective correspondence is fundamental in counting. This provides us with a definition of the concept of two sets having the same number of elements.

In the examples we have suggested it has been possible in each case to set up a bijective map onto the set of natural numbers from 1 to n for some n. There is no reason why our ideas cannot be extended to cases where such a map (on this standard set $\{1, \cdot \cdot \cdot ,n\}$) does not exist. The following definition of cardinal number includes this more general case.

DEFINITION

Two sets A and B have the same *cardinal number* (written card A = card B) if there is a bijective map $f : A \rightarrow B$.

We say that card $A \leq$ card B (read: the cardinal number of A is less than or equal to the cardinal number of B) if there is an injective map $f : A \rightarrow B$.

This definition does not alter our previous ideas about sets with the same number of elements. The cases that we have considered so far are all finite sets.

It can be proved rigorously[10] that there is no bijective map between the set

$$A = \{1,2, \cdot \cdot \cdot ,n\}$$

and a proper subset $B \subset A$. It is, however, possible to give a bijective map between the set N of all positive integers and a proper subset of N. For example, let E be the set of even positive integers. Then $f : N \rightarrow E$, where $f(n) = 2n$ is a bijective map.

We can use these ideas to define *finite* and *infinite*.

DEFINITION

A set A is called *infinite* if there is a proper subset $B \subset A$ and a bijective map $f : A \rightarrow B$. A set A is called *finite* if, for every proper subset $B \subset A$, there is no bijective map $f : A \rightarrow B$.

---

[10] The rigorous proof requires an axiomatic development of the natural numbers. This is touched upon in Chapter 5, but the details of the proof remain beyond the scope of this book.

There are other ways to define finite and infinite. We cannot go into a comparison of the various possible definitions. The details of what we have done and many other properties of cardinal numbers can be found in books devoted to a more complete study of the theory of sets.

3.7   Some standard maps and standard construction of maps

In this section we shall discuss several particular functions that have simple definitions. Some of these, although they are simple, are of considerable importance. We shall also discuss some ways in which new functions can be constructed from known functions.

I. The Identity Map

For a given set A the simplest map to define with A as domain and codomain is:

$$i_A : A \to A, \qquad \text{where } i_A(x) = x \text{ for all } x \in A.$$

The function i_A is called the *identity map* (or function) on A.

It is obvious that the identity map is a bijective map of A onto itself, that is, a permutation. The graph of i_A is the diagonal of $A \times A$.

II. The Inclusion Map

Suppose B is any set and A is a subset $A \subset B$. Consider the map

$$j : A \to B, \qquad \text{where } j(x) = x \text{ for all } x \in A.$$

We call this function the *inclusion map* of A into B. The inclusion map is injective, but not one-to-one unless $A = B$. The graph of j is

$$G_j = \{ p | p = (x,x), x \in A \}.$$

G_j is not the diagonal of $B \times B$ but a subset of it. $G_j \subset A \times B$ and $A \times B$ does not have a diagonal set if $A \neq B$.

As a particular example, suppose $A = \{x | 0 \le x \le 1\}$ and $B = R$ (the real numbers). Then the graph G_j of the inclusion is shown in Figure 3.13. The set $A \times B$ is the vertical strip, not the whole plane; hence $A \times B$ does not have a diagonal.

III. The Constants

Another easily defined set of functions is the constants. We say that a map $f : A \to B$ is a *constant function* if, for each $x \in A$ and $x' \in A, f(x) = f(x')$.

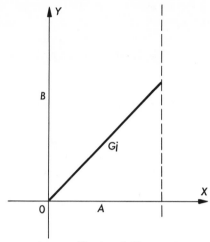

FIGURE 3.13

It is obvious that with each $b \in B$ we can associate one constant map $f(x) = b$ for all $x \in A$. Thus we can say that the set of constant maps with domain A and codomain B has the same cardinal number as the set B.

IV. The Characteristic Function

We have emphasized that from our point of view a function is defined by its domain, codomain, and graph. The simplest codomain for $f : A \to B$ consists of a single element. In this case there is exactly one function $f : A \to B$.

As a next step in complexity, the codomain may be a set of exactly two elements, say $B = \{0,1\}$. Then a function $f : A \to B$ will take as value either 0 or 1 for each $x \in A$. We can associate with this function $f : A \to \{0,1\}$ the set

$$E = \{x | x \in A, f(x) = 1\}.$$

We call this function the *characteristic function* of $E \subset A$.

For each $E \subset A$ we can define the characteristic function $f_E : A \to \{0,1\}$ as

$$f_E(x) = 1 \qquad \text{if } x \in E,$$
$$= 0 \qquad \text{if } x \notin E.$$

For instance, if $A = \{1,2,3,4\}$ and $E = \{3,4\}$, then the characteristic function $f_E : A \to \{0,1\}$ has the graph

$$G_{f_E} = \{(1,0),(2,0),(3,1),(4,1)\}.$$

In general for $E \subset A$ the graph of $f_E : A \to \{0,1\}$ is

$$G_{f_E} = \{p | p = (x,1) \text{ for } x \in E\} \cup \{p | p = (x,0) \text{ for } x \in \mathbf{C}_A E\}.$$

This is illustrated in Figure 3.14.

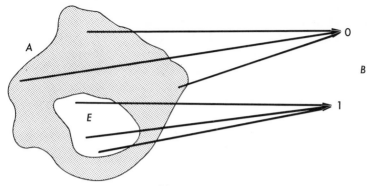

FIGURE 3.14

By associating with each subset $E \in \mathcal{P}(A)$ the characteristic function $f_E : A \to \{0,1\}$, we construct a bijective map between $\mathcal{P}(A)$ and the set of all the characteristic functions with domain A. That is, the two sets have the same cardinal number.

V. Restriction and Extension of Functions

We shall now consider one of the simplest ways of constructing a new function from a known function. Suppose we have a function $f : A \to B$ and a subset $E \subset A$. We denote by $f|E$ a function $f|E : E \to B$, which we call the *restriction* of f to E and whose graph is

$$G_{f|E} = \{p \mid p = (x, f(x)), x \in E\}.$$

We also refer to f as the *extension* of $f|E$ to A. This idea of extension can also be stated as follows. If two maps $f : A \to B$ and $g : E \to B$ are given such that $E \subset A$ and for each $x \in E$, $f(x) = g(x)$, then we say that f is an extension of g to A. These ideas are illustrated in Figure 3.15.

The graph $G_{f|E}$ is a subset of the graph G_f, that is, $G_g \subset G_f$.

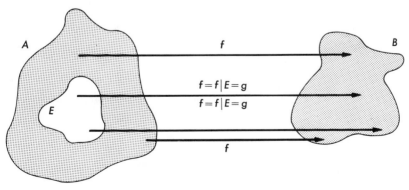

FIGURE 3.15

By way of an example, we point out that the inclusion map $j : E \to A$, where $E \subset A$ and $j(x) = x$, is a restriction of the identity $i_A : A \to A$ to E. Also i_A is an extension of j to A. If $E \neq A$ there are other extensions.

Many inportant problems in mathematics are concerned with constructing or proving the existence of an extension of a given map. We have seen that it is easy to define a restriction of a map to some subset of the domain, and it is clear that the restriction is unique. It may not be as easy to construct an extension map, especially if we further complicate the problem by requiring that the extension satisfy certain conditions. It may happen that there is no extension that satisfies the conditions or, at the other extreme, there may be many such extensions.

For example, consider the functions we refer to as length, area, and volume. The ancient Greek mathematicians successfully defined these for a limited class of geometric figures. When the calculus came into use these functions were extended to a domain that included as a proper subset the geometric figures that the Greeks had handled. At the beginning of the twentieth century a further extension was accomplished and these concepts are now used in a very general context, but this generality is limited by the requirement that the functions satisfy certain conditions suggested by the geometric figures. Some of these restrictions were listed as properties when we used these functions as examples in Section 3.4.

VI. Inverse Functions

If $f : A \to B$ is a bijective map, we can obtain from it a map with domain B and codomain A. If f is a bijective map, then for each $b \in B$ the equation $f(x) = b$ has a unique solution $a \in A$. Define $g : B \to A$ as follows: $g(b) =$ unique solution of $f(x) = b$. We call the map g the *inverse map* (or *inverse function*) of f. If f is a bijective map, we usually denote its inverse by f^{-1}. It is clear that domain of $f^{-1} =$ codomain of f and codomain of $f^{-1} =$ domain of f. The inverse function is illustrated in Figure 3.16.

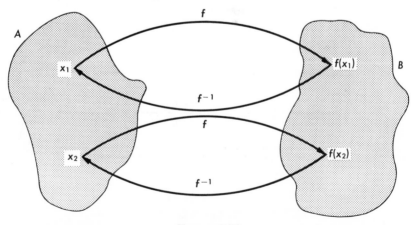

FIGURE 3.16

The graph of f^{-1} is

$$G_{f^{-1}} = \{p \mid p = (b,a), a \in A, b \in B, f(a) = b\}.$$

Also $G_f \subset A \times B$ and $G_{f^{-1}} \subset B \times A$.

The inverse map of the identity $i_A : A \to A$ is i_A itself, that is, $i_A^{-1} = i_A$. There are permutations other than the identity for which $f = f^{-1}$. For example, consider the power set $\mathcal{P}(A)$ and the permutation

$$f : \mathcal{P}(A) \to \mathcal{P}(A),$$

where $f(X) = \complement X$ for each $X \in \mathcal{P}(A)$. For the inverse function we want

$$f^{-1}(X) = \text{the unique set } Y \text{ such that } \complement Y = X.$$

Then

$$f(X) = f(\complement Y) = \complement(\complement Y) = Y,$$

and therefore $f^{-1}(X) = f(X)$.

A permutation that is its own inverse is called an *involution*. Any permutation has an inverse permutation, but not all permutations are involutions.

As a further example of an involution consider the bijective map $f : R \times R \to R \times R$ of the plane $R \times R$ into itself defined by the reflection of each point $p \in R \times R$ with respect to a fixed line $L \subset R \times R$ as in Figure 3.17. It is left to the reader to prove that f is bijective and $f^{-1} = f$.

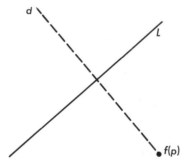

FIGURE 3.17

VII. The Reduced Map

Another map that has a simple definition in terms of a given map $f : A \to B$ is the *reduced map* of f, that is, the map $g : A \to f(A)$ such that $g(a) = f(a)$ for all $a \in A$. The maps f and g have the same domain, the same range, and the same graph, but they do not have the same codomain. The codomain of the reduced map of f is the range of f. We have already emphasized that we distinguish between functions with different codomains. We must not confuse a map with its reduced map.

If $f : A \to B$ is injective, but is not onto, we cannot talk about its inverse, since there are elements $b \in B$ such that there is no $a \in A$ for which $f(a) = b$.

If $f:A \to B$ is injective, then its reduced map $g:A \to f(A)$ is bijective and has an inverse $g^{-1}:f(A) \to A$.

As an example let A be any set, E any subset $E \subset A$, and let $j:E \to A$ be the inclusion map of E into A, that is, $j(x) = x$ for all $x \in E$. The reduced map of j is $i_E:E \to E$ where $i_E(x) = x$ for all $x \in E$, that is, the identity map on E.

3.8   Composition of functions

A most common method of constructing a new function from given functions is the *composition of functions*. Suppose we have functions $f:A \to B$ and $g:C \to D$, where $f(A) \subset C$, that is, the range of f is a subset of the domain of g. For every $a \in A$ there is a corresponding value of the function $f(a) \in B$. For every $c \in C$ there is a value of the function $g(c) \in D$. In particular, $f(a) \in C$, and therefore there is a value $g(f(a)) \in D$. Thus for any $a \in A$ we have defined $g(f(a)) \in D$. Consider the set

$$G_{gf} = \{p|p = (x,g(f(x))),x \in A\}.$$

Since $g(f(x)) \in D$, we have $G_{gf} \subset A \times D$, so that it is the graph of a relation. If (x,z) and (x,z') are both elements of G_{gf}, then there must be $y,y' \in f(A)$ such that $g(y) = z$ and $g(y') = z'$ and also $f(x) = y$ and $f(x) = y'$. But this can be true only if $y = y'$ and hence $z = z'$. Thus G_{gf} is the graph of a function with domain A and codomain D. We call this function the *composite function* or *composition of f and g* and denote it by $g \cdot f$. Thus we have $g \cdot f:A \to D$, where $(g \cdot f)(x) = g(f(x))$.

The order in which we write the symbols of a composite function is important. That is, $f \cdot g$ and $g \cdot f$ are not generally the same function. In fact, the existence of $g \cdot f$ does not prove the existence of $f \cdot g$. If $f:A \to B$, $g:C \to D$, and both $g \cdot f$ and $f \cdot g$ are defined, it does not follow that $g \cdot f$ and $f \cdot g$ are the same function. We shall see by examples that we may have one but not both composites defined and that even when they are both defined they need not be equal.

The idea of a composite function is represented by the diagram in Figure 3.18. The sets A, B, C, D are represented by regions. The arrows,

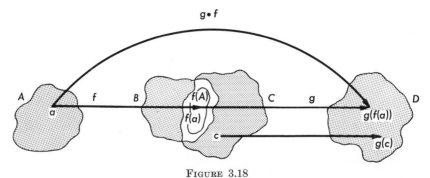

FIGURE 3.18

marked by the symbol of a function, relate an element of the domain to its value with respect to the function in the codomain.

EXAMPLE 3.11

Consider the sets $A = \{1,2,3,4\}$, $B = \{3,5,7,11\}$, $C = \{5,7,11,12\}$, $D = \{6,8,9,10\}$, and the maps $f:A \to B$ with

$$G_f = \{(1,7),(2,11),(3,5),(4,7)\},$$

and $g:C \to D$ with

$$G_g = \{(5,6),(7,8),(11,8),(12,9)\}.$$

The composite $g \cdot f:A \to D$ has the graph

$$G_{g \cdot f} = \{(1,8),(2,8),(3,6),(4,8)\}.$$

The composite $f \cdot g$ is not defined, since $g(C) \not\subset A$.

EXAMPLE 3.12

Consider the permutations $f:A \to A$ and $g:A \to A$, where

$$A = \{1,2,3,4\},$$
$$G_f = \{(1,2),(2,3),(3,4),(4,1)\},$$

and

$$G_g = \{(1,4),(2,3),(3,2),(4,1)\}.$$

The permutations can conveniently be written

$$f = \begin{pmatrix} 1 & 2 & 3 & 4 \\ 2 & 3 & 4 & 1 \end{pmatrix} \quad \text{and} \quad g = \begin{pmatrix} 1 & 2 & 3 & 4 \\ 4 & 3 & 2 & 1 \end{pmatrix}.$$

This notation gives all the information needed to determine the function. The first row gives the domain, the second row the range, which for a permutation is also the codomain, and each column gives an ordered pair of the graph. This notation can be used for any bijective map of a finite set onto a finite set, not just for permutations, and can be used to represent the graph of any function with a finite domain.

The composite functions $g \cdot f$ and $f \cdot g$ can be represented

$$g \cdot f = \begin{pmatrix} 1 & 2 & 3 & 4 \\ 2 & 3 & 4 & 1 \\ 3 & 2 & 1 & 4 \end{pmatrix} \quad \text{and} \quad f \cdot g = \begin{pmatrix} 1 & 2 & 3 & 4 \\ 4 & 3 & 2 & 1 \\ 1 & 4 & 3 & 2 \end{pmatrix}.$$

The small figures in the middle row do not form a part of the usual notation. They represent $f(x)$ in $g \cdot f$ and $g(x)$ in $f \cdot g$. They are included to make clear the way in which the composites are formed. In this case the two composite functions $g \cdot f$ and $f \cdot g$ are distinct maps of A onto itself.

EXAMPLE 3.13

Consider the plane $R \times R$ and the maps $f:R \times R \to R \times R$ and $g:R \times R \to R \times R$, where

$$f(x,y) = (x + 4, y + 5),$$
$$g(x,y) = (x + 2, y + 1).$$

These transformations are represented in Figure 3.19, where we consider the effect of the various maps on the points $(0,0)$ and $(-7,1)$. The

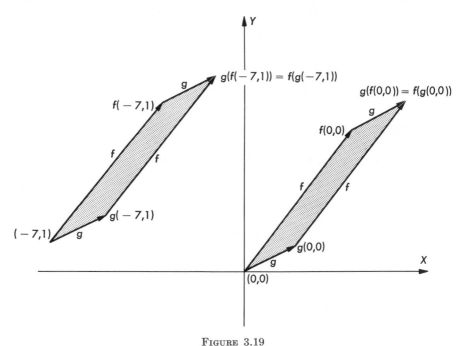

FIGURE 3.19

arrows labeled f and g relate points of $R \times R$ to their values under the corresponding function.

The transformations considered here are called *translations*. If f is a translation, then all line segments $[(x,y), f(x,y)]$ are congruent. If f and g are translations, then $f \cdot g = g \cdot f$.

We mentioned in Section 3.3 that the symbol for the function is sometimes written to the right of the element from the domain. This is done in the case of the mth power x^m. Some authors prefer this notation in general and write xf instead of $f(x)$. In this notation the composite of f and g (which we denote by $g \cdot f$) is written $f \cdot g$ to be consistent with the notation $x(f \cdot g) = (xf)g$.

Consider the functions u, v with R as domain and codomain and such that $u(x) = x^m$, $v(x) = x^n$. In our notation we have $(uv)(x) = (x^n)^m$ and

$(vu)(x) = (x^m)^n$. In this case the order of the symbols in uv is the reverse of the order in $(x^n)^m$. In this example the order is of no importance, since $uv = vu$.

3.9 The associativity of composition

Consider the three maps

$$f:A \to B, \qquad g:C \to D, \qquad h:E \to F,$$

where $f(A) \subset C$, $g(C) \subset E$. Then the composite of f and g is defined

$$g \cdot f:A \to D,$$

and also the composite of g and h:

$$h \cdot g:C \to F.$$

Now we observe that the range of $g \cdot f$ is a subset of the domain of h. Thus we can define

$$h \cdot (g \cdot f):A \to F.$$

The maps $h \cdot (g \cdot f)$ and $(h \cdot g) \cdot f$ have the same domain A and the same codomain F. Theorem 3.1 shows that these maps are equal.

THEOREM 3.1

The functions $h \cdot (g \cdot f):A \to F$ and $(h \cdot g) \cdot f:A \to F$ are equal.

Proof

We have already shown that the two functions have the same domain and the same codomain. We must now show that they have the same graph, that is, for each $a \in A$ the values of the functions are equal, $(h \cdot (g \cdot f))(a) = ((h \cdot g) \cdot f)(a)$.

For convenience we write $h \cdot (g \cdot f)$ as s and $(h \cdot g) \cdot f$ as t. Then, since s is the composite of $g \cdot f$ and h, we have $s(a) = h(g \cdot f(a))$. Also $g \cdot f$ is the composite of f and g; therefore $g \cdot f(a) = g(f(a))$ and

$$s(a) = h(g(f(a))).$$

The function t is the composite of f and $h \cdot g$, therefore $t(a) = h \cdot g(f(a))$. Also $h \cdot g$ is the composite of g and h; therefore $h \cdot g(f(a)) = h(g(f(a)))$ and $t(a) = h(g(f(a)))$.

From this we see that for each $a \in A$, $s(a) = t(a)$ and therefore $s = t$. •

The result of this theorem is often referred to as the "associativity of the composition of maps." In view of this theorem we can write $h \cdot g \cdot f$ to denote the two equal maps $h \cdot (g \cdot f)$ and $(h \cdot g) \cdot f$. We see that the position of brackets in the expression does not matter, but the order of the symbols h, g, f does matter.

Composition is one of the main tools for constructing new functions from given functions. It is particularly useful in the case of functions whose domain and codomain are equal, for then the existence of the composite functions is assured. If $f:A \rightarrow A$ and $g:A \rightarrow A$, then the composites $g \cdot f:A \rightarrow A$ and $f \cdot g:A \rightarrow A$ are defined as well as $f \cdot f:A \rightarrow A$, $g \cdot g$, $f \cdot f \cdot f$, $f \cdot g \cdot f \cdot f$, etc.

The reader has some appreciation of the power of this method to create from a few known functions a large collection of new functions. This method is widely used in mathematics.

It is convenient to have a simpler notation for such functions as $f \cdot f$. If $f:A \rightarrow A$, then

$$f \cdot f:A \rightarrow A \text{ is denoted by } f^2,$$
$$f \cdot f \cdot f:A \rightarrow A \text{ is denoted by } f^3,$$
$$\cdots$$
$$f \cdots f:A \rightarrow A \text{ is denoted by } f^n, \text{ where}$$
$$f \text{ appears } n \text{ times in } f \cdots f.$$

We call these functions, respectively, the *first iteration, second iteration,* . . . , $(n - 1)$th *iteration* of f.

For some maps there is a positive integer n such that $f^n = i_A$ (the identity). In these cases the method of iteration produces only a finite set of distinct maps. In other cases f^m and f^n are distinct whenever $m \neq n$. In these cases we can start with a single function f and use iteration to obtain an infinite set of maps of A into A. Example 3.14 is designed to show a simple case in which the set of maps obtained by iteration is infinite.

EXAMPLE   3.14

Consider the set N of positive integers and the map $\sigma:N \rightarrow N$, where $\sigma(x) = x + 1$ for all $x \in N$. This map is called the *successor function*. It is studied in greater detail in Chapter 5.

The addition of $n \in N$ to a number $x \in N$ is a function $s_n:N \rightarrow N$ where $s_n(x) = x + n$. It is obvious that $s_n(x) = \sigma^n(x)$, that is, s_n is the $(n - 1)$th iteration of the successor function. In this case it is clear that $\sigma^m \neq \sigma^n$ if $m \neq n$.

The student is warned that some writers use f^n *not* to denote an iteration of f, but rather to denote the composite of f and g, where $g(x) = x^n$. For example, $\log^2 x$ is written for $(\log x)^2$, rather than for $\log(\log x)$. Thus $\log^2$ is the composite of $f(x) = \log x$ and $g(x) = x^2$. Similarly, $\sin^3 x$ denotes $(\sin x)^3$, not $\sin(\sin(\sin x))$. Thus $\sin^3$ is the composite of $h(x) = \sin x$ and $k(x) = x^3$.

3.10 Functions of two or more variables

Many of the functions used in mathematics and in applications to physics and other subjects have as their domain a set which is the Cartesian product of two or more sets. These are traditionally referred to as functions of several variables (in particular functions of two variables, three variables, etc.).

As an example, consider the problem of describing the temperature in a country during a certain year. If we let Y represent the year and C represent the set of weather stations, then we want to associate with each pair (t,x)— where t is a moment in Y and x is a weather station in C—a number that represents the temperature at the place x at the moment t. That is, we have a map

$$T : C \times Y \to R.$$

Several mathematical examples are given in Part II, where addition and multiplication for the number systems are introduced and these ideas are extended to algebraic systems. Example 3.6 has already considered the sum $s : R \times R \to R$ and product $p : R \times R \to R$ of real numbers.

The reader will recall that early in his training in arithmetic he encountered an addition (or multiplication) table such as the one reproduced in part in Table 3.1. Each cell of this table represents an element of the Cartesian product $N \times N$, the domain of the function. In each cell appears the element of N that is the value of the function for this element of the domain. This device is useful for describing the graph of a function whose domain is $A \times B$ where A and B are finite sets.

Table 3.1

+	1	2	3	4	5
1	2	3	4	5	6
2	3	4	5	6	7
3	4	5	6	7	8
4	5	6	7	8	9
5	6	7	8	9	10

From a function of two variables $f : A \times B \to C$ we can obtain two new functions, one with domain A and one with domain B, called the *partial functions associated with f*. These functions are constructed by the method referred to as holding one variable constant.

We shall study these partial functions by means of an example. Let $f : R \times R \to R$ be a function such that $f(x,y) = 2x^2y$. When we say that we "hold x constant," we mean that we select some $a \in R$ and consider the function

$$\varphi_a : R \to R, \qquad \text{where } \varphi_a(y) = 2a^2y.$$

In particular when $a = 5$ we have

$$\varphi_5 : R \to R, \qquad \text{where } \varphi_5(y) = 50y.$$

When we speak of "holding y constant," we select $b \in R$ and consider the function

$$\psi_b : R \to R, \qquad \text{where } \psi_b(x) = 2bx^2.$$

In particular when $b = 7$, we have

$$\psi_7 : R \to R, \qquad \text{where } \psi_7(x) = 14x^2.$$

The functions φ_a and ψ_b are called the partial functions associated with f.

The partial functions can also be obtained by the composition of f with one of two simple functions.

Consider the injective map

$$j_a : R \to R \times R, \qquad \text{where } j_a(y) = (a,y).$$

Then $\varphi_a = f \cdot j_a$, since $j_a(y) = (a,y)$, $f(a,y) = 2a^2y$, and hence $\varphi_a(y) = f(j_a(y))$. Similarly, $\psi_b = f \cdot k_b$, where

$$k_b : R \to R \times R \qquad \text{and} \qquad k_b(x) = (x,b).$$

The function $k_3 : R \to R \times R$ is represented in Figure 3.20 where R and $R \times R$ are represented on separate diagrams. The heavy line labeled $k_3(R)$ is the range of k_3, that is, the set of points $(x,3)$.

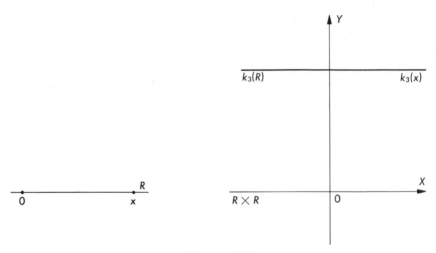

FIGURE 3.20

3.11   The set of all functions of A into B

In all our discussion of functions or maps of A into B we have seen that, when the domain A and codomain B are given, the only additional information needed to determine the function is the graph, that is, a subset of $A \times B$ or an element of the power set $\mathcal{P}(A \times B)$. From this we see that the set of all possible graphs of functions with domain A and codomain B will be described by some subset of $\mathcal{P}(A \times B)$. We denote the *set of all functions of A into B* by $\mathcal{F}(A,B)$ or by B^A. As a memory device for the latter notation the student might think of the superscript (representing the domain) being mapped or thrown down on the base (the codomain).

As an example, let $A = \{a,b,c\}$ and $B = \{0,1\}$. In this case we can write out the graph for each possible function. We choose to do this in terms of the notation we introduced for permutations of a finite set. That is, for $f_1: A \to B$ such that $f_1(a) = 0, f_1(b) = 0, f_1(c) = 0$, we write $f_1 = \begin{pmatrix} a & b & c \\ 0 & 0 & 0 \end{pmatrix}$.

Then $\mathcal{F}(A,B) = \{f_1,f_2,f_3,f_4,f_5,f_6,f_7,f_8\}$, where

$$f_1 = \begin{pmatrix} a & b & c \\ 0 & 0 & 0 \end{pmatrix},$$

$$f_2 = \begin{pmatrix} a & b & c \\ 0 & 0 & 1 \end{pmatrix},$$

$$f_3 = \begin{pmatrix} a & b & c \\ 0 & 1 & 0 \end{pmatrix},$$

$$f_4 = \begin{pmatrix} a & b & c \\ 1 & 0 & 0 \end{pmatrix},$$

$$f_5 = \begin{pmatrix} a & b & c \\ 1 & 1 & 0 \end{pmatrix},$$

$$f_6 = \begin{pmatrix} a & b & c \\ 1 & 0 & 1 \end{pmatrix},$$

$$f_7 = \begin{pmatrix} a & b & c \\ 0 & 1 & 1 \end{pmatrix},$$

$$f_8 = \begin{pmatrix} a & b & c \\ 1 & 1 & 1 \end{pmatrix}.$$

This example shows that, if A has 3 elements and B has 2 elements, then $\mathcal{F}(A,B)$ has 8 elements. Can we find for any finite sets A and B the number of elements in $\mathcal{F}(A,B)$? As a first step suppose $A = \{1,2, \cdots ,n\}$ and B has m elements. In this case each function is an n-tuple which we may write as $(b_1,b_2, \cdots ,b_n)$, where $b_i \in B$. How many such n-tuples are there? Each b_i is chosen from B and hence there are m choices for it. Thus there are m^n possible n-tuples and hence m^n elements in $\mathcal{F}(A,B)$. This means that in fact $\mathcal{F}(A,B)$ is the Cartesian product $B \times B \times \cdots \times B$, where B appears n times. Instead of the special case $A = \{1,2, \cdots ,n\}$, we now consider any set C with n elements. There is a bijective function $g: C \to A$. We can now define a function $h: \mathcal{F}(A,B) \to \mathcal{F}(C,B)$, where $h(f) = f \cdot g$ for $f \in \mathcal{F}(A,B)$. It is left for the reader to show that h is bijective and hence $\mathcal{F}(A,B)$ and $\mathcal{F}(C,B)$ have the same number of elements. This completes the proof that, if A has n elements and B has m elements, then $\mathcal{F}(A,B)$ has m^n elements. This result shows why the notation B^A is sometimes used instead of $\mathcal{F}(A,B)$, since it resembles the formula for the number of elements.

As a further example, consider the set of functions $\mathfrak{F}(N,B)$, where N is the set of natural numbers and $B = \{0,1,2,3,4,5,6,7,8,9\}$. Each function $f:N \to B$ is a sequence of digits from B. We know that, for each such sequence $S_1, S_2, S_3, \cdots, S_n, \cdots$, we have a real number $x = 0.\,S_1 S_2 S_3 \cdots S_n \cdots$ and $0 \le x \le 1$. This gives a mapping of $\mathfrak{F}(N,B)$ *onto* $\{x|0 \le x \le 1\}$. This mapping is not bijective. For example, the numbers $0.5000 \cdots$ and $0.4999 \cdots$ are equal, but are associated with different sequences. It can be shown that, if in each such case we select one of these forms and exclude the function (or sequence) associated with the other, the exclusion of these functions does not affect the cardinal number of $\mathfrak{F}(N,B)$. In view of our definition of cardinal number we can now say that $\mathfrak{F}(N,B)$ has the same cardinal number as the set of all x for which $0 \le x \le 1$.

3.12   Historical note

The word *function* appeared in the mathematical literature with increasing frequency from the beginning of the calculus. In spite of its frequent use it lacked a clear definition for many years. The notation $f(x)$ appears to be due to L. Euler in 1734. His treatise *Introductio in Analysis Infinitarum* was described as a text on the theory of functions. Euler's concept of a function, however, was very close to the concept of many high school students, that a function is something given by a formula. He spoke of an "analytic expression," which was a combination of all the arithmetic operations together with limits and other techniques of the calculus as the way to present a function. We have emphasized by means of examples the inadequacy of such a concept.

At the beginning of the nineteenth century, Jean B. J. Fourier discovered (1807) that a single trigonometric series could represent objects that mathematicians had considered distinct functions, because they were represented by different formulas. This discovery led to research into the question of which functions could be represented by a trigonometric series. It was while working in this area that the German mathematician Pierre G. Lejeune-Dirichlet formulated (1829) a definition of function closely related to the one we have used. Later the theory of sets provided the tools and language for a clear statement of this concept.

EXERCISES

3.25. Which of the following permutations are involutions?

(a) $\begin{pmatrix} 1 & 2 & 3 & 4 \\ 2 & 1 & 4 & 3 \end{pmatrix}$.

(b) $\begin{pmatrix} 1 & 2 & 3 \\ 3 & 2 & 1 \end{pmatrix}$.

(c) $\begin{pmatrix} 1 & 2 & 3 & 4 & 5 \\ 5 & 1 & 4 & 2 & 3 \end{pmatrix}$.

3.26. Which of the following functions are injective? Which are onto? For each bijective function describe the inverse function.

(a) $f:R \rightarrow R$, $f(x) = x^2$.

(b) $f:R \rightarrow R$, $f(x) = x^3$.

(c) $f:R \rightarrow R_+ \cup \{0\}$, $f(x) = \dfrac{x + |x|}{2}$,

where $R_+ \cup \{0\}$ is the set of nonnegative real numbers.

(d) $f:A \rightarrow A$, where $A = \{a,b,c,d\}$ and $f = \begin{pmatrix} a & b & c & d \\ d & a & d & c \end{pmatrix}$.

3.27. Let $A = \{a,b,c,d,e\}$, $B = \{b,d,e\}$, N be the set of natural numbers.

(a) List the ordered pairs in the graph of the characteristic function of $B \subset A$.

(b) Let $f:A \rightarrow N$ be the function whose graph is

$$G_f = \{(a,2),(b,5),(c,10),(d,16),(e,2)\}.$$

List the ordered pairs in the graph of $f|B$, the restriction of f to B.

(c) Give the domain, codomain, and graph for the reduced map of f.

3.28. Let $A = \{a,b,c\}$, $E = \{a,b,c,d,e\}$, $C = \{0,1,2\}$. Let $f:A \rightarrow C$ be the function whose graph is

$$G_f = \{(a,0),(b,1),(c,1)\}.$$

How many extensions of f to the domain E are there?

3.29. Let $f:\{1,2,3,4,5\} \rightarrow \{a,b,c,d,e,f,g\}$ be the function whose graph is

$$G_f = \{(1,a),(2,c),(3,g),(4,f),(5,d)\}.$$

How many bijective extensions of f to the domain $\{1,2,3,4,5,6,7\}$ are there?

3.30. Prove that the function $f:R \times R \rightarrow R \times R$ is an involution of $R \times R$, where, for each $p \in R \times R$, $f(p)$ is its reflection in a fixed line $L \subset R \times R$.

3.31. Let $Z = \{\cdots, -2, -1, 0, 1, 2, \cdots\}$. Prove card $Z =$ card N.

3.32. If a, b are real numbers, we write

$$\max (a,b) = \begin{cases} a & \text{if } b \leq a \\ b & \text{if } a \leq b \end{cases}$$

$$\min (a,b) = \begin{cases} a & \text{if } a \leq b \\ b & \text{if } b \leq a. \end{cases}$$

If $f:A \rightarrow R$ and $g:A \rightarrow R$, we define two new functions $\max (f,g):A \rightarrow R$ and $\min (f,g):A \rightarrow R$, where $(\max (f,g))(x) = \max (f(x),g(x))$ and $(\min (f,g))(x) = \min (f(x),g(x))$. For $A = \{x | -2 \leq x \leq 2\}$ and $f(x) = x^2 + 1$, $g(x) = x/2 + 1$, draw the graphs of $\max (f,g)$ and $\min (f,g)$.

3.33. (a) Consider the function $f: A \rightarrow B$. Define a relation on A as follows: "For each $x \in A$, $y \in A$, $x \rho y$ if and only if $f(x) = f(y)$." Prove that ρ is an equivalence relation. Is ρ necessarily a functional relation? (*Hint:* See 3.33b.)

(b) Let $E = \{1,2, \cdots, n\}$ and $A = \mathcal{P}(E)$. The function $f:A \rightarrow N \cup \{0\}$ is such that $f(X) =$ number of elements in X for $X \in \mathcal{P}(E)$. The relation ρ is defined as in 3.33a. How many equivalence classes are there with respect to ρ? Describe them.

3.34. The relation ρ_1 is defined in terms of ρ as in Exercise 2.38. Show that, if ρ is an injective function, then ρ_1 is the identity map. Show that, if ρ is a function which is not injective, then ρ_1 is not a function.

3.35. If $A \subseteq E$, we write $f_A : E \to \{0,1\}$ for the characteristic function of A. Prove that f_E is the constant function 1.

3.36. Using the notation of Exercise 3.35, prove that $f_\varnothing$ is the constant function 0.

3.37. Using the notation of Exercise 3.35, prove that

$$f_{\complement A}(x) = 1 - f_A(x) \qquad \text{for all } x \in E.$$

3.38. Using the notation of Exercises 3.32 and 3.35, prove that

$$f_{A \cup B} = \max (f_A, f_B).$$

3.39. Using the notation of Exercise 3.35, prove that

$$f_{A \cap B}(x) = f_A(x) f_B(x) \qquad \text{for all } x \in E.$$

3.40. Using the notation of Exercise 3.35, prove that

$$f_{A - B}(x) = f_A(x) - f_{A \cap B}(x) \qquad \text{for all } x \in A.$$

3.41. Let P, Q be propositions that are meaningful for any natural number $n \in N$. Let R be the conjunction "P and Q." Let $T(P)$ be the subset of N consisting of all natural numbers for which P is true. $T(Q)$, $T(R)$ are defined similarly. Let $f_{T(P)} : N \to \{0,1\}$ be the characteristic function of $T(P)$. Prove that $f_{T(R)}(n) = f_{T(P)}(n) f_{T(Q)}(n)$ for all $n \in N$.

3.42. Consider the functions $f : R \to R$ and $g : R \to R$, where $f(x) = x^2 + 2$ and $g(x) = x^3$. Draw the graph of each function. What is the range of each? Is either function injective? Are the two composites $g \cdot f$ and $f \cdot g$ equal? Are they injective? Are they onto?

3.43. Consider the sets $A = \{a,b,c\}$, $B = \{1,2,3\}$, $C = \{\alpha,\beta,\gamma\}$ and the functions $f : A \to B$, $g : B \to C$ where $f = \begin{pmatrix} a & b & c \\ 2 & 1 & 3 \end{pmatrix}$, that is, $G_f = \{(a,2),(b,1),(c,3)\}$ and $g = \begin{pmatrix} 1 & 2 & 3 \\ \alpha & \beta & \gamma \end{pmatrix}$. Prove that f^{-1} and g^{-1} are defined and give their graphs. Prove that $(g \cdot f)^{-1} = f^{-1} \cdot g^{-1}$.

3.44. If $f : N \times N \to N$ where $f(x,y) = xy$, $g : N \to N$, where $g(x) = x + 1$, and $g \cdot f$ is the composite of f with g, find $(g \cdot f)(x,y)$.

3.45. If $f : N \to N \times N$ where $f(n) = (n, n + 1)$, $g : N \times N \to N$ where $g(m,n) = mn$, and $g \cdot f$ is the composite, find $(g \cdot f)(n)$.

3.46. If $A = \{a,b,c,d,e,f\}$ and f is the permutation

$$f = \begin{pmatrix} a & b & c & d & e & f \\ c & b & d & f & a & e \end{pmatrix},$$

how many distinct functions can be obtained by iteration?

3.47. (a) If $f : A \to B$ is a bijective function, prove that $f^{-1} \cdot f = i_A$, the identity function on A, and $f \cdot f^{-1} = i_B$.

(b) Let $f : A \to A$ be any permutation. Prove that $f^{-1} \cdot f^n = f^n f^{-1} = f^{n-1}$.

(c) If B is a finite set and $f : B \to B$ is a permutation, prove that $f^n = i_B$ for some $n \in N$.

3.48. Consider $f : A \to B$ and $g : B \to A$. If $g \cdot f : A \to A$ is injective, prove that f is injective.

3.49. If $f: A \to B$ is onto and $g: B \to C$ is injective, is $g \cdot f$ injective? Is $g \cdot f$ onto? Give reasons for your answers.

3.50. Let f, g be as in Exercise 3.48. If $g \cdot f$ is onto, prove that g is onto.

3.51. Let f, g be as in Exercise 3.48. If $g \cdot f$ and $f \cdot g$ are permutations, use the results of Exercises 3.48 and 3.50 to prove that f and g are bijective.

3.52. Let f, g be as in Exercise 3.48. If $g \cdot f = i_A$ and $f \cdot g = i_B$, prove that $f^{-1} = g$.

3.53. Use the notation of Section 3.11 to list all the functions in $\mathfrak{F}(A,B)$ and $\mathfrak{F}(A,C)$ where $A = \{a,b\}$, $B = \{0,1\}$, $C = \{0,1,2\}$.

3.54. Show that the function $h: \mathfrak{F}(A,B) \to \mathfrak{F}(A,C)$ of Section 3.11 is bijective.

3.55. Prove that $\mathfrak{F}(A,B) \cap \mathfrak{F}(A',B') = \varnothing$ unless $A = A'$ and $B = B'$.

4

Order Relations

4.1   Definitions

We are familiar with a property of the various number systems (except the complex numbers) that allows us to say that one number is less than or equal to another number. We write this as $x \leq y$. From our knowledge of relations it is clear that this is a relation. For any pair (x,y) of numbers (natural numbers, integers, rationals, reals), we have either $x \leq y$ or $x \nleq y$. If $x \leq y$, then (x,y) is in the graph of the relation.

If we consider this relation for real numbers, we can represent its graph $G_\leq$ by the shaded region together with the diagonal in Figure 4.1.

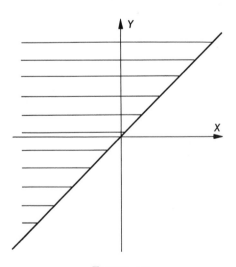

FIGURE 4.1

This relation "$\leq$" for the real numbers has the following properties:

1. By $x \leq y$ we mean "either $x = y$ or $x < y$." Since for each $x \in R$ we have $x = x$, it follows that "either $x = x$ or $x < x$," although the second alternative is impossible. Thus $x \leq x$, that is, $(x,x) \in G_{\leq}$. That is, $\leq$ is *reflexive*.

2. If $x \leq y$ and $y \leq x$, then $x = y$. Another way of expressing this is to say that there is no pair (x,y) of real numbers with $x \neq y$ for which $x \leq y$ and $y \leq x$. We describe this by saying that the relation is *antisymmetric*.

3. If $x \leq y$ and $y \leq z$, then $x \leq z$, that is, the relation is *transitive*.

4. For any real numbers x, y we have either $x \leq y$ or $y \leq x$. We call this the *trichotomy property*. This word implies *three* choices, although we have described only two. The use of the word arises from a consideration of the relation $x < y$. In that case exactly one of the following holds: $x < y$, $x = y$, or $y < x$.

The relation $\leq$ is plainly not an equivalence relation, although it does have the reflexive and transitive properties.

The relation expressed as $x \geq y$ also has properties 1 through 4. The relations $\leq$ and $\geq$ are *not* the same relation. The graph $G_{\geq}$ (see Figure 4.2) is the reflection in the diagonal of the graph $G_{\leq}$.

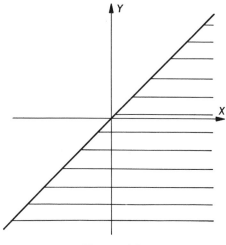

FIGURE 4.2

Consider the set $A = \{1,2,3,4\}$ and the usual relation $\leq$. The graph $G_{\leq}$ is a subset of $A \times A$:

$$G_{\leq} = \{(1,1),(2,2),(3,3),(4,4),(1,2),(1,3),(1,4),(2,3),(2,4),(3,4)\}.$$

The symbol $\leq$ here represents a different relation from the inequality for the integers because they have different domains.

We can define a relation ρ on A which is different from $\leq$ and $\geq$ but which has properties 1 through 4. For example, ρ can be defined by the graph

$$G_\rho = \{(1,1),(2,2),(3,3),(4,4),(2,3),(2,4),(2,1),(3,4),(3,1),(4,1)\}.$$

In this relation we consider 2 as being "before" 3, 3 "before" 4, 4 "before" 1.

We can show that for this set $A = \{1,2,3,4\}$ there are 4! different relations that are reflexive, antisymmetric, transitive, and obey the law of trichotomy.

We mentioned in Section 1.4 that the inclusion relation $\subset$ is reflexive, antisymmetric, and transitive, but it does not satisfy the trichotomy property. We shall meet other relations that have these properties. It will be convenient to have a name for such a relation.

DEFINITION

A relation ρ with A as domain and codomain is called an *order relation* or a *partial order* on A if it satisfies the following conditions:

1. $x \rho x$ for each $x \in A$ (reflexivity).
2. If $x \rho y$ and $y \rho x$, then $x = y$ (antisymmetry).
3. If $x \rho y$ and $y \rho z$, then $x \rho z$ (transitivity).

We also say that ρ *orders* A or ρ *partially orders* A.

DEFINITION

A relation ρ that orders A and that satisfies the trichotomy property (that is, if $x \neq y$, then $y \rho x$) is called a *total order* on A. We also call this a *linear order* on A and say A is *linearly or totally ordered* by ρ.

The word *linear* is used to indicate that this relation is similar to the ordering of points on the line. If an order relation is defined on A we call A an ordered set.

We sometimes study relations that are antisymmetric and transitive, but not reflexive. A familiar example is the relation $x < y$ (without equality) between real numbers. In this example the antisymmetry property is satisfied. The property states that if, $x < y$ and $y < x$, then $x = y$. Since it can never happen that $x < y$ and $y < x$, the property is satisfied trivially.

Let ρ be an antisymmetric, transitive relation on the set A. Let G_ρ represent the graph of ρ and let Δ_A be the diagonal of $A \times A$. Then $G_\rho \cup \Delta_A$ is the graph of an order relation. In view of this fact it is not necessary to make a special study of antisymmetric, transitive relations.

For example, consider the set $A = \{1,2,3,4\}$ and the relation $x < y$ whose graph is

$$G_< = \{(1,2),(1,3),(1,4),(2,3),(2,4),(3,4)\}.$$

Also $\Delta_A = \{(1,1),(2,2),(3,3),(4,4)\}$. Then $G_< \cup \Delta_A$ is the graph $G_\le$ defined above.

There is another type of relation that is closely connected with order. Let A be a set of people and, for $x \in A$, $y \in A$, write $x \rho y$ to mean x is not taller than y. Is ρ an order relation? The reader can easily verify that it is reflexive and transitive. Suppose x and y are two different persons of the same height. Then $x \rho y$ and $y \rho x$ but $x \ne y$. Thus ρ is not antisymmetric and so is not an order relation. Now define a relation τ with A as domain and codomain such that $x \tau y$ if and only if x and y have the same height. It is clear that τ is an equivalence relation. Let B be the quotient set A/τ. We now define a relation $\bar{\rho}$ with B as domain and codomain. For $\bar{x} \in B$, $\bar{y} \in B$ we say that $\bar{x} \bar{\rho} \bar{y}$ if and only if $x \rho y$ for some $x \in \bar{x}$, $y \in \bar{y}$. We leave the reader to verify that this definition is independent of the choice of representatives, that is, if $x \in \bar{x}$, $x' \in \bar{x}$, $y \in \bar{y}$, $y' \in \bar{y}$, and $x \rho y$, then $x' \rho y'$. The reader can also verify that $\bar{\rho}$ is an order relation on B.

4.2 Notations and terminology

The symbols $\le$ or $\preceq$ are often used to denote order relations other than the usual order of the number systems. Since these relations generally have a domain other than a number system, there is no danger of confusion. We read $x \le y$ or $x \preceq y$ as *x is before y*, or *x preceeds y*, or *y succeeds x*, or *x is less than or equal to y*, or *x is smaller than or equal to y*. "Smaller" here has a different meaning from its use for number systems, but it is useful figurative language. A relation that is not reflexive is denoted by $<$, and we read $x < y$ as "*x is strictly less than y.*"

If a relation $x \le y$ is given we often say that y *comes after* x or y is *greater* than or equal to x. If $x \le y$ we sometimes say that x is a *predecessor* or an *antecedent* of y, or that y is a *successor* of x. This does not imply that there is no element between x and y.

If x, y are elements of a set ordered by the relation $\le$ and we have $x \le y$ and $y \le x$, then we say that x and y are *incomparable elements*, that is, we cannot say either that x is smaller than y or that x is greater than or equal to y. For example, in the power set $\mathcal{P}(A)$ of any set A, the subsets B and C are incomparable with respect to inclusion if neither $B \subset C$ nor $C \subset B$ holds.

4.3 Hasse diagrams

To visualize an order relation, we make use of a diagram called a *Hasse diagram*, after the contemporary German mathematician Helmut Hasse. This device is particularly useful in the case of a finite set. We represent the elements of the set by points on the plane and join these points by arrows in such a way that, if $x \, \rho \, y$ then there is a path of arrows starting from x, possibly passing through other points, and ending at y.

EXAMPLE   4.1

Let A be the set $\{1,2,3\}$. Then the power set $\mathcal{P}(A)$ has 2^3 elements, represented by the vertices in Figure 4.3. $\mathcal{P}(A)$ is ordered by the inclusion relation. This order relation is represented in Figure 4.3.

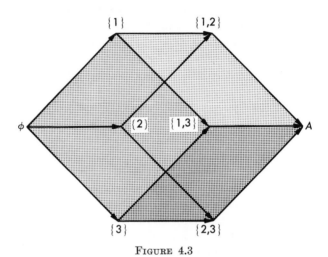

FIGURE 4.3

EXAMPLE   4.2

We shall now use the method of the Hasse diagram to determine all the order relations on the set $A = \{a,b,c\}$. The set of graphs of all the relations with A as domain and codomain is the power set $\mathcal{P}(A \times A)$. This set has $2^9 = 512$ elements, but not all are order relations. To determine the number of order relations, we classify them according to the type of Hasse diagram. There are six order relations of Type I as shown in Figure 4.4.

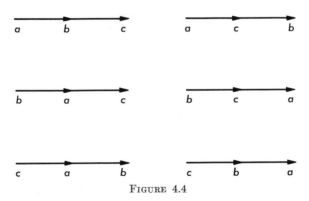

FIGURE 4.4

The order relations of Type I are linear orders. All the rest are partial orders.

There are three order relations of Type II as shown in Figure 4.5, since interchanging b and c in the left-hand diagram does not change the graph.

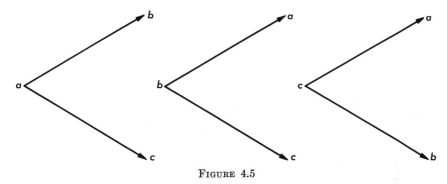

FIGURE 4.5

Similarly, there are three order relations of Type III as shown in Figure 4.6.

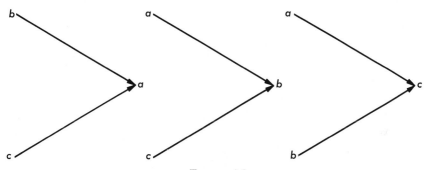

FIGURE 4.6

There are six order relations of Type IV as shown in Figure 4.7.

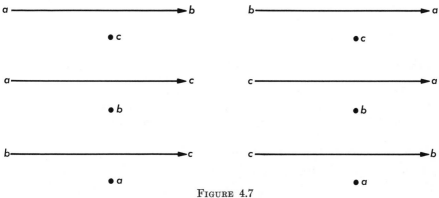

FIGURE 4.7

• a

There is only one order relation of Type V as shown in Figure 4.8, since the graph is the diagonal and is unchanged by permutations of the elements indicated by the dots.

We thus see that there are 19 different order relations on

• b   the set $A = \{a,b,c\}$.

4.4   Some special order relations

• c

FIGURE 4.8   We have just seen that for a set with three elements there are 19 different order relations. The student can gain some appreciation of how rapidly the number of order relations increases as the number of elements increases by attempting to determine the number of order relations for a set with four elements.

Instead of wanting all the order relations for some set, we are sometimes interested in the connection between order relations, or we may be given an order relation on a set and want to construct from it other order relations on the same set or on subsets or product sets of it. We shall be concerned with such problems in this section.

I. Inverse Order

In Section 4.1 we gave two different order relations on the set R of real numbers. These were denoted $x \leq y$ and $x \geq y$. We observed that their graphs $G_\leq$ and $G_\geq$ were reflections with respect to the diagonal. This same idea can be applied to order relations on other sets.

Let ρ be an order relation on a set A. We want to show that the *inverse relation* ρ^{-1} is also an order relation. We define ρ^{-1} as follows: The domain and codomain of ρ are both A. Similarly, the domain and codomain of ρ^{-1} are A. Whenever $y \rho x$, then $x \rho^{-1} y$. Therefore $x \rho^{-1} x$ for all $x \in A$ and ρ^{-1} is reflexive. If $x \rho^{-1} y$ and $y \rho^{-1} x$, then $y \rho x$ and $x \rho y$. But ρ is antisymmetric; therefore $x = y$ and hence ρ^{-1} is also antisymmetric. Finally, if $x \rho^{-1} y$ and $y \rho^{-1} z$, then $y \rho x$ and $z \sigma y$. But ρ is transitive; therefore $z \rho x$ and hence $x \rho^{-1} z$. Therefore ρ^{-1} is also transitive. This completes the proof Theorem 4.1.

THEOREM   4.1

If the relation ρ orders the set A, then the inverse relation ρ^{-1} also orders A.

We have mentioned that an order relation is frequently denoted by $\leq$ even when the domain is not a number system. In this case the inverse relation, called the *opposite order* or the *inverse order*, is denoted by $\geq$.

II. Induced Order on a Subset

If a relation ρ with domain A and codomain B is given, we can easily define a new relation ρ' with domain $A' \subset A$ and codomain $B' \subset B$. This idea is similar to the restricted function and reduced functions obtained from a given functional relation (see Section 3.7). We can use this idea to define an order on a subset $A' \subset A$ if A is ordered by the relation ρ. We have already done this in defining the relation $\leq$ on the set $\{1,2,3,4\}$, which is a subset of R.

The graph of the relation ρ' is $G_{\rho'} = (A' \times A') \cap G_\rho$, that is, if $x \in A'$ and $y \in A'$, then $x \rho' y$ if and only if $x \rho y$. It can easily be verified that, if ρ is an order relation on A, then ρ' will be an order relation on A'. We call ρ' the *order on A' induced by ρ*.

Two different order relations ρ_1 and ρ_2 on a set A may induce the same order relation on a subset A'.

If the symbol $\leq$ is used for an order relation on a set A, we ordinarily use the same symbol for the induced order on $A' \subset A$. Seldom would this lead to confusion; if it would, another notation must be used.

III. Order on the Cartesian Product

Let A and B be two sets ordered by the relations ρ_1 and ρ_2, respectively. Define a relation ρ on $A \times B$ as follows: $(a,b) \rho (a',b')$ if and only if $a \rho_1 a'$ and $b \rho_2 b'$. We shall prove that ρ is an order relation on $A \times B$. We call ρ *the product order of ρ_1 and ρ_2*. For any $(a,b) \in A \times B$ we have $(a,b) \rho (a,b)$ because $a \rho_1 a$ and $b \rho_2 b$. Therefore ρ is reflexive. If $(a,b) \rho (a',b')$, then $a \rho_1 a'$ and $b \rho_2 b'$. If also $(a',b') \rho (a,b)$ then $a' \rho_1 a$ and $b' \rho_2 b$. But ρ_1, ρ_2 are antisymmetric; therefore $a' = a$, $b' = b$, and $(a',b') = (a,b)$. Hence ρ is antisymmetric. Finally, if $(a,b) \rho (a',b')$ and $(a',b') \rho (a'',b'')$, then $a \rho_1 a'$, $b \rho_2 b'$, $a' \rho_1 a''$, $b' \rho_2 b''$. Therefore $a \rho_1 a''$, $b \rho_2 b''$, and hence $(a,b) \rho (a'',b'')$. Therefore ρ is transitive.

As an example, consider the usual order $\leq$ for the real numbers R. The product order of this order with itself is an order on the set $R \times R$. If we denote this product order by $\leq$ we have $(a,b) \leq (a',b')$ if and only if $a \leq a'$ and $b \leq b'$. This means that (a',b') must be to the right of (a,b) or they are on the same vertical line, and also (a',b') must be above (a,b) or they are on the same horizontal line. This is illustrated in Figure 4.9. In particular we

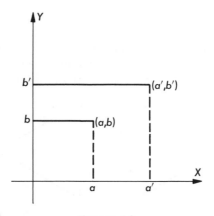

FIGURE 4.9

have $(2,3) \leq (2,5)$, but neither $(2,3) \leq (3,2)$ nor $(3,2) \leq (2,3)$. From this we see that the product order is not linear, even though the order on each factor is linear.

IV. Order on a Set of Functions

We want to define an order on the set $\mathfrak{F}(A,B)$ of all functions of the set A into the ordered set B, ordered by the relation $\leq$. If we write $\preceq$ for the order on $\mathfrak{F}(A,B)$ we can define it as follows: "$f \preceq g$ if and only if for each $x \in A$, $f(x) \leq g(x)$."

As an example, consider the set $\mathfrak{F}(R,R)$ of all real valued functions of a real variable where R has the usual order $\leq$. For the functions $f(x) = x^2$, $g(x) = x^3$ and $h(x) = 2x^2$ we have $f \preceq h$, but $f \npreceq g$, $g \npreceq f$, $h \npreceq g$, and $g \npreceq h$.

4.5 Special elements of an ordered set

In an ordered set A there are sometimes elements with special properties that are worth mentioning.

I. First Element

In a set A ordered by the relation $\leq$ there may be an element p such that, for each $x \in A$, we have $p \leq x$. Such an element p is called the *first element* of the set A (ordered by $\leq$). The element p is also called the *smallest element* of A.

Let $A = \{a,b,c,d\}$ be ordered by the relation represented in the Hasse diagram of Figure 4.10. In this case a is the first element.

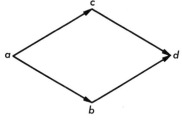

FIGURE 4.10

If A is ordered as in Figure 4.11, then b is the first element.

An ordered set does not always have a first element. For example consider $A = \{a,b,c,d\}$ and the order represented in Figure 4.12.

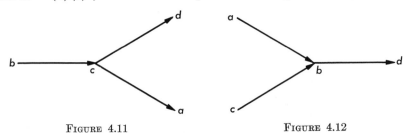

FIGURE 4.11　　　　　　　　　　FIGURE 4.12

The set N of natural numbers with the usual order has 1 as its first element.

The set $Z = \{\cdots ,-n, \cdots ,0,1, \cdots ,n, \cdots \}$ of all the integers ordered by the usual $\leq$ has no first element.

The power set $\mathcal{P}(A)$ of any set A ordered by inclusion has the empty set as its first element.

THEOREM   4.2

If an ordered set A has a first element, then the first element is unique.

Proof

Suppose p and p' are both first elements. Since p is a first element, we have $p \leq p'$. Since p' is a first element we have $p' \leq p$. Thus by the anti-symmetric property we have $p = p'$. •

II. Last Element

In the same way an ordered set A may contain an element q such that $x \leq q$ for every $x \in A$. Such an element q is called the *last element* (or *largest element*) of the set A.

A proof similar to the one for the case of a first element shows that, *if there is a last element, it is unique.*

For example, consider the set of all negative integers ordered by $\leq$, that is $\cdots \leq -n \leq \cdots \leq -3 \leq -2 \leq -1$. Then -1 is the last element.

In the ordered set represented by Figure 4.10, d is the last element. In the ordered set of Figure 4.11 there is no last element.

The set N of natural numbers ordered by $\leq$ has no last element. For the inverse order $\geq$, 1 is the last element and there is no first element.

In general, if ρ is an order relation on a set A and p is a first element, then the set ordered by the inverse order ρ^{-1} has p as its last element. Also if q is the last element for the order ρ, it will be the first element for the order ρ^{-1}.

III. Minimal Elements

Consider the ordered set A represented by the Hasse diagram in Figure 4.13. We observe that a has the property that, for each $x \in A$, if $x \neq a$ then

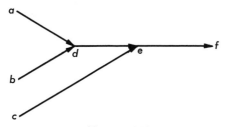

FIGURE 4.13

$x \nleq a$. A similar statement is true for b and c also. We call such an element a *minimal element* of the ordered set A. A minimal element a is an element such that there is no element in the ordered set that is strictly less than a.

An ordered set need not have minimal elements, but in order to have an ordered set with no minimal elements we must have an infinite set. This result is proved in Theorem 4.3.

THEOREM   4.3

If A is a finite set, then there are minimal elements for any order relation on A.

Proof

Let $\leq$ represent any order relation on A. For any $x \in A$, consider the set

$$L_x = \{y|y \in A, y \leq x, y \neq x\}.$$

If x is not a minimal element, then $L_x \neq \varnothing$. Also L_x is finite, since A is finite.

Pick any $x_1 \in L_x$. If x_1 is not a minimal element of A ordered by $\leq$, then the set

$$L_{x_1} = \{y|y \in A, y \leq x_1, y \neq x_1\}$$

is not empty. Thus we can choose $x_2 \in L_{x_1}$ and form L_{x_2}.

But if A has n elements, then L_x has fewer than n elements, L_{x_1} has fewer than $n - 1$ elements, and before we reach L_{x_n} we must have some $L_{x_i} = \varnothing$; that is, x_i is a minimal element. Therefore A has some minimal element. •

A simple example of an *ordered set without minimal elements* is provided by the set of all integers with the usual order $\leq$.

As a second example consider the set N of positive integers and the relation $\leq$ defined "$x \leq y$ if x is a multiple of y." Since $x = 1 \cdot x$, we have $x \leq x$ and $\leq$ is reflexive. If $x \leq y$ and $y \leq x$, then $x = ky$ and $y = k'x$. Then $x = kk'x$ and hence $k = k' = 1$, since k, k' are positive integers. Therefore $x = y$ and $\leq$ is antisymmetric. Finally, if $x \leq y$ and $y \leq z$ we have $x = k_1 y$, $y = k_2 z$. Therefore $x = k_1 k_2 z$, $x \leq z$, and hence $\leq$ is transitive.

The relation $\leq$ partially orders N; the order is not linear, since we have, for example, $3 \nleq 4$, and $4 \nleq 3$.

There are no minimal elements for N ordered in this way. If $a \in N$, then any multiple ka satisfies $ka \leq a$ and hence no element a can be minimal. The set does have a largest element 1, since for any x we have $x = x \cdot 1$ and hence $x \leq 1$.

The proofs of the following two theorems are left as exercises.

THEOREM   4.4

If an ordered set has a first element this first element is a minimal element.

THEOREM   4.5

If a linearly ordered set has a minimal element, this element must be the first element.

IV. Maximal Elements

Consider the ordered set A represented by the Hasse diagram in Figure 4.14. We observe that m has the property that, for each $x \in A$, if $x \neq m$,

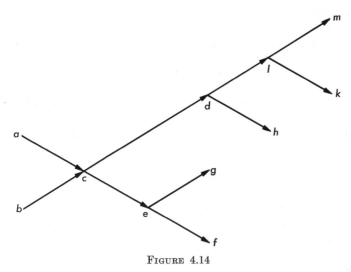

FIGURE 4.14

then $m \not< x$. The same property holds for f, g, h, k. We call these elements *maximal elements* of the ordered set A. A maximal element of an ordered set A is an element $m \in A$ such that there is no element of A strictly greater than m.

Each minimal element of a set A ordered by $\leq$ becomes a maximal element for A ordered by the inverse relation $\geq$. We leave it to the reader to state the properties and give examples of maximal elements analogous to those for minimal elements.

4.6   Densely ordered sets

Here we shall restrict ourselves to a consideration of totally ordered sets. These sets are of considerable importance because they include all the subsets of the real numbers and also the sets of points on a line. It will simplify our notation if we agree to write $a < b$ wherever $a \leq b$ and $a \neq b$ in a set ordered by the relation $\leq$. If a, b, c are elements of the ordered set and $a < b < c$, we say that b *is between a and c*.

DEFINITION

If A is a totally ordered set and $a < b$, where $a \in A$, $b \in A$, then the subset

$$\{x | x \in A, a \leq x \leq b\}$$

is called the *closed interval* with end points (or extremities) a and b. This subset is denoted by $[a,b]$.

DEFINITION

If A is a totally ordered set and $a \in A$, $b \in A$ with $a < b$, then the subset

$$\{x | x \in A, a < x < b\}$$

is called the *open interval* with end points (or extremities) a and b. It is denoted[1] by $]a,b[$.

It is sometimes convenient to deal with half-open intervals:

$$]a,b] = \{x | x \in A, a < x \leq b\},$$
$$[a,b[= \{x | x \in A, a \leq x < b\}.$$

A closed interval $[a,b]$ always contains at least two elements a and b. An open interval may be the empty set. In particular, for the set N of natural numbers the open intervals of the form $]n,n + 1[$ are always empty.

DEFINITION

In a totally ordered set A, we call two elements a and b, where $a < b$, *adjacent* or *consecutive* if $]a,b[= \varnothing$. We also say that a is the *immediate predecessor* of b and b is the *immediate successor* of a.

There are ordered sets in which each element has an immediate successor and predecessor.

EXAMPLE   4.3

Consider set Z of integers ordered by the usual relation $\leq$. Then $\cdots \leq -n \leq \cdots \leq -2 \leq -1 \leq 0 \leq 1 \leq 2 \leq \cdots \leq n \leq \cdots$ It is clear in this case that each element has an immediate successor and predecessor.

There are also totally ordered sets in which no element has an immediate successor or predecessor.

----

[1] Many books use (a,b) to denote an open interval. We have chosen the less common notation to avoid confusion with an ordered pair.

EXAMPLE   4.4

Consider the set of all points on a line L (see Figure 4.15). This set is ordered by the relation $\leq$, where we write $a \leq b$ if a is to the left of b or if a

FIGURE 4.15

coincides with b. Our geometric intuition tells us that, for any choice of a and b such that $a < b$, there is a point c between them. This means that no points a and b can be adjacent elements, that is, the open interval $]a,b[$ is never empty.

The property illustrated in this example is important enough to be given a special name.

DEFINITION

A totally ordered set is called *dense* (or *densely ordered*) if, for each pair of elements $a < b$, the interval $]a,b[$ is not empty.

The rational numbers with the usual order relation provide another example of a densely ordered set. This example is considered in Chapter 6.

4.7   Well-ordered sets

There is one more important type of order relation for us to study. Consider the set N of natural numbers. We know that N has a first or smallest element 1. But also every subset of N has a first or smallest element.[2] This property is not shared by all ordered sets; the set Z of *all* integers has no first element. This property is also found in sets other than the natural numbers, as seen in the following example.

EXAMPLE   4.5

Consider the set

$$A = \{(a,b)|a \in N, b \in N\},$$

that is, $A = N \times N$, and the relation defined as follows: $(a,b) \leq (a',b')$ if and only if one of the following conditions holds: (1) $a < a'$ or (2) $a = a'$ and $b \leq b'$. In particular $(3,8) \leq (4,2)$ and $(3,5) \leq (3,7)$. It is left for the reader

[2] This fact will be considered in more detail in Chapter 5.

to verify that this relation is a linear order. This linear order can be described:

$$(1,1) \leq (1,2) \leq (1,3) \leq \cdots \leq (2,1) \leq (2,2) \leq \cdots \leq (n,1)$$
$$\leq (n,2) \leq \cdots .$$

The element $(1,1)$ is the first element of A. Each element (m,n) has an immediate successor $(m,n + 1)$, but the elements $(2,1),(3,1), \cdots ,(n,1), \cdots$ do not have an immediate predecessor. Also A has no last element.

Let B be any subset of A. Let $X_B = \{x|x \in N,(x,y) \in B$ for some $y \in N\}$. Since X_B is a subset of N, it has a first element, say a. Let $Y_B = \{y|y \in N,(a,y) \in B\}$. Since Y_B is a subset of N, it has a first element, say b. Then (a,b) is a first element of B. Thus any subset of A has a first element.

We give this property, possessed by some ordered sets, a name in the following definition.

DEFINITION

A set A ordered by the relation $\leq$ is called a *well-ordered* set if each nonempty subset $B \subset A$ has a first element.

4.8   Monotone functions

An ordered set is a more complicated object than a set without an order relation. The ordered set is one of the many objects we can construct from a set by introducing certain relations. Sets are the basic objects from which the number systems and the algebraic systems are constructed in Part II.

Functions are also of major importance in all branches of mathematics. It is therefore reasonable to ask what interesting properties a function $f:A \rightarrow B$ may have in terms of order relations on A and B. This question will be our chief concern in this section.

DEFINITION

A function $f:A \rightarrow B$, where A is a set ordered by $\leq$ and B is ordered by $\preceq$, is called an *order-preserving map* if $x_1 \leq x_2$ for $x_1 \in A$, $x_2 \in A$ implies $f(x_1) \preceq f(x_2)$.

When there is no danger of confusion, we write $\leq$ for the order relation on both A and B. If this is likely to cause confusion, we use two different symbols. (We used different symbols in the definition to emphasize the fact that A and B are in general different ordered sets.)

Let A and B be ordered sets with order relations denoted by $\leq$ and $\preceq$, respectively. If $f:A \rightarrow B$ is an order-preserving function, we say that f is a *nondecreasing function*. If we now consider the set B with the inverse order

$\geq$, then an order-preserving function $g:A \to B$ is called a *nonincreasing function*. Whether a function is nondecreasing or nonincreasing depends on the order relations we define on the sets A and B.

When A and B are subsets of the real numbers we follow the convention of taking the usual order $\leq$ for each, and referring to $\geq$ as the inverse order. Then $f:A \to B$ is nondecreasing if $f(x_1) \leq f(x_2)$ whenever $x_1 \leq x_2$, and $g:A \to B$ is nonincreasing if $g(x_1) \geq g(x_2)$ whenever $x_1 \leq x_2$.

DEFINITION

The nonincreasing functions and the nondecreasing functions of an ordered set A into an ordered set B are called the *monotone functions* of A into B.

If $f:A \to B$ is injective, then $f(x_1) \neq f(x_2)$ for $x_1 \neq x_2$, $x_1 \in A$, $x_2 \in A$. If f is nondecreasing and injective, then $f(x_1) < f(x_2)$ whenever $x_1 < x_2$. Such a function is called an *increasing function*.

If $g:A \to B$ is nonincreasing and injective, then $g(x_1) > g(x_2)$ whenever $x_1 < x_2$ for $x_1 \in A$, $x_2 \in A$. Such a function is called a *decreasing function*.

EXAMPLE 4.6

The function $f:A \to R$, where $A = \{x|x \in R, -\pi/2 \leq x \leq \pi/2\}$ and $f(x) = \sin x$, is an increasing map of A into R. Its graph is shown in Figure 4.16.

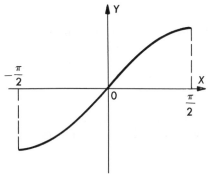

FIGURE 4.16

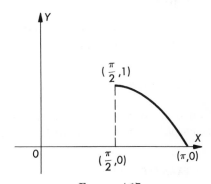

FIGURE 4.17

EXAMPLE 4.7

The function $f:B \to R$, where $B = \{x|x \in R, \pi/2 \leq x \leq \pi\}$ and $f(x) = \sin x$ is a decreasing map. Its graph is shown in Figure 4.17.

EXAMPLE   4.8

Let $A = \{1,2,3\}$ be ordered by the usual relation $\leq$. Let $B = \{a,b,c\}$ be partially ordered by $\leq$ as shown in the Hasse diagram of Figure 4.18.

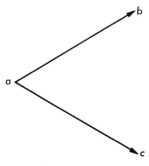

FIGURE 4.18

The map $f = \begin{pmatrix} 1 & 2 & 3 \\ a & b & b \end{pmatrix}$ preserves the order $\leq$, that is, it is nondecreasing, but it is not injective; $g = \begin{pmatrix} 1 & 2 & 3 \\ b & a & a \end{pmatrix}$ preserves the inverse order $\geq$, that is, it is nonincreasing, but it is not injective; $h = \begin{pmatrix} 1 & 2 & 3 \\ b & c & a \end{pmatrix}$ does not preserve either order and hence is not a monotone function.

DEFINITION

A bijective order-preserving map whose inverse is also order-preserving is called an *order isomorphism*.

DEFINITION

Two ordered sets A and B are said to be *isomorphically ordered* or *order isomorphic* if there is a map $f: A \to B$ that is an order isomorphism.

EXAMPLE   4.9

Let $A = \{a,b,c\}$ and consider the two order relations represented in Figure 4.19. The maps $f = \begin{pmatrix} a & b & c \\ b & c & a \end{pmatrix}$ and $g = \begin{pmatrix} a & b & c \\ b & a & c \end{pmatrix}$ are order isomorphisms. These two order relations were said to be of the same type in Section 4.3. The reader can check that any two order relations of the same type in that example are isomorphically ordered.

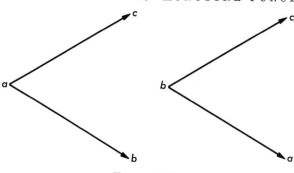

FIGURE 4.19

EXAMPLE 4.10

Consider the set $A = \{1,2,3,4\}$ with the order induced by the usual order on N as shown in Figure 4.20a and also with the order as shown in Figure 4.20b. Then the permutation $f = \begin{pmatrix} 1 & 2 & 3 & 4 \\ 2 & 4 & 3 & 1 \end{pmatrix}$ is an order isomorphism.

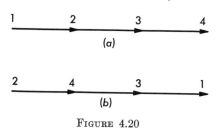

FIGURE 4.20

It can be shown that any totally ordered set A with n elements is order isomorphic to a totally ordered set B with n elements.

THEOREM 4.6

Let A and B be ordered sets and let $f: A \to B$ be an order isomorphism.
   a. If a_0 is the first element of A, then $f(a_0)$ is the first element of B.
   b. If a_1 is the last element of A, then $f(a_1)$ is the last element of B.
   c. If a_2 is a minimal element of A, then $f(a_2)$ is a minimal element of B.
   d. If a_3 is a maximal element of A, then $f(a_3)$ is a maximal element of B.
   e. If a_4 and a_5 are adjacent elements of A, then $f(a_4)$ and $f(a_5)$ are adjacent elements of B.

Proof

Let $\leq$ denote the order on both A and B. We shall prove parts a and e and leave the rest as an exercise.
   a. For any $b \in B$ we must show that $f(a_0) \leq b$. But f is a bijective

function and hence there is exactly one $a \in A$ such that $f(a) = b$. But a_0 is the first element of A; therefore $a_0 \leq a$ and, since f is order-preserving, $f(a_0) \leq f(a) = b$.

e. Let $f^{-1}:B \to A$ be the inverse function of f. Since f is an order iso-morphism, f^{-1} is bijective and order-preserving. We want to show that $]f(a_4),f(a_5)[= \varnothing$. Suppose it is not, that is, $f(a_4) < b < f(a_5)$ for some $b \in B$. Then $f^{-1}(f(a_4)) < f^{-1}(b) < f^{-1}(f(a_5))$ [that is, $a_4 < f^{-1}(b) < a_5$], which is impossible since a_4 and a_5 are adjacent elements. Therefore $]f(a_4),f(a_5)[= \varnothing$. •

THEOREM   4.7

If $f:A \to B$ and $g:B \to C$ are monotone functions, then their composite $g \cdot f$ is also a monotone function.

Proof

We denote the order on all these sets by $\leq$. If $a_1 \in A$, $a_2 \in A$, and $a_1 \leq a_2$, then $f(a_1) \leq f(a_2)$ if f is nondecreasing and $f(a_1) \geq f(a_2)$ if f is nonincreasing.

Consider the case in which $f(a_1) \leq f(a_2)$. If g is nondecreasing, then $g(f(a_1)) \leq g(f(a_2))$. If g is nonincreasing, then $g(f(a_1)) \geq g(f(a_2))$.

Now suppose $f(a_1) \geq f(a_2)$. If g is nondecreasing, then $g(f(a_1)) \geq g(f(a_2))$. If g is nonincreasing, then $g(f(a_1)) \leq g(f(a_2))$.

In each case $g \cdot f$ is monotone. •

EXERCISES

4.1. Let A be any set. A relation ρ on A is both an equivalence relation and an order relation. Describe its graph.

4.2. Let B be the set of all people who have ever lived in a certain country. For $x \in B$, $y \in B$ we define $x \rho y$ to mean $x = y$ or x is an ancestor of y. Prove that ρ is an order relation. Is it a total order?

4.3. Show that there are 4! linear orders for the set $A = \{a,b,c,d\}$.

4.4. Let ρ be an antisymmetric transitive relation with A as domain and codo-main. Let G_ρ be its graph and let Δ_A be the diagonal of $A \times A$. Show that $G_\rho \cup \Delta_A$ is the graph of an order relation on A.

4.5. Let A be the set of teams in a basketball league. If $x \in A$ and $y \in A$, we say that $x \rho y$ if and only if either $x = y$ or x has defeated y. Is this relation reflexive? Is it always antisymmetric? Is it always transitive?

4.6. Under what conditions can a relation with the same set as domain and codomain be both a functional relation and an order relation?

4.7. Let A be any set of people. We say that $x \rho y$ if x is not taller than y. Show that this relation is reflexive and transitive.

4.8. Show that the relation in Exercise 4.7 is not always antisymmetric.

Define an equivalence relation on A and a new relation $\bar{\rho}$ on the quotient set as in the last paragraph of Section 4.1.

4.9. Show that the definition of $\bar{\rho}$ in the last paragraph of Section 4.1 is independent of the choice of representatives; that is, if $x \tau x'$, $y \tau y'$, and $x \rho y$, then $x' \rho y'$.

4.10. Prove that $\bar{\rho}$ in the last paragraph of Section 4.1 is an order relation on B.

4.11. Consider a set of people E. If $x \in E$ and $y \in E$, we say $x \rho y$ if either x is not taller than y or x is not heavier than y. Is this relation reflexive? Is it antisymmetric? Is it transitive?

4.12. Let Z be the set of integers. We say that $x \rho y$ if and only if x divides y (without remainder). Is ρ an order relation?

4.13. Let $C = \{1,2\}$. Draw the Hasse diagram for $\mathcal{P}(C)$ ordered by inclusion. Is the order linear?

4.14. Let $B = \{1,2,3\}$, $C = \{1,2,3,4\}$. Let θ_B be the set of all graphs of order relations on B, and θ_C the similar set for C. Which of the following statements are true? Give reasons for your answers.

  (a) $\theta_B \subset \theta_C$.
  (b) For each $G \in \theta_C$ there is $H \in \theta_B$ such that $H \subset G$.
  (c) $\theta_B \cap \theta_C = \varnothing$.

4.15. How many order relations are there for $A = \{1,2,3,4\}$ that induce linear orders on $B = \{1,2,3\}$? Draw a Hasse diagram for each type.

4.16. Prove that the relation on $A \subset B$ induced by an order relation on B is an order relation on A. Prove that, if the order on B is linear, so is the induced order on A.

4.17. Find all the linear orders on $A = \{1,2,3,4,5\}$ that induce the usual order $\leq$ on $B = \{1,2,3\}$. Draw the Hasse diagram for each one.

4.18. Let A be a set with more than two elements ordered by the relation ρ_1 and also by ρ_2. Prove that, if ρ_1 and ρ_2 induce the same order on every *proper* subset of A, they are the same order.

4.19. Let $A = \{1,2\}$, $B = \{a,b\}$. How many order relations are there for each? How many products orders of ρ_1 and ρ_2 on $A \times B$ can be formed where ρ_1 is an order on A and ρ_2 is an order on B? Draw a Hasse diagram for each.

4.20. Let A be a set ordered by ρ_1, B a set ordered by ρ_2. For $(a,b) \in A \times B$ and $(a',b') \in A \times B$ we say that $(a,b) \rho (a',b')$ if either $a \rho_1 a'$ or $b \rho_2 b'$. Is ρ always reflexive? Is it always antisymmetric? Is it always transitive?

4.21. Let $A = [-1,1]$ and let $f : A \to R$, $g : A \to R$. We define $f \leq g$ if $f(x) \leq g(x)$ for all $x \in A$. Draw a Hasse diagram for the order on $\{f,g,h,j\}$, where $f(x) = x^2$, $g(x) = x^3$, $h(x) = x^4$, $j(x) = x^5$.

4.22. Repeat Exercise 4.21 with A replaced by $\mathbf{C}_R[-1,1]$.

4.23. An order on $\mathcal{F}(R,R)$ is defined in a manner analogous to Exercise 4.21. Draw the Hasse diagram for the set $\{f,g,h\}$, where $f(x) = x^2 + 1$, $g(x) = x + 1$, $h(x) = |x|$.

4.24. With the order defined as in Exercise 4.21, what is the largest subset $A \subset R$ such that $f \leq g$ in $\mathcal{F}(A,R)$, where $f(x) = 0$, $g(x) = [x]$?

4.25. How many order relations are there for $\{1,2,3,4\}$ for which there is a first element? Draw a Hasse diagram for each type.

4.26. How many order relations are there for $\{1,2,3,4\}$ such that there is a first and a last element? Draw a Hasse diagram for each type.

4.27. Prove that, if an ordered set has a last element, then the last element is unique.

4.28. Prove that, if p is the first element of a set ordered by ρ, it is the last element of the set ordered by ρ^{-1}, and that, if q is the last element of a set ordered by ρ, it is the first element of the set ordered by ρ^{-1}.

4.29. What are the minimal elements and the maximal elements for the order relation of Exercise 4.2?

4.30. Let N be the set of positive integers; let $A = N - \{1\}$ be ordered by the relation "$a \leq b$ if and only if a divides b." What are the minimal elements?

4.31. Let B be the set of 19 order relations on the set $\{a,b,c\}$ (see Section 4.3). An order relation is defined on B as: "$\rho_1 \leq \rho_2$ if $G_{\rho_1} \subset G_{\rho_2}$, where G_{ρ_1}, G_{ρ_2} are the graphs of ρ_1, ρ_2." Draw the Hasse diagram for the set B with this order. What are the maximal elements?

4.32. Let B be the set of all order relations for any set A. An order relation is defined on B as in Exercise 4.31. Prove that the linear orders are maximal elements.

4.33. Prove Theorem 4.4.

4.34. Prove Theorem 4.5.

4.35. State and prove an analogue of Theorem 4.4 concerning a last element.

4.36. State and prove an analogue of Theorem 4.5 concerning a maximal element.

4.37. Prove that, if p is a minimal element of a set ordered by ρ, it is a maximal element of the set ordered by ρ^{-1}; prove that, if q is a maximal element of the set ordered by ρ, it is a minimal element of the set ordered by ρ^{-1}.

4.38. Give an example (other than the usual order for a number system) of an ordered set that has no maximal elements.

4.39. State and prove an analogue of Theorem 4.3 concerning maximal elements.

4.40. Prove that a densely ordered set containing more than one element must have an infinite number of elements.

4.41. Show that not all totally ordered infinite sets are densely ordered.

4.42. If an infinite set is totally ordered and has a first and last element, is it necessarily densely ordered?

4.43. Let $f: N \to A$ be a bijective function. Define an order relation on A such that A is well-ordered with respect to this relation.

4.44. Define an order relation on Z such that Z is well-ordered with respect to this relation.

4.45. Show that a set that has more than one element cannot be both well-ordered and densely ordered by the same relation.

4.46. Prove that the relation defined for $N \times N$ in the example of Section 4.7 is a linear order.

4.47. Consider the functions with domain and codomain the set of integers Z, $f(n) = -n$, $g(n) = 5n$, $h(n) = n^2$. In terms of the usual order $\leq$ on Z, which are order-preserving?

4.48. Let $A = \{1,2,3,4\}$ with the usual order $1 < 2 < 3 < 4$. Let $B = \{a,b,c\}$ be ordered by ρ_1 and also by ρ_2, where $a \, \rho_1 \, b$, $b \, \rho_1 \, c$, and $c \, \rho_2 \, b$, $c \, \rho_2 \, a$. Consider the function $f: A \to B$ with the graph

$$G_f = \{(1,a),(2,b),(3,b),(4,c)\}.$$

Show that f is nondecreasing with respect to ρ_1 and nonincreasing with respect to ρ_2.

4.49. Let A and B be two sets ordered by the relations ρ_1 and ρ_2, respectively, and such that A and B are isomorphically ordered. Prove that ρ_1 is a linear order if and only if ρ_2 is a linear order.

4.50. If $f:R \to R$ and $g:R \to R$, we define $f + g:R \to R$ by $(f + g)(x) = f(x) + g(x)$ for all $x \in R$. If f and g are both nondecreasing, show that $f + g$ is nondecreasing. If f is nondecreasing and g is nonincreasing, show that $f + g$ need not be monotone.

4.51. Consider the function $f:R \to R$, where $f(x) = x^n$. For what values of $n \in N$ is f monotone?

4.52. From each type (except V) of order for the set $A = \{a,b,c\}$ in Section 4.3, select two orders and show that there is an order isomorphism between A with the first of the orders and A with the second.

4.53. Prove that on a finite set A with n elements there are $n!$ different linear order relations. Let ρ and ρ' be two such linear order relations and prove that A ordered by ρ is order isomorphic to A ordered by ρ'. How many order isomorphisms are there between these sets? Give the graphs for the linear orders on $\{1,2\}$. Also show all the order isomorphisms among these ordered sets.

4.54. Complete the proof of Theorem 4.6.

Part Two

NUMBER SYSTEMS AND

ALGEBRAIC SYSTEMS

5
The Integers

5.1 Introduction

In our study of sets and relations we have frequently used examples that involve one of the number systems, especially the set of positive integers and the set of real numbers. We used these examples because the reader is expected to have an adequate intuitive understanding of the number systems. But intuition is not enough, and so this chapter and the two succeeding ones are devoted to a development of the number systems based on the results we have obtained for sets. We shall not attempt to include every detail, but we shall use methods that are adequate to provide the details. Some of these details will be found in the exercises.

We shall start with the simplest number system and extend this to more and more complicated systems. Each extension will be motivated by a problem that can be stated but not solved in the systems developed up to that point.

5.2 Definition of the natural numbers

The simplest of the number systems is the set of numbers used in counting. This set is called the set of natural numbers. We shall denote it[1] by the letter N. In Section 3.6 we encountered the notion of cardinal number or, in the case of a finite set, the number of elements in the set. This idea could be further developed to motivate the definition of the natural numbers and the operations on them. We choose, however, to introduce the natural numbers

---

[1] We have so far used N to represent the set of positive integers. The reader will realize by the end of this chapter that these two uses of the symbol are consistent. In fact it is not necessary to distinguish between the natural numbers and the positive integers.

in an axiomatic way, that is, we shall state certain properties of the natural numbers and prove the other properties from these. These properties from which we start are called the *axioms of the system.*

The reader is reminded that the word *axiom* is not meant to imply that these statements are obviously true. A little thought should convince the reader that the axioms are consistent with his intuitive knowledge of the numbers used in counting, but he probably will not see why these particular properties have been selected. We do not claim that this is the only possible set of axioms, but it is the usual one.

These axioms are called *Peano's axioms* after the Italian mathematician Giuseppe Peano (1858–1932), who about 1894 called attention to the fact that all theorems of the arithmetic of natural numbers can be proved from these axioms. In fact these axioms were first used by the German mathematician Richard Dedekind (1831–1915), in his book *Was sind und was sollen die Zahlen?*, published in 1888.

In their classical form as given by Peano these axioms are:

1. There is a natural number[2] 1.
2. With each natural number a there is associated in a unique way another natural number, written $\sigma(a)$, which is called the *successor of a.* We call a the *predecessor of $\sigma(a)$.*
3. The number 1 has no predecessor.
4. If $\sigma(a) = \sigma(b)$, then $a = b$.
5. Consider a set of natural numbers A such that (a) A contains 1, and (b) if a is in A, then $\sigma(a)$ is in A. Then A must be the set of *all* natural numbers.

These axioms can also be written in the language of sets and functions as follows:

The system of natural numbers is a set N for which a function $\sigma:N \to N$, called the *successor function,* is defined. This is the content of axiom 2. The set N together with the function σ satisfies the following conditions:

a. There exists in N an element, denoted by e, such that $\sigma(x) \neq e$ for each $x \in N$. (This is equivalent to axioms 1 and 3.)

b. The function σ is injective. (This is axiom 4.)

c. If $A \in \mathcal{P}(N)$ (that is, $A \subset N$) and $e \in A$ and, if $x \in A$ implies that $\sigma(x) \in A$, then $A = N$ (axiom 5).

The reader will observe that we have written e in the second formulation instead of 1. The system we obtain has the same structure no matter what symbol we write. By writing e instead of 1 we emphasize that in the axiomatic system it is the behavior of the elements rather than the symbols used that is important. In fact there may be many ways of representing such a system. Since the reader should already have a complete intuitive knowledge of the natural numbers, he will realize that the number 1 plays the role

---

[2] Some books use: "There is a natural number 0." Both approaches are satisfactory. We have chosen to start with 1 and introduce 0 in Section 5.10.

of e in this system of axioms. It is useful to write e when we refer to a system in which not all the axioms hold. When we use the natural number system we shall usually write 1.

From these axioms it is possible to define in the set N the usual order relation, the operations of addition and multiplication, all the functions of the arithmetic of natural numbers, and to prove all their properties. We shall undertake to define order, addition, and multiplication, but before we do so we must look more carefully at the last of Peano's axioms.

5.3 Induction

The fifth of Peano's axioms (or c in the second formulation) is called the *principle of finite induction*. We want to consider the role of this axiom in the proofs of propositions concerning natural numbers. To do this we shall consider some cases in which all the axioms, except the last one, hold.

We first point out certain facts concerning Peano's axioms. They state properties that must be satisfied by the set N and the successor function $\sigma : N \to N$. There is a difference between the formulation of the principle of finite induction and the formulation of the other axioms. In each of the other axioms there is a condition concerning an arbitrary element of N:

a. For each $n \in N$, $\sigma(n) \neq e$.
b. For each $n_1 \in N$ and $n_2 \in N$, $\sigma(n_1) = \sigma(n_2)$ implies $n_1 = n_2$.

On the other hand, the principle of finite induction expresses a condition concerning, not elements of N, but elements of $\mathcal{P}(N)$, that is, subsets of the natural numbers.

We can state the principle of finite induction as follows. Let $\mathfrak{A}$ denote the class of all subsets of N that contain e. Then $\mathfrak{A} \subset \mathcal{P}(N)$. Let $\mathfrak{I} \subset \mathcal{P}(N)$ denote the class of subsets $M \subset N$ which satisfy the condition that, if $n \in M$, then $\sigma(n) \in M$. The principle of finite induction states that $\mathfrak{A} \cap \mathfrak{I} = \{N\}$, that is, the only element common to $\mathfrak{A}$ and $\mathfrak{I}$ is N.

We shall now give an example of a set A and a function σ that satisfy Peano's axioms except for the principle of finite induction. This example will be constructed from the set N of natural numbers. In doing this we make use of the reader's previous knowledge of the natural numbers.

EXAMPLE 5.1

Let us consider the set $A = N \times \{0,1\}$, that is, the set of all pairs $(n,0)$ or $(n,1)$, where $n \in N$. We define $\sigma : A \to A$ as

$$\sigma(n,0) = (n + 1,0),$$
$$\sigma(n,1) = (n + 1,1).$$

The element $e = (1,0)$ is an element of A, and for every $a \in A$ we have $\sigma(a) \neq e$. Thus axiom a is satisfied. It is easy to see that, if $\sigma(a) = \sigma(b)$, then $a = b$; that is, σ is an injective map. Thus axiom b is satisfied.

The principle of finite induction is not satisfied. If it were, we would have $\mathfrak{A} \cap \mathfrak{I} = \{A\}$, where $\mathfrak{A}$ is the class of all subsets of A that contain e and $\mathfrak{I}$ is the class of subsets $M \subset A$ such that, if $n \in M$, then $\sigma(n) \in M$. But we can easily see that the set $B = N \times \{0\}$, that is, the set of all pairs $(n,0)$ is an element of $\mathfrak{A} \cap \mathfrak{I}$. The reader can verify that the sets

$$C_m = B \cup \{a | a = (n,1), n \in N, n \geq m\}$$

are also elements of $\mathfrak{A} \cap \mathfrak{I}$, and in fact that $\mathfrak{A} \cap \mathfrak{I}$ consists of A, B, and C_m for $m = 1,2,3, \cdots$.

From this example we see that the principle of finite induction is not implied by the other axioms. We shall now consider the use of this principle in proving statements about the natural numbers.

5.4 Proof by induction

The principle of finite induction can often be used to determine whether some statement about natural numbers is true for all natural numbers. A statement about natural numbers defines a subset of N consisting of those natural numbers for which the statement is true. If we can prove that this subset, say A, is an element of $\mathfrak{A} \cap \mathfrak{I}$, where $\mathfrak{A}$ and $\mathfrak{I}$ are defined for N as before, then we know that $A = N$, and hence the statement is true for all natural numbers. This use of the principle of finite induction will be clarified in the following examples.

EXAMPLE 5.2

Prove that the range of the map $\sigma : N \to N$ is $\complement_N \{1\}$.

Proof

Let L denote the range of σ. By axiom a, $1 \notin L$. Let $M = \{1\} \cup L$. It is now sufficient to prove that $M = N$. By definition, $1 \in M$. If $a \in M$, then $\sigma(a) \in M$, because $\sigma(a)$ is in the range of σ. Therefore $M \in \mathfrak{A} \cap \mathfrak{I}$ and hence $M = N$. •

EXAMPLE 5.3

Prove that the map $\sigma : N \to N$ leaves no element invariant, that is, there is no $n \in N$ for which $\sigma(n) = n$.

Proof

It is sufficient to prove that the set $M = \{n | n \in N, \sigma(n) \neq n\}$ is equal to N. By axiom a, $\sigma(n) \neq 1$ for any n and in particular for $n = 1$. Therefore

$1 \in M$. If $a \in M$, then $\sigma(a) \neq a$. Since σ is injective this implies that $\sigma(\sigma(a)) \neq \sigma(a)$ and hence $\sigma(a) \in M$. Therefore $M = N$. •

5.5 Addition of the natural numbers

The addition of natural numbers is familiar to anyone who has the most rudimentary knowledge of arithmetic. We shall not attempt to teach facts that the reader has known from childhood. We shall, however, emphasize certain important properties that are often passed over in an elementary presentation as being so natural that they are not worthy of mention. To emphasize these properties we shall describe addition in the language of set theory.

The addition of two natural numbers is an operation that associates with each pair (a,b) of natural numbers a natural number, called the *sum of a and b* and denoted by $a + b$. That is, addition is a function

$$s:N \times N \to N,$$

where $s(a,b) = a + b$.

In our elementary classes this function was defined by a list of values of the function for certain pairs of natural numbers, which was called the addition table and which we were required to memorize.

We want to define this function in terms of Peano's axioms, that is, in terms of the set N, the successor function $\sigma:N \to N$, and their properties.

In Section 4.8 we considered how a function could interact with an order relation on its domain and codomain. We were concerned with sets having a structure determined by the order relation. For A ordered by ρ and B by ρ', we were interested in a function $f:A \to B$ such that, if $x \rho y$ for $x \in A$, $y \in A$, then $f(x) \rho' f(y)$. In the case of the set N, the function σ determines a structure. If we write, in the notation for relations, $x \sigma y$ whenever $\sigma(x) = y$, we can ask whether there are functions $f:N \to N$ such that, if $x \in N, y \in N$, and $x \sigma y$, then $f(x) \sigma f(y)$. That is, we ask whether there are functions such that $f(\sigma(x)) = \sigma(f(x))$ for all $x \in N$ or, in other words, such that the two composites $\sigma \cdot f$ and $f \cdot \sigma$ are the same function.

This situation can be represented by Figure 5.1. We want a function f such that, if we move from the upper left corner to the lower right corner by

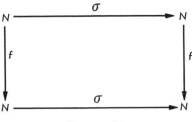

FIGURE 5.1

way of either set of arrows, we get the same result. In this case we say that the diagram is commutative.

The existence of such a function is trivial: For example, the identity map has the required properties. We might next ask how many such functions there are. Theorem 5.1 is a first step toward answering this.

THEOREM   5.1

If $f:N \to N$ and $g:N \to N$ are such that $f \cdot \sigma = \sigma \cdot f$ and $g \cdot \sigma = \sigma \cdot g$ and if $f(1) = g(1)$, then $f = g$.

Proof

We want to prove that $f(n) = g(n)$ for all $n \in N$. We shall do this by finite induction. Let $M = \{n|n \in N, f(n) = g(n)\}$. We want to prove that $M = N$. We are given that $f(1) = g(1)$ and hence $1 \in M$. If $n \in M$, then $f(n) = g(n)$. Then $f(\sigma(n)) = \sigma(f(n)) = \sigma(g(n)) = g(\sigma(n))$, and hence $\sigma(n) \in M$. Therefore $M = N$ and $f = g$. •

From this theorem we can see that a function $f:N \to N$, such that $f \cdot \sigma = \sigma \cdot f$ is completely determined by the value $f(1)$. But since $f(1) \in N$, we see that the cardinal number of the set of such functions cannot be greater than the cardinal number of N. Are these cardinal numbers equal? To answer this we must know whether for each $n \in N$ there is a function with the required properties and such that $f(1) = n$. This question is answered in Theorem 5.2.

THEOREM   5.2

For each $n \in N$ there is exactly one map $f:N \to N$ such that $f(1) = n$ and $\sigma \cdot f = f \cdot \sigma$.

Proof

Let $M = \{n|n \in N$, there is $f:N \to N, f(1) = n, f \cdot \sigma = \sigma \cdot f\}$. We can easily see that the identity map $i_N:N \to N$ is such that $i_N(1) = 1$ and $i_N \cdot \sigma = \sigma \cdot i_N$. Then $1 \in M$. If $n \in M$, there is a function $f:N \to N$ such that $f(1) = n$ and $f \cdot \sigma = \sigma \cdot f$. Consider the map $g = \sigma \cdot f$. Then $g:N \to N$, $g(1) = \sigma(f(1)) = \sigma(n)$, and $\sigma \cdot g = \sigma \cdot \sigma \cdot f = \sigma \cdot f \cdot \sigma = g \cdot \sigma$. Therefore $\sigma(n) \in M$ and by the principle of finite induction $M = N$. Therefore such a function f exists. Theorem 5.1 shows that f is unique. •

From our discussion we see that, for each $n \in N$, there is one and only one function $s_n:N \to N$ such that

$$s_n(1) = \sigma(n)$$
$$s_n \cdot \sigma = \sigma \cdot s_n.$$

We can now define $s: N \times N \to N$ where $s(n,m) = s_n(m)$. We usually write $s(n,m) = n + m$. We refer to the function s_n as the *addition of n*. In particular we see that $\sigma(n) = n + 1$.

There are some results contained in the proofs of Theorems 5.1 and 5.2 to which we want to make reference in terms of this new notation $s(n,m) = n + m$. To present these results explicitly we list them as corollaries.

Corollary 1

For any $n \in N$, $s_{\sigma(n)}(x) = s_n(\sigma(x))$ for all $x \in N$.

Proof

If we compare the definition of s_n with the proof of Theorem 5.2, we see that $g = s_n$ and also that $\sigma \cdot g = s_{\sigma(n)}$. But $\sigma \cdot g = g \cdot \sigma$, and therefore $s_{\sigma(n)}(x) = \sigma \cdot g(x) = g \cdot \sigma(x) = s_n(\sigma(x))$. •

Corollary 2

For all $a \in N$ and $b \in N$, $\sigma(a) + b = \sigma(a + b) = a + \sigma(b)$.

Proof

By the definition of s_n and Corollary 1 we see that $\sigma(a) + b = s_{\sigma(a)}(b) = s_a(\sigma(b))$. But $s_a(\sigma(b)) = a + \sigma(b)$ and also $s_a(\sigma(b)) = \sigma(s_a(b)) = \sigma(a + b)$. •

THEOREM 5.3

For any $a \in N$ the function $s_a: N \to N$ is injective.

Proof

Consider the natural numbers x and y such that $x \neq y$. Let M be the set of all natural numbers n, such that $s_n(x) \neq s_n(y)$.

Since $x \neq y$ and σ is injective, we have $\sigma(x) \neq \sigma(y)$. From the definition of s_n we see that σ has the properties required of s_1. But s_1 is unique. Therefore $s_1 = \sigma$ and $s_1(x) \neq s_1(y)$. Thus $1 \in M$.

Suppose that $n \in M$, that is, $s_n(x) \neq s_n(y)$. By Corollary 1 to Theorem 5.2 we know that $s_{\sigma(n)} = \sigma \cdot s_n$. Because $s_n(x) \neq s_n(y)$ and σ is injective, we have $\sigma(s_n(x)) \neq \sigma(s_n(y))$. But this means $s_{\sigma(n)}(x) \neq s_{\sigma(n)}(y)$; hence $\sigma(n) \in M$ and $M = N$.

Therefore each $s_a: N \to N$ is an injective map. •

Theorem 5.4 states three fundamental properties of the addition of natural numbers. These properties are, of course, well-known, but the names by which they are called are not so well-known. It is important to learn these names and the properties to which they refer, because they are frequently used in mathematics and not always in such a simple context as here.

THEOREM   5.4

1. The addition of natural numbers obeys the commutative law, that is, $a + b = b + a$, where a and b are natural numbers.
2. The addition of natural numbers obeys the associative law, that is, $a + (b + c) = (a + b) + c$, where a, b, c are natural numbers.
3. The addition of natural numbers obeys the cancellation law, that is, if $a + b = a + c$, then $b = c$, where a, b, c are natural numbers.

Proof

1. Let $M = \{a | a \in N, a + b = b + a \text{ for all } b \in N\}$. We have seen that $s_1 = \sigma$. Then $1 + b = s_1(b) = \sigma(b) = b + 1$ and hence $1 \in N$. If $n \in M$, then $n + b = b + n$. By Corollary 2 to Theorem 5.2 we see that $\sigma(n) + b = \sigma(n + b) = \sigma(b + n) = b + \sigma(n)$. Therefore $\sigma(n) \in M$. Thus by the principle of induction, $M = N$ and $a + b = b + a$ for all $a \in N$, $b \in N$.

2. Let $M_1 = \{c | c \in N, (a + b) + c = a + (b + c) \text{ for all } a \in N, b \in N\}$. By Corollary 2 to Theorem 5.2 we know that $(a + b) + 1 = \sigma(a + b) = a + \sigma(b) = a + (b + 1)$. Therefore $1 \in M_1$. If $c \in M_1$ then $(a + b) + c = a + (b + c)$. Therefore $\sigma((a + b) + c) = \sigma(a + (b + c))$. But $\sigma((a + b) + c) = (a + b) + \sigma(c)$ and $\sigma(a + (b + c)) = a + \sigma(b + c) = a + (b + \sigma(c))$, by Corollary 2. Therefore $(a + b) + \sigma(c) = a + (b + \sigma(c))$ and $\sigma(c) \in M_1$. Therefore $M_1 = N$ and the addition of natural numbers is associative.

3. If $a + b = a + c$, then $s_a(b) = s_a(c)$. But s_a is injective by Theorem 5.3. Therefore $a = b$. •

The reader may feel that this definition of addition is unnecessarily involved. Could we not give a definition as follows:[3] For each $x \in N$ we define

$$x + 1 = \sigma(x),$$
$$x + \sigma(y) = \sigma(x + y).$$

This might be supported by saying that we know what $x + 1$ means and, whenever we know $x + y$, we know $x + \sigma(y)$; thus $x + y$ is defined for all $y \in N$.

To see the fallacy of such an argument we replace "$x +$" by the functional notation $f_x : N \to N$. The "definition" then becomes

$$f_x(1) = \sigma(x),$$
$$f_x(\sigma(y)) = \sigma(f_x(y)).$$

This simply means that we require a function with certain properties; it does not prove that such a function exists or, if it does exist, whether it is unique.

---

[3] This definition was used by Peano and his successors, up to the first edition of E. Landau, *Foundations of Analysis*. It was corrected in a later edition (1929) when challenged by Grandjot, a student of Landau.

5.6 Multiplication of the natural numbers

We can introduce multiplication of the natural numbers in a way similar to the introduction of addition. We shall give a very brief outline and leave the reader to supply the details.

Analogues of Theorems 5.1 and 5.2 show that there is a unique function $p_n : N \to N$ such that

$$p_n(1) = n,$$
$$p_n(\sigma(x)) = p_n(x) + n.$$

We define a function $p : N \times N \to N$, where $p(x,y) = p_x(y)$. We usually write xy, $x \cdot y$, or $x \times y$ for $p(x,y)$ and call it the multiplication of the natural number x by the natural number y.

Multiplication has properties like those stated in Theorem 5.4 for addition. The same names are used to describe these properties.

1. The multiplication of natural numbers obeys the commutative law, that is, $ab = ba$ for a and b natural numbers.
2. The multiplication of natural numbers obeys the associative law, that is, $a(bc) = (ab)c$, where a, b, c are natural numbers.
3. The multiplication of natural numbers obeys the cancellation law, that is, if $ab = ac$, then $b = c$ if a, b, c are natural numbers.

So far we have discussed the properties of addition and multiplication independently without considering any interdependence. But multiplication is defined in terms of addition and so we might expect a connection. We also know from elementary arithmetic that such a connection exists, as described in Theorem 5.5.

THEOREM 5.5

The addition and multiplication of the natural numbers obey the left distributive law, that is, $a(b + c) = ab + ac$ for all natural numbers a, b, c, and the right distributive law, that is, $(b + c)a = ba + ca$ for all natural numbers a, b, c.

Proof

It is clear that, if we prove the left distributive law, the right distributive law follows by the commutative law of multiplication.

Let a,b be fixed natural numbers. Let $M = \{c | c \in N, a(b + c) = ab + ac\}$. Since $a(b + 1) = p_a(\sigma(b)) = p_a(b) + a = ab + a$, we see that $1 \in M$. If $c \in M$, then $a(b + c) = ab + ac$. Then $a(b + \sigma(c)) = a(\sigma(b + c)) = p_a(\sigma(b + c)) = p_a(b + c) + a = (ab + ac) + a = ab + (ac + a) = ab + a\sigma(c)$. Therefore $\sigma(c) \in M$ and $M = N$. Thus $a(b + c) = ab + ac$ for all natural numbers a, b, c. •

5.7   Definition by induction

To show that a relation is a function, it is necessary to show that each element of the domain is related to a unique element of the codomain. For many functions whose domain is the set of natural numbers the relation is defined in such a way that the principle of finite induction can be used to show that the relation is a function. A definition of this form is known as a *definition by induction*.

Suppose we are dealing with a relation f with domain N and codomain some set B, and such that the following properties are satisfied:

1. There is a *unique* element in B, which we denote by $f(1)$, such that the relation f holds between 1 and $f(1)$.

2. A means is known whereby, if we know $f(n) \in B$ such that n and $f(n)$ are related, we can determine a unique $f(\sigma(n)) \in B$ such that the relation f holds between $\sigma(n) \in N$ and $f(\sigma(n))$.

For such a method to be satisfactory, we must give a precise meaning to "a means is known" in condition 2. To do this we introduce a function[4] $g : N \times B \to B$ and define $f(\sigma(n)) = g(n, f(n))$.

From these properties it is clear by the principle of finite induction that the set M of all $n \in N$, for which there is a unique $f(n) \in B$ such that the relation f holds between n and $f(n)$, is in fact the set N. The uniqueness of $f(n)$ for each $n \in N$ shows that f is a function mapping N into B.

We have defined addition and multiplication directly. They could also be defined as special cases of definition by induction.

As a simple example, we consider the function $f : N \to N$, where $f(n) = n!$ To define this by induction we use $g : N \times N \to N$, where $g(n, m) = \sigma(n)m$. Then $f(1) = 1$ and $f(\sigma(n)) = g(n, f(n))$ define the factorial function.

5.8   Order for the natural numbers

Consider the list of natural numbers

$$1, \sigma(1), \sigma(\sigma(1)), \; \cdots .$$

The reader can prove by the principle of finite induction that this list contains all the natural numbers. Since σ is injective, it can be shown that no natural number appears twice in the list.

We define the *order of the natural numbers* by saying that, if $a \in N$, $b \in N$, and a appears before b in this list, then $a < b$. The method of Exercise 2.25 can be used to show that this relation is transitive.

Since $\sigma(a) = a + 1$, we see that we can replace the above list of natural numbers by

$$1, 1 + 1, 1 + 1 + 1, 1 + 1 + 1 + 1, \; \cdots .$$

[4] For many purposes it is possible to replace g by $h : B \to B$, but g is more convenient for defining some functions, for example $n!$.

From this we see that, if a appears in the list before b, then there is a natural number x such that $a + x = b$, and, conversely, if there exists a natural number x such that $a + x = b$, where a and b are natural numbers, then a appears before b in the list. This gives us a second, and equivalent, characterization of the order: $a < b$ if and only if there exists a natural number x such that $a + x = b$.

We can now prove three important properties of the order of the natural numbers.

THEOREM 5.6

1. If a, b, c are natural numbers and if $a < b$ and $b < c$, then $a < c$ (transitivity).
2. If a, b are natural numbers, then exactly one of the following is true (trichotomy):
$$a < b, \qquad a = b, \qquad a > b.$$
3. If a, b, c are natural numbers and if $a < b$, then $ac < bc$ and $a + c < b + c$.

Proof

1. Since $a < b$, there exists a natural number x such that $a + x = b$. Since $b < c$, there exists a natural number y such that $b + y = c$. Therefore $(a + x) + y = b + y = c$. By the associative law $a + (x + y) = c$. But $x + y$ is a natural number. Therefore $a < c$.

2. Find a, b in the list $1, 1 + 1, 1 + 1 + 1, \cdots$. Then exactly one of the following is true:

   (a) a appears before b.
   (b) a and b appear in the same position.
   (c) a appears after b.

These possibilities correspond, respectively, to $a < b$, $a = b$, and $a > b$.

3. Since $a < b$, there exists a natural number x such that $a + x = b$. Therefore $(a + x) + c = b + c$. By the associative law $a + (x + c) = b + c$. By the commutative law $a + (c + x) = b + c$. By the associative law $(a + c) + x = b + c$. Therefore $a + c < b + c$.

The proof that $ac < bc$ is similar. •

As usual we write $b > a$ to mean the same as $a < b$. We also write $a \leq b$ to mean "either $a < b$ or $a = b$." We leave the reader to prove that the relation $\leq$ is a linear order on N.

5.9 The well-ordering principle

There is a useful property of the natural numbers that can be proved from the axiom of induction.

THEOREM   5.7

The natural numbers are well-ordered, that is, in every nonempty set of natural numbers there is a smallest member.

Proof

Suppose M is a subset of N without a smallest member. We want to prove that $\complement M = N$, that is, $M = \varnothing$. Let $S = \{n | n < m, n \in N,$ for all $m \in M\}$, that is, the set of all natural numbers smaller than every member of M. It is clear that $S \subset \complement M$. Also $1 \in S$, since otherwise $1 \in M$ and M has a smallest element. Consider $n \in S$. If $n + 1 \notin S$, then $n + 1 \in M$ and $n + 1$ is the smallest element of M. But this is impossible. Therefore $n + 1 \in S$. Then, by the principle of finite induction, $S = N$. Therefore $N = \complement M$ and hence $M = \varnothing$. •

We say that a subset of the natural numbers is *bounded above* if there is a natural number n such that $a < n$ for all a in the set. We prove Theorem 5.8 as an important example of the use of the well-ordering principle.

THEOREM   5.8

Every nonempty set S of natural numbers that is bounded above contains a greatest member.

Proof

Let A denote the set of all $n \in N$ such that $n > x$ for all $x \in S$. A has a smallest element a_0 and $a_0 > x$ for all $x \in S$. The number $s \in N$, such that $\sigma(s) = a_0$, must be in S for otherwise it would be in A, which is impossible since $s < a_0$. Also $s \geq x$ for all $x \in S$ for otherwise $\sigma(s) \notin A$. Thus s is the largest element in S. •

The reader is familiar with the process of division of natural numbers—a process that associates with an ordered pair of natural numbers a quotient and a remainder, where the remainder may be zero. We use the well-ordering principle to prove that this process can always be carried out.

THEOREM   5.9 (THE DIVISION ALGORITHM)

Let x and y be natural numbers such that $x < y$. Then either there exists $q \in N$ such that $y = xq$, or there exist $q_1 \in N$ and $r \in N$ such that $y = xq_1 + r$ and $r < x$.

Proof

Consider the set $M = \{m | m \in N, y \leq xm\}$. Since $y < x(y + 1)$, we see that $M \neq \varnothing$. Then by the well-ordering principle, M contains a smallest element, call it m_1. If $y = xm_1$, we take $q = m_1$ and the theorem is proved in this case. If $y \neq xm_1$, let m_2 be the predecessor of m_1, that is, $\sigma(m_2) = m_1$. (Since $x < y$, we know that $m_1 > 1$ and hence m_1 has a predecessor.) Then $xm_2 < y < xm_1$, since otherwise m_2 is an element of M and m_1 would not be the smallest element. Then there exists r such that $xm_2 + r = y$. If we take $q_1 = m_2$, we have $y = xq_1 + r$. It remains to be proved that $r < x$. If $r \not< x$, then $y = xm_2 + r \geq x(m_2 + 1) = xm_1$. But this contradicts $y \neq xm_1$. Therefore $r < x$. •

If there is a $q \in N$ such that $y = xq$, we sometimes write $q = y/x$ and say that x divides y or that x is a divisor of y.

5.10 Unique factorization

In this section we shall introduce the idea of prime numbers and prove an important theorem about the representation of a natural number as a product of prime numbers.

It is clear from our definition of divisors in the last section that divisibility is a transitive relation, that is, if a is a divisor of b and b is a divisor of c, then a is a divisor of c. Theorem 5.10 shows a connection between divisibility and order.

THEOREM 5.10

If $a \in N$ is a divisor of $b \in N$, then $a \leq b$.

Proof

Since a is a divisor of b, we have $b = ac$ for some $c \in N$. It is thus sufficient to prove that $a \leq an$ for all $n \in N$. We shall leave the proof of this as an exercise. •

The following corollary is an immediate consequence, since the order relation is antisymmetric.

Corollary 1

If a is a divisor of b and b is a divisor of a, then $a = b$.

It is clear that any natural number $a \neq 1$ has at least two divisors, a and 1. We call these *trivial divisors*.

DEFINITION

A number $p \in N$ is called a *prime number* if $p \neq 1$ and if p has only trivial divisors.

We shall now ask whether there are prime numbers. This is answered in the following theorem.

THEOREM 5.11

There are prime numbers.

Proof

For any $a \in N$, consider the set $D_a = \{b | b \text{ divides } a\}$. It is clear that $1 \in D_a$ and $a \in D_a$. If $E_a = D_a - \{1,a\} = \varnothing$, then a is a prime and the theorem is proved. Suppose $E_a \neq \varnothing$. Since $E_a \subset N$ and N is well-ordered, there is a smallest element $c \in E_a$. Then c is a prime, for otherwise there is a divisor e of c and hence of a by the transitivity of divisibility. Theorem 5.10 shows that $e < c$, a contradiction. •

Much of the arithmetic of natural numbers (and of integers) depends on Theorem 5.12, sometimes called the *fundamental theorem of arithmetic.*

THEOREM 5.12

Any $n \in N$, $n \neq 1$, can be written as a product of primes, and this product is unique except for the order of the primes.

Proof

Consider any $a \in N$. Let E_a be as defined in the proof of Theorem 5.11. If $E_a = \varnothing$, then a is a prime and hence is the product of primes (one prime in this case). If $E_a \neq \varnothing$, we have seen that its smallest element is a prime denoted by p_1. Then $a = p_1 a_1$. If we now consider E_{a_1}, we see that either a_1 is a prime or there is a smallest prime p_2 such that $a = p_1 p_2 a_2$. Also $a_1 < a$. Then in fewer than a steps we get $E_{a_i} = \varnothing$ for some i, and $a = p_1 p_2 \cdots p_i$. This proves the existence of the prime decomposition. Suppose $a = p_1 p_2 \cdots p_i p_{i+1} \cdots p_r = p_1 p_2 \cdots p_i q_{i+1} \cdots q_s$ are decompositions in which the primes are arranged in nondecreasing order. By the cancellation law $p_{i+1} \cdots p_r = q_{i+1} \cdots q_s$. Then $p_{i+1} = q_{i+1}$, since each is the smallest element of $E_{p_{i+1} \cdots p_r}$. Therefore the decomposition is unique. •

We conclude this section with a theorem dealing with division by a prime number.

THEOREM 5.13

A natural number $n \neq 1$ is a prime if and only if, whenever n divides a product ab with $a \in N$, $b \in N$, it follows that n divides either a or b.

Proof

1. Suppose n is a prime dividing ab, where $a = p_1 p_2 \cdots p_r$ and $b = q_1 q_2 \cdots q_s$ are prime decompositions. If n does not divide a or b, we

have

$$ab = p_1p_2 \cdots p_r q_1 q_2 \cdots q_s = nm.$$

But this leads to two decompositions of ab, one involving the prime n and the other not. This is a contraduction, and hence n divides either a or b.

2. If n is not a prime, then $n = cd$ with $c < n$ and $d < n$. Thus n divides the product cd but divides neither c nor d. •

EXERCISES

5.1. Using the notation of Example 5.1, prove that B, C_m are elements of $\mathfrak{C} \cap \mathfrak{I}$ and that $\mathfrak{C} \cap \mathfrak{I} = \{A, B, C_m, m \in N\}$.

5.2. Prove that $s_a : N \to N$ does not leave any element of N invariant, that is, $s_a(n) \neq n$ for $n \in N$.

5.3. Prove that $s_n = \sigma^n$.

5.4. Use induction to prove that

$$r + r^2 + \cdots + r^n = \frac{r(1 - r^n)}{1 - r}.$$

5.5. Use induction to prove that

$$1 + 2 + \cdots + n = \frac{n(n + 1)}{2}$$

for all $n \in N$.

5.6. Use induction to prove that

$$1^2 + 2^2 + \cdots + n^2 = \frac{n(n + 1)(2n + 1)}{6}$$

for all $n \in N$.

5.7. Use induction to prove that

$$1^3 + 2^3 + \cdots + n^3 = \frac{n^2(n + 1)^2}{4}$$

for all $n \in N$.

5.8. Prove the analogue of Theorem 5.1 for multiplication; that is, if $f : N \to N$ and $g : N \to N$ such that $f(\sigma(x)) = f(x) + f(1)$, $g(\sigma(x)) = g(x) + g(1)$, and $f(1) = g(1)$, then $f = g$.

5.9. Prove the analogue of Theorem 5.2 for multiplication; that is, for each $n \in N$ there is exactly one map $f : N \to N$ such that $f(1) = n$ and $f(\sigma(x)) = f(x) + n$.

5.10. Prove that $p_{\sigma(x)}(y) = p_x(y) + y$, where $p_n : N \to N$ is defined as in Section 5.6.

5.11. Prove the analogue of Theorem 5.3 for multiplication; that is, $p_a : N \to N$ is injective.

5.12. Prove the cancellation law for multiplication of the natural numbers.

5.13. Prove the commutative law for the multiplication of the natural numbers (see Exercise 5.10).

5.14. Prove that the left distributive law for natural numbers implies the right distributive law.

5.15. If $g:N \times N \to N$, where $g(x,y) = 2y$, describe the function $f:N \to N$ defined by induction as in Section 5.7.

5.16. Find a function $g:N \times N \to N$ such that $f:N \to N$ defined by induction as in Section 5.7 is the function $s_m:N \to N$.

5.17. Prove that the list 1, $\sigma(1)$, $\sigma(\sigma(1))$, $\cdots$ in Section 5.8 contains all natural numbers with no repetitions.

5.18. Prove that, if a, b, c are natural numbers and $a < b$, then $ac < bc$.

5.19. Prove that, if a, b, c are natural numbers and $a + c < a + b$, then $c < b$.

5.20. Prove that if a, b, c are natural numbers and $ab < ac$, then $b < c$.

5.21. Prove that the relation $\leq$ linearly orders the natural numbers.

5.22. Use induction (*not* the binomial theorem) to prove that, if a is a natural number, then $(1 + a)^n \geq 1 + na$ for all $n \in N$.

5.23. Consider the set $A = \{e,b,c\}$ and the function $f = \begin{pmatrix} e & b & c \\ b & c & b \end{pmatrix}$.

    (a) Prove that $f(x) \neq e$ for all $x \in A$. (Hence axiom a is satisfied by A and f.)

    (b) Let

$$\mathcal{Q} = \{X | X \subset A, e \in X\}$$

and

$$\mathcal{J} = \{X | X \subset A, \text{ if } x \in X \text{ then } f(x) \in X\}.$$

Prove that $\mathcal{Q} \cap \mathcal{J} = \{A\}$ (hence axiom c is satisfied).

    (c) Prove that f is not injective (thus axiom b is not satisfied).

This exercise shows that axiom b is not a consequence of axioms a and c.

5.24. Consider the set $A = \{a,b,c,d\}$ and the function $f = \begin{pmatrix} a & b & c & d \\ b & c & d & a \end{pmatrix}$.

    (a) Show that there is no $e \in A$ such that $f(x) \neq e$ for all $x \in A$.

    (b) Prove that f is injective.

    (c) If

$$\mathcal{E} = \{X | X \subset A, a \in X\}$$

and

$$\mathcal{J} = \{X | X \subset A, \text{ if } x \in X \text{ then } f(x) \in X\},$$

prove that $\mathcal{E} \cap \mathcal{J} = \{A\}$.

This exercise shows that axiom a is not a consequence of axioms b and c.

5.25. Let X be a set, $f:X \to X$. We say that $A \subset X$ is invariant under f if $f(a) \in A$ for all $a \in A$. Prove that, if X is the only invariant subset of X, then X is a finite set. [*Hint:* Observe that $B = \{x, f(x), \cdots, f^n(x), \cdots\}$ and $C = \{f(x), f^2(x), \cdots, f^n(x), \cdots\}$ are invariant.]

5.26. For $a \in N$ prove that $a \leq an$ for all $n \in N$.

5.11   Zero

In our study of order for the natural numbers, we saw that, if $a \in N$ and $b \in N$, then the equation $a + x = b$ has a solution $x \in N$ if and only if $a < b$. If such a solution exists, we write $x = b - a$ and call the operation subtraction. We shall now attempt to find a larger set of numbers that contains N as a subset and in which this equation can always be solved.

As a first step we attempt to solve $a + x = a$. To do this we introduce a new symbol 0, defined in terms of the properties we want it to have. The first of these we have already seen:

$$a + 0 = a \text{ for all natural numbers } a.$$

Now consider $(a + 0)b$. Since $a + 0 = a$, we have $ab = (a + 0)b$. We want the distributive law to hold, that is, we want

$$ab = (a + 0)b = ab + 0 \cdot b.$$

This will be satisfied if we define $0 \cdot b = 0$ for all natural numbers b. Similarly, we define $b \cdot 0 = 0$ and $0 \cdot 0 = 0$.

5.12 Construction of the integers

We still cannot solve $a + x = b$ in all cases. To do this we want to obtain a set of numbers called the *integers*. There are two ways in which this set can be constructed. One is by means of equivalence classes of natural numbers. This method is similar to the way in which we shall introduce the rational numbers. We shall mention this method briefly and leave the details as exercises. The second method is to associate with each natural number a new symbol called a negative integer. We choose this second method, which will be used again in Chapter 6 to introduce the negative real numbers.

With each natural number n we associate a new symbol $(-n)$ so that no symbol $(-n)$ is equal to any natural number and $(-a) = (-b)$ if and only if $a = b$. We call $(-n)$ a *negative integer*.

We now consider the system of numbers consisting of the natural numbers (frequently called the *positive integers*), zero, and the negative integers. We call this new system the *integers*. We shall reserve the symbol Z to represent the set of integers. We want as many as possible of the properties of the natural numbers, such as the associative and commutative laws, to hold for the integers. These various properties guide our definition of addition for the integers.

We shall not go through the details of motivating the definition, which can be stated as follows, where a and b are natural numbers:

1. $a + b$ as defined for natural numbers;
2. $a + 0 = a = 0 + a; 0 + 0 = 0;$
3. $(-a) + (-b) = (-(a + b));$
4. $(-a) + 0 = (-a) = 0 + (-a);$
5. $a + (-b) = (-b) + a = \begin{cases} a - b & \text{if } a > b, \\ (-(b - a)) & \text{if } a < b, \\ 0 & \text{if } a = b. \end{cases}$

It can be proved that addition defined in this way obeys the associative, commutative, and cancellation laws.

The definition of multiplication is also motivated by a desire to have the associative, commutative, and distributive laws hold. These lead to the following definition, where a and b are natural numbers:

1. $a \cdot b$ as defined for natural numbers,
2. $a \cdot 0 = 0 = 0 \cdot a,\ (-a) \cdot 0 = 0 = 0 \cdot (-a);\ 0 \cdot 0 = 0,$
3. $(-a)b = a(-b) = (-ab),$
4. $(-a)(-b) = ab.$

Multiplication defined in this way obeys the associative and commutative laws. Addition and multiplication together obey the distributive laws.

There is also a cancellation law for multiplication, but it must be stated with special care:

If a, b, c are integers, if $a \neq 0$, and if $ab = ac$, then $b = c$.

This cancellation law can be proved by using the fact that the function $m_a : Z \to Z$, where $m_a(b) = ab$ is injective if and only if $a \neq 0$. The reader should note this close connection between injectivity and cancellation.

In future we shall not be so careful in our notation for the negative integers. We shall write $-a$ instead of $(-a)$ and $a - b$ instead of $a + (-b)$.

Since we now can subtract natural numbers, we want to define $a - (-b)$ and $(-a) - (-b)$. To be able to solve $a + x = b$ for all integers a and b, we choose the definitions

$$a - (-b) = a + b,$$
$$(-a) - (-b) = b - a.$$

If $a = 0$, the first definition becomes $0 - (-b) = 0 + b$ and hence $-(-b) = b$.

We have now extended the set of natural numbers to the set of integers in such a way that the natural numbers are included in the new set. (We say the natural numbers are embedded in the integers.) The new system has the advantage that subtraction can always be performed.

If we had chosen to introduce the integers by means of an equivalence relation, we would have considered the set $N \times N$ and defined a relation ρ such that $(a,b)\ \rho\ (c,d)$ if and only if $a + d = b + c$. The reader can verify that this is an equivalence relation. The quotient set of this relation would be called the set of integers.

To add two integers we choose a representative from each, say, (a,b) and (c,d) and form the ordered pair $(a + c, b + d)$. The equivalence class containing this pair is called the sum of the integers. Also the product is the equivalence class containing $(ac + bd, ad + bc)$. The reader can show that the sum and product are independent of the choice of representatives. Addition and multiplication defined in this way satisfy the associative, commutative, cancellation, and distributive laws.

The reader can verify that the diagonal, that is, the set of ordered pairs of the form (a,a), is an equivalence class. This class is called zero. The identification of positive and negative integers will be found in the exercises.

5.13 Order for the integers

We saw that the order for *natural numbers* could be characterized by the statement "$a < b$ if and only if there is $x \in N$ such that $a + x = b$." We know that, for *integers* a and b, there is always $x \in Z$ such that $a + x = b$. If x is a positive integer (that is, a natural number), we say $a < b$.

Since we have used addition in the definition of order, it is reasonable to expect that order and addition will interact. This can be stated precisely by saying that the function $s_a : Z \to Z$, where $s_a(x) = a + x$, is an increasing function for every $a \in Z$.

The reader can also prove that the function $m_a : Z \to Z$, where $m_a(b) = ab$ is increasing if $a > 0$, decreasing if $a < 0$, and constant if $a = 0$.

The relation $\leq$ is a linear order on Z. We leave the proof of this fact together with several important properties of order for the integers as exercises.

EXERCISES

5.27. Prove the associative law for the addition of integers.

5.28. Prove the commutative law for the addition of integers.

5.29. Prove that the function $s_a : Z \to Z$, where $s_a(x) = a + x$, is injective for every $a \in Z$.

5.30. Use Exercise 5.29 to prove the cancellation law for addition of integers.

5.31. Prove the associative law for the multiplication of integers.

5.32. Prove the commutative law for the multiplication of integers.

5.33. Prove that the function $m_a : Z \to Z$, where $m_a(x) = ax$, is injective if and only if $a \neq 0$.

5.34. Use Exercise 5.33 to prove the cancellation law for the multiplication of integers.

5.35. Prove the two distributive laws for the integers.

5.36. Prove that the relation ρ defined at the end of Section 5.12 is an equivalence relation.

5.37. Prove that the addition defined at the end of Section 5.12 is independent of the choice of representatives, i.e., if $(a,b) \; \rho \; (a',b')$ and $(c,d) \; \rho \; (c',d')$, then $(a + c, b + d) \; \rho \; (a' + c', b' + d')$.

5.38. Prove that the multiplication defined at the end of Section 5.12 is independent of the choice of representatives, i.e., if $(a,b) \; \rho \; (a',b')$ and $(c,d) \; \rho \; (c',d')$, then $(ac + bd, ad + bc) \; \rho \; (a'c' + b'd', a'd' + b'c')$.

5.39. Prove that $\{(a,a) | a \in N\}$ is an equivalence class for ρ as defined in Section 5.12.

5.40. Prove that $\{(a + n,a)|a \in N\}$, where $n \in N$ is an equivalence class for ρ as defined in Section 5.12.

5.41. Prove that $\{(a,a + n)|a \in N\}$, where $n \in N$ is an equivalence class for ρ as defined in Section 5.12.

5.42. Prove that every equivalence class for ρ as defined in Section 5.12 has one of the forms listed in Exercises 5.39–5.41.

5.43. What equivalence class for ρ in Section 5.12 plays the role of the natural number 2? Give reasons for your answer.

5.44. What equivalence class for ρ in Section 5.12 represents the negative integer -3? Give reasons for your answer.

5.45. Let a, b, c be natural numbers such that $a < b$. Prove that $-ca > -cb$.

5.46. Let a, b be integers such that $a < b$. If c is a negative integer, prove that $ca > cb$.

5.47. Prove that, for any integer, "$a > 0$" is equivalent to "a is a positive integer", and "$a < 0$" is equivalent to "a is a negative integer."

5.48. Prove that the function $s_a : Z \to Z$, where $s_a(x) = a + x$, is an increasing function.

5.49. Prove that the function $m_a : Z \to Z$, where $m_a(x) = ax$, is an increasing function if $a > 0$, a decreasing function if $a < 0$, a constant function if $a = 0$.

5.50. Prove that the relation $\leq$ linearly orders the integers.

5.51. If a, b, c are integers, $c > 0$, and $ac > bc$, prove that $a > b$. State a similar result for $c < 0$.

6

Rational Numbers
and Real Numbers

6.1 Introduction

The system of integers was adequate for dealing with many problems man encountered in his cultural development, but soon problems arose both in everyday life and also in the early study of geometry that required a new system of numbers. We shall not consider these historical developments, but simply point out that the main failure of the system of integers is that it does not always provide us with a solution for the equation $ax = b$. To solve such an equation or, in other words, to carry out division for any two numbers, the system of rational numbers is needed.

We shall make use of our knowledge of set theory and also our knowledge of the system of integers to define the rational numbers and their arithmetic operations and to point out a few important properties of the system.

6.2 Definition of rational numbers

To divide a by b is to find a number q, called the *quotient*, such that $a = bq$. If we limit ourselves to the integers, we can solve such a problem in the following cases:

1. $a = 0$, $b = 0$, in which case q can be any integer since $0q = 0$.
2. $b \neq 0$ and a is an integer multiple of b (possibly zero). In this case there is a unique solution q such that $bq = a$.

The case $b = 0$ and $a \neq 0$ has no solution because we know that $bq = 0q = 0 \neq a$ for any q. Thus it makes no sense to speak of division by zero.

We want to construct a new system, which we shall call the *rational numbers*, and define the operations of addition and multiplication in this system. We want to be able to solve $bx = a$ for all cases in the new system.

The reader, of course, has a thorough knowledge of operations with rational numbers and has a clear picture of what they represent. Our purpose here is not to teach new facts, but rather to present a rigorous development of these facts.

Consider the set $Z \times C_z \{0\}$, that is, the set of all ordered pairs (a,b) of integers with $b \neq 0$. In Section 2.3 we defined a relation on this set as

$$(a,b) \; \rho \; (c,d) \qquad \text{if} \qquad ad = bc.$$

We shall not repeat the proof that this is an equivalence relation. *We define a rational number to be an equivalence class of pairs under this equivalence relation.* We often refer to a representative (a,b) of the equivalence class as a rational number. This abuse of terminology should not cause any confusion.

The reader will realize that the difference between writing (a,b) and a/b is merely a matter of notation. The integer in the first position (a) is called the *numerator;* the integer in the second position (b) is called the *denominator.* The representative a/b is called a *fraction* or the *ratio* of a and b. Any other pair c/d such that $ad = bc$ can also be taken as a representative of the equivalence class, that is, of the rational number. We make the convention, as in common usage, of writing $a/b = c/d$ if $(a,b) \; \rho \; (c,d)$. This is in fact giving two names to the same rational number in terms of two different representatives.

We have some preference for a special set of representatives of the equivalence classes. These preferred representatives are fractions a/b, where a and b are not multiples of the same integer other than 1 or -1. We call such representatives *irreducible fractions* or *fractions in lowest terms.* To show that every rational number has an irreducible representative we consider *any* representative a/b. If this is not an irreducible representative, then $a = a_1 k_1$, $b = b_1 k_1$ for some $k_1 \in Z$, $k_1 \neq 0, 1, -1$. The reader can prove that a_1/b_1 is a representative of the same rational number as a/b. If a_1/b_1 is not an irreducible representative, then $a_1 = a_2 k_2$, $b_1 = b_2 k_2$ for some $k_2 \in Z$, $k_2 \neq 0$, $1, -1$. Then a_2/b_2 is a representative of the same number as a/b. Since a cannot have more than a factors $k_1, k_2, \cdots$, we must have an irreducible representative a_j/b_j for some $j \in N$.

The irreducible representative of a rational number is also unique. Suppose there are two irreducible representatives $a/b = c/d$. Then $ad = bc$. If we write out the prime decomposition for each a, b, c, d as in Section 5.10, we see that $a = (\pm 1)p_1 p_2 \cdots p_i$, $b = (\pm 1)q_1 q_2 \cdots q_j$, $c = (\pm 1)r_1 r_2 \cdots r_k$, $d = (\pm 1)s_1 s_2 \cdots s_l$, where $p_m \neq q_n$, $r_m \neq s_n$ for all m, n. Then we have the decomposition $(\pm 1)p_1 \cdots p_i s_1 \cdots s_l = (\pm 1)q_1 \cdots q_j r_1 \cdots r_k$ for ad. But this decomposition is unique; therefore, for each m, $p_m = r_n$ for some n and, for each n, $r_n = p_m$ for some m. Therefore $p_1, \cdots, p_i$ are the same as $r_1, \cdots, r_k$ except for their order and $a = c$. Similarly, $b = d$ and the irreducible representative is unique.

Any other representative c/d of the class containing the irreducible fraction must have the form $c = ka$, $d = kb$, where k is a nonzero integer. It is for this reason that we consider the irreducible fraction the simplest representative of the rational number.

The rational numbers that can be represented by irreducible fractions of the form $a/1$ are called the *rational integers*. We can identify these with the integers without causing confusion.

The set of rational numbers is denoted by Q.

6.3   Operations with rational numbers

We know that the sum of the fractions a/b and c/d is a new fraction, in fact

$$\frac{a}{b} + \frac{c}{d} = \frac{ad + bc}{bd}.$$

Since the rational numbers are equivalence classes and not just ratios, we can use this as a definition of addition for rational numbers only if we can show that the result is independent of our choice of representatives. The reader can verify that, if $a/b = a'/b'$ and $c/d = c'/d'$, then

$$\frac{ad + bc}{bd} = \frac{a'd' + b'c'}{b'd'},$$

that is, $(ad + bc, bd) \, \rho \, (a'd' + b'c', b'd')$. Thus the definition of addition of rational numbers is satisfactory.

We also know that the product of two fractions is

$$\frac{a}{b} \cdot \frac{c}{d} = \frac{ac}{bd}.$$

The reader can verify that, if $a/b = a'/b'$ and $c/d = c'/d'$, then $a/b \cdot c/d = a'/b' \cdot c'/d'$, that is, $(ac, bd) \, \rho \, (a'c', b'd')$. Therefore this gives a satisfactory definition for the product of two equivalence classes, that is, of two rational numbers.

These operations for rational numbers have many of the same properties as the operations for the integers. The addition of rational numbers r, s, t satisfies

1. the associative law, $r + (s + t) = (r + s) + t$;
2. the commutative law, $r + s = s + r$;
3. the cancellation law, if $r + s = r + t$ or $s + r = t + r$, then $s = t$.

The multiplication of rational numbers r, s, t satisfies

1. the associative law, $r(st) = (rs)t$;
2. the commutative law, $rs = sr$;
3. the cancellation law, if $rs = rt$ or $sr = tr$ and $r \neq 0$, then $s = t$.

The addition and multiplication of rational numbers r, s, t satisfy the distributive laws: $r(s + t) = rs + rt$ and $(s + t)r = sr + tr$.

We shall prove one of these laws as an example, the others being left as exercises.

EXAMPLE 6.1

Prove the left distributive law for rational numbers.

Proof

We want to show that $a/b \cdot (c/d + e/f) = a/b \cdot c/d + a/b \cdot e/f$. We have

$$\frac{a}{b} \cdot \frac{c}{d} + \frac{a}{b} \cdot \frac{e}{f} = \frac{ac}{bd} + \frac{ae}{bf} \qquad \text{(definition of multiplication)},$$

$$= \frac{acbf + bdae}{bdbf} \qquad \text{(definition of addition)}.$$

Also

$$\frac{a}{b} \cdot \frac{c}{d} + \frac{e}{f} = \frac{a}{b} \cdot \frac{cf + de}{df} \qquad \text{(definition of addition)},$$

$$= \frac{acf + ade}{bdf} \qquad \text{(definition of multiplication)},$$

$$= \frac{(acf + ade)b}{bdfb} \qquad \text{(definition of equality)}.$$

The commutative and distributive laws for integers show that these two rational numbers are equal. •

6.4   Order for rational numbers

The usual order relation for the rationals is defined in terms of the order for the integers. We first observe that, since $a/b = (-a)/(-b)$, it is always possible to choose as representative of a rational number a fraction whose denominator is a positive integer. With this choice of representative, that is, with $b > 0$, $d > 0$, we define

$$\frac{a}{b} < \frac{c}{d} \qquad \text{if } ad < bc.$$

We can show that the relation $\leq$ is a linear order for the rationals. For example, we can prove transitivity as follows: If we choose representatives with positive denominators and if $a/b \leq c/d$ and $c/d \leq e/f$, then $ad \leq bc$ and $cf \leq de$. Since b and f are positive, it follows that $adf \leq bcf$ and $bcf \leq bde$. By the transitive property of the order relation for integers, it follows that $adf \leq bde$. Hence $af \leq be$ by the cancellation property for order of the integers, since $d > 0$. Therefore $a/b \leq e/f$.

There is one property of order in which the rationals differ sharply from the integers. We can talk about adjacent or consecutive integers, since there is no integer between a and $a + 1$. Theorem 6.1 shows that in contrast to this the *rationals are densely ordered*.

THEOREM 6.1

Between any two rational numbers there is a rational number.

Proof

Let the given rationals be represented by a/b and c/d, where b and d are positive. Suppose $a/b < c/d$. Consider the rational number

$$\frac{ad + bc}{2bd}.$$

Since $a/b < c/d$, $ad < bc$ and hence $abd < b^2c$, since $b > 0$. Then $2abd = abd + abd < abd + b^2c$. But this is the condition that

$$\frac{a}{b} < \frac{ad + bc}{2bd}.$$

Similarly, we can prove that

$$\frac{ad + bc}{2bd} < \frac{c}{d},$$

and hence we have a rational number between a/b and c/d. •

Corollary 1

Between any two rational numbers there is an infinite number of rational numbers.

Proof

Let the two rationals be r_1 and r_2. By Theorem 6.1 there exists an r_3 between r_1 and r_2. Also by Theorem 6.1 there exists an r_4 between r_2 and r_3. This process can be continued indefinitely, and hence there is an infinite number of rationals $r_3, r_4, r_5, \cdots$ between r_1 and r_2. •

There is a connection between the order relation and addition. To see this we choose some $a \in Q$ and define the function $s_a : Q \to Q$, where $s_a(x) = x + a$ for all $x \in Q$. Then s_a is an increasing function.

Similarly, if we define $m_a : Q \to Q$, where $m_a(x) = ax$ for all $x \in Q$, we have a monotone function. If $a > 0$, m_a is an increasing function; if $a < 0$, then m_a is decreasing.

6.5   The Archimedean property

The property we shall consider in this section seems to have been discovered by Eudoxus (400–347 B.C.) but it is usually associated with Archimedes (287–212 B.C.), who emphasized its importance. This property states that, if we take any positive rational a, no matter how small, and form a sum with a sufficiently large number (n) of terms each equal to a, we can obtain a rational number na that is larger than any given positive rational b. More precisely, we have the following theorem.

THEOREM   6.2

For any two given rational numbers $q > 0$ and $r > 0$, there is a natural number n such that $nq > r$.

Proof

Choose representatives a/b of q and c/d of r, where a, b, c, d are natural numbers. By applying the division algorithm to cb and ad, we get $cb = adk + m$, where $k \geq 0$ and $0 \leq m < ad$. If we set $n = k + 1$ we have $cb < adn$, therefore $cb/ad < n$, $c/d < n(a/b)$, and hence $r < nq$. •

This theorem shows that in the set of rational numbers there are no "infinitely large" or "infinitely small" numbers.

Corollary 1

For each rational number $q > 0$, there is a natural number n such that $1/n < q$.

Proof

In the proof of the theorem we choose $r = 1$, that is, $1 < nq$, and therefore $1/n < q$. •

6.6   Exponents

The reader is familiar with the notation a^2 for aa, a^3 for aaa, etc. One of the advantages of this notation is that computations can be simplified by the "laws of exponents," one of which states that $a^{n+m} = a^n a^m$. If we think of a^n as a function $f: Z \to Q$, where $f(n) = a^n$, we see that this rule is equivalent to $f(n + m) = f(n)f(m)$. We have studied functions that interacted with the structure of the domain and codomain. Here we have a function that turns addition in the domain into multiplication in the codomain. We might ask two questions. Is there such a function? This is a genuine question, since we have not yet defined a^n for all $n \in Z$. If there is such a function, is it unique?

We shall prove two lemmas that will be useful in proving the uniqueness of such a function.

LEMMA 6.1

If $f:Z \to Q$ is a function such that $f(n + m) = f(n)f(m)$ for all $n \in Z$, $m \in Z$ and if $f(n) \neq 0$ for some $n \in Z$, then $f(0) = 1$.

Proof

We know that $f(n) = f(n + 0) = f(n)f(0)$. But $f(n) \in Q$ and $f(n) \neq 0$; therefore the cancellation law for the multiplication of rational numbers shows that $f(0) = 1$. •

LEMMA 6.2

If $f:Z \to Q$ is a function such that $f(n + m) = f(n)f(m)$ for all $n \in Z$, $m \in Z$, if $f(n) \neq 0$ for some $n \in Z$ and if $k \in Z$, then $f(-k) = 1/f(k)$.

Proof

Let k be any integer. We know that $f(k)f(-k) = f(k - k) = f(0) = 1$. Hence $f(k) \neq 0$, and also $f(-k) = 1/f(k)$. •

The following theorem proves the uniqueness of such functions.

THEOREM 6.3

For each $a \in Q$, $a \neq 0$, there is at most one function $f:Z \to Q$ such that

$$f(1) = a,$$
$$f(n + m) = f(n)f(m).$$

Proof

Suppose both $f:Z \to Q$ and $g:Z \to Q$ have the properties of Theorem 6.3. We want to show that $f(n) = g(n)$ for all $n \in Z$. We can use induction to prove that this is true for all $n \in N$. Let $M = \{n|n \in N, f(n) = g(n)\}$. Since $f(1) = a = g(1)$, we see that $1 \in M$. If $n \in M$, then $f(n) = g(n)$ and $f(n + 1) = f(n)f(1) = g(n)g(1) = g(n + 1)$. Therefore $n + 1 \in M$ and $M = N$. Thus we have $f(n) = g(n)$ for all $n \in N$.

Lemma 6.1 shows that $f(0) = 1 = g(0)$. If $n \in N$, Lemma 6.2 shows that $f(-n) = 1/f(n)$ and $g(-n) = 1/g(n)$. But we have proved that $f(n) = g(n)$, therefore $f(-n) = g(-n)$. This completes the proof that $f(n) = g(n)$ for all $n \in Z$. •

We are left with the question of whether such a function exists. We shall answer the question by defining a function $f: Z \to Q$ and showing that it has the required properties.

If we have $f(n) \neq 0$ for some $n \in Z$, then Lemmas 6.1 and 6.2 show that $f(0) = 1$ and that the value of $f(-n)$ for $n \in N$ is determined by $f(n)$. From this we see that it is sufficient to define $f(n)$ for $n \in N$. We shall give this definition by induction as discussed in Section 5.7. We define

$$f(1) = a,$$
$$f(n + 1) = f(n) \cdot a.$$

This meets the requirements for definition by induction; $f(1)$ is uniquely defined and $f(n + 1)$ is uniquely defined in terms of $f(n)$. The reader can prove that $f(n) \neq 0$ for all $n \in Z$, provided $a \neq 0$ and that $f(n + m) = f(n)f(m)$ for all $n \in Z$, $m \in Z$. This completes the proof of the existence of the required function.

We have shown that, for each $a \in Q$, $a \neq 0$, there is a unique function f such that $f(n + m) = f(n)f(m)$. In view of this it is natural to use a notation for $f(n)$ that shows the number a. The usual notation is $f(n) = a^n$. In this notation the laws of exponents state that, for all $n \in Z$, $m \in Z$,

$$a^n a^m = a^{n+m},$$
$$(a^n)^m = a^{nm}.$$

The first of these we have proved in the form $f(n + m) = f(n)f(m)$. The proof of the second is left as an exercise.

EXERCISES

6.1. If a/b is an irreducible representative of a rational number, then c/d is a representative of the same rational number if and only if $c = ka$, $d = kb$ for $k \in C_z \{0\}$.

6.2. Prove that the addition of rational numbers is independent of the choice of representatives, that is, if $(a,b) \rho (a',b')$ and $(c,d) \rho (c',d')$ then $(ad + bc, bd) \rho (a'd' + b'c', b'd')$.

6.3. Prove that the multiplication of rational numbers is independent of the choice of representatives, that is, if $(a,b) \rho (a',b')$ and $(c,d) \rho (c',d')$, then $(ac,bd) \rho (a'c',b'd')$.

6.4. Prove that $a/b = ac/bc = ca/cb$ for integers a, $b \neq 0$, $c \neq 0$.

6.5. Prove that $a/b + c/b = (a + c)/b$ for integers a, $b \neq 0$, c.

6.6. Prove the associative law for the multiplication of rational numbers.

6.7. Prove the associative law for the addition of rational numbers.

6.8. Prove the commutative law for the multiplication of rational numbers.

6.9. Prove the commutative law for the addition of rational numbers.

6.10. Prove the cancellation law for the addition of rational numbers.

6.11. Prove the cancellation law for the multiplication of rational numbers.

6.12. Prove that, if a, b are rational numbers, then $a + x = b$ has a unique rational solution.

6.13. Prove that, if a, b are rational numbers and $a \neq 0$, then $ax = b$ has a unique rational solution.

6.14. Prove that the relation $\leq$ is a linear order on the rationals.

6.15. Prove the "rule of signs" for the multiplication of rational numbers, that is, the product of two positive rationals is positive, the product of two negative rationals is positive, the product of a negative rational, and a positive rational is negative.

6.16. Complete the proof of Theorem 6.1 by proving that

$$\frac{ad + bc}{2bd} < \frac{c}{d}.$$

6.17. Prove that, if $f : N \to Q$ is defined by

$$f(1) = a,$$
$$f(n + 1) = f(n)a,$$

and $a \neq 0$, then $f(n) \neq 0$ for all $n \in N$.

6.18. Prove that, for the function defined in Exercise 6.17 extended to the domain Z as at the end of Section 6.6, $f(n + m) = f(n)f(m)$ for all $n \in Z$, $m \in Z$.

6.19. Prove that $(a^n)^m = a^{nm}$ for all $a \in Q$, $n \in Z$, $m \in Z$.

6.20. Do $(a^n)^n$ and $a^{(n^n)}$ always represent the same rational number? Give reasons for your answer.

6.21. Prove that $(ab)^n = a^n b^n$ for all $a \in Q$, $b \in Q$, $n \in Z$, $a \neq 0$, $b \neq 0$.

6.22. If a is a negative rational and $n \in N$, prove that $a^{2n} > 0$ and $a^{2n-1} < 0$.

6.23. If a/b and c/d are representatives of natural numbers such that $a/b < c/d$, prove that $a/b < (a + c)/(b + d) < c/d$.

6.7 Irrational numbers

We saw in Section 6.4 that, between any two rationals, there exists another rational. This means that there are no gaps in the rational numbers, that is, that we never get a situation where two rationals are a fixed distance apart and there are no rationals between them. If the rationals are represented as points whose distances from the origin along a line are the given rational numbers, then there is no segment of the line that does not contain the representative of a rational number. But the rational numbers by themselves are inadequate for the purposes of geometry and analysis.

As an example of this inadequacy, consider the problem of finding the length of the hypotenuse of a right triangle whose other two sides each have length 1. We know by the theorem of Pythagoras that if x is this length, then $x^2 = 1^2 + 1^2 = 2$. We shall show that there is no rational number whose square is 2.

The proof is by *reductio ad absurdum*. Assume that there is such a rational. Write it in irreducible form as p/q, that is, there is no integer other than 1 or -1 that divides both p and q. Then $(p/q)^2 = 2$ and hence $p^2 = 2q^2$.

Therefore 2 is a factor of p^2 and hence of p, since 2 is a prime. Then 4 is a factor of p^2 and hence of $2q^2$. Therefore 2 is a factor of q^2 and hence of q. But then p/q is not irreducible. Thus we have a contradiction and hence there is no rational square root of 2.

To solve this and similar problems, we introduce a new system of numbers called the *real numbers*. Real numbers that are not rational numbers are called *irrational*. There are various ways to introduce the real numbers. The method we choose has the advantage of describing the real numbers in a familiar form. No matter which definition we choose, we are faced with more difficult proofs than anything we have seen so far in our study of number systems.

6.8   Decimal notation

We shall assume that the student is familiar with the use of decimal notation. We can obtain a decimal representation for a rational number simply by carrying out the division in the decimal system. For example, $\frac{1}{4} = 0.25$ and $\frac{1}{3} = 0.3333 \cdots$. The first of these is said to *terminate*, the second to *repeat*. Terminating decimals can be thought of as having a repeating zero. When we speak of repeating decimals, we include terminating decimals. It can be proved that in carrying out the division for a rational number we always obtain a repeating decimal. This may have a single digit repeating such as $0.184444 \cdots$ or may have a sequence of digits repeating such as $0.2945945945 \cdots$. The proof is not difficult. We observe that in the division process, only a finite number of remainders can occur. Hence one of them must be repeated. When this remainder reappears, after the stage where zeros must be attached to the dividend in order to continue the division, the same sequence of digits also reappears in the quotient. This description lacks some of the details, but it gives an idea of the nature of the proof.

Let us now return to the problem of finding the square root of 2. The reader is aware, at least intuitively, that the function $f: Q_+ \to Q_+$ where $f(x) = x^2$ is an increasing function. From this fact we find by experiment that 1 is too small for the square root of 2, and that 2 is too large. Further experiment shows that 1.4 is too small, 1.5 is too large; 1.41 is too small, 1.42 is too large; 1.414 is too small, 1.415 is too large. This suggests that a decimal $1.414 \cdots$ can be used to represent the sequence of numbers 1.4, 1.41, $1.414 \cdots$, whose values come closer and closer to the square root of 2. The method of "too big and too small" that we have been using enables us always to find one more decimal place in this representation. This decimal can never repeat because we have proved that there is no rational square root of 2.

The example suggests the possibility of considering the set of infinite sequences $a_0.a_1a_2a_3 \cdots$ (which we call *infinite decimals*) with $a_0 \in Z$, $a_i \in \{0,1,2, \cdots ,9\}$ for $i \in N$, as a new number system that will enable us to carry out some operations that are impossible in the rational numbers.

This is the basic idea behind our definition of real numbers, but we shall make some refinements in it. It is convenient to consider first the positive and then the negative real numbers.

To clarify our definition of positive real numbers we shall consider the problem of finding a decimal representation for a point on a line. Since any rational number can be represented by a point on a line at a distance from a fixed point O equal to the rational number, this provides us with a representation for any rational number. It will also be clear when we have completed our study of real numbers that the set of real numbers can be identified with the set of points on the line.

We have said that the method we are about to describe is suitable for any point associated with a rational number. For the sake of simplicity we shall deal only with the point associated with $\frac{1}{2}$. We know that it is the midpoint of the half-open interval $[0,1[$. If we divide the line into intervals $A_n = [n,n+1[$ for $n \in Z$, we can write 0. to show that $\frac{1}{2}$ is represented by a point in A_0. If we divide A_0 into ten intervals $A_{0i} = [i/10,(i+1)/10[$, where $i = 0,1,2, \cdots ,9$, we can write 0.5 to show that $\frac{1}{2}$ is represented in A_{05}. We can now subdivide A_{05} into $A_{05i} = [\frac{5}{10} + i/100, \frac{5}{10} + (i+1)/100[$ with $i = 0,1,2, \cdots ,9$. Then $\frac{1}{2}$ is represented in A_{050} and we write 0.50. If we continue in this way we get $0.5000 \cdots$ as the representation for $\frac{1}{2}$.

We shall now consider the situation if we use half-open intervals that contain the *right* end point. In this case we divide the line into intervals $B_n =]n,n+1]$. We write 0. to indicate that the point representing $\frac{1}{2}$ is in the interval B_0. We can divide B_0 into 10 subintervals, $B_{0i} =]i/10,(i+1)/10]$, where $i = 0,1,2, \cdots ,9$. We see that $\frac{1}{2}$ is represented in B_{04} and we write 0.4 to indicate this. We now divide B_{04} into 10 subintervals $B_{04i} =]\frac{4}{10} + i/100, \frac{4}{10} + (i+1)/100]$. Then $\frac{1}{2}$ is represented in B_{049} and we write 0.49. If we continue in this way, we get $0.4999 \cdots$ as the decimal representation for $\frac{1}{2}$.

From this example we see that for some rational numbers we have two decimal representations, one with a repeating zero and one with a repeating 9. To avoid confusion we want to limit ourselves to only one of these. For most purposes the repeating zero is more natural, but we choose the repeating nine for the sake of convenience in proving Theorem 6.5. We are now ready to define a positive real number.

Consider the set of digits $B = \{0,1,2, \cdots ,9\}$ and a function $f:N \to B$ such that $f(n) \neq 0$ for an infinite number of $n \in N$. Then the ordered pair (a_0,f) where $a_0 \in N$ is called a *positive real number*. We shall usually denote this pair by $a_0.a_1a_2a_3 \cdots$, where $a_n = f(n)$ for all $n \in N$. We shall denote the set of positive real numbers by R_+. We shall see later that the positive rational numbers can be identified with a subset of R_+. When we speak of the rational numbers being "identified" with a subset of the real numbers, we mean that there is a subset $A \subset R_+$ and a bijective function $f:Q \to A$ which preserves the order and also preserves the operations of addition and multiplication.

We can now extend the set of positive real numbers to the set of all real numbers in the same way we extended the set of natural numbers to the set of integers. With each positive real number a we associate a symbol $(-a)$, called a *negative real number*, in such a way that $(-a) = (-b)$ if and only if $a = b$. We call the set consisting of all the positive real numbers, all the negative real numbers, and 0 the *set of real numbers*. We have represented this set by R.

6.9   Order for the positive real numbers

If a and b are positive real numbers with decimal representations $a = a_0.a_1a_2a_3 \cdots$ and $b = b_0.b_1b_2b_3 \cdots$, we say $a \leq b$ if $a_i = b_i$ for all i or if, for the smallest index i such that $a_i \neq b_i$, we have $a_i < b_i$.

THEOREM   6.4

The relation $\leq$ is a linear order on R_+.

Proof

We have defined the relation $\leq$ so that $a \leq a$, since there is no index i for which the digits a_i differ. Therefore the relation is reflexive.

Suppose $a \leq b$ and $a \neq b$. Then there is a smallest $i \in N \cup \{0\}$ such that $a_i < b_i$ and $a_j = b_j$ for all $j < i$. To have $a \geq b$ also, we must have $a_n > b_n$ for the smallest n such that $a_n \neq b_n$. But we know that $n = i$ and $a_i < b_i$. Thus we cannot have $a \leq b$ and $a \geq b$ unless $a = b$. Therefore the relation is antisymmetric.

Suppose $a \leq b$ and $a_i = b_i$, $0 \leq i \leq n - 1$, $a_n < b_n$. Also suppose $b \leq c$ and $b_i = c_i$, $0 \leq i \leq m - 1$, $b_m < c_m$. Let k be the smaller of m, n. Then $a_i = c_i$, $0 \leq i \leq k - 1$, and $a_k < c_k$. Thus $a \leq c$ and the relation is transitive.

Let a, b be two distinct real numbers. Let i be the smallest index such that $a_i \neq b_i$. Then either $a_i < b_i$ or $b_i < a_i$. Also, either $a \leq b$ or $b \leq a$, so that the relation satisfies the trichotomy property. •

6.10   Least upper bound

The concepts of upper bound and least upper bound can be defined for any ordered set. We shall apply these concepts only for subsets of the real numbers. We have not yet defined order for the set of all reals, only for the positive reals. We shall, however, give definitions here in terms of the order for the reals. We shall use these concepts only for the positive real numbers until we have extended the definition of order.

Let S be a set of real numbers. If there is a real number u such that $s \leq u$ for all $s \in S$, we say that u is an *upper bound* for S. We also say that S is *bounded above*.

If u is an upper bound for S and if for any other upper bound u_0 we have $u \leq u_0$, then u is called[1] the *least upper bound* (lub) or *supremum* (sup) of S. We write $u = \text{lub } S$ or $u = \text{sup } S$.

If S has no upper bound, we write $\text{lub } S = +\infty$ or $\text{sup } S = +\infty$. This does not mean that we have introduced an infinitely large number; it is simply a notation for the fact that S is not bounded above.

We can define a lower bound in a similar way. If the real number l is such that $l \leq s$ for all $s \in S$, we say that l is a *lower bound* for S and that S is *bounded below*. If l is a lower bound for S and if for any lower bound l_0 we have $l_0 \leq l$, then l is called[2] the *greatest lower bound* (glb) or *infinum* (inf) of S. We write $l = \text{glb } S$ or $l = \text{inf } S$.

After we have introduced the order relation for the set of all real numbers, we shall write $\text{glb } S = -\infty$ or $\text{inf } S = -\infty$ to express the statement that S is not bounded below.

We shall now prove some theorems concerning the least upper bound and greatest lower bound of sets of *positive* real numbers. These will later be extended to sets of real numbers.

Theorem 6.5 is one of the most important properties of real numbers. This property is essential to mathematical analysis, as we shall see in our study of the calculus in Part IV.

THEOREM 6.5

Every nonempty set of positive real numbers that is bounded above has a least upper bound.

Proof

Let E be a set of positive real numbers bounded above. Consider the set of all upper bounds of the form $a_0.999 \cdots$, where $a_0 \in N \cup \{0\}$ (this will later be identified with $a_0 + 1$). The set N and hence $N \cup \{0\}$ is well-ordered; therefore there is a smallest upper bound of this form which we denote by $m_0.999 \cdots$. Now consider all the upper bounds of the form $m_0.a_1 999 \cdots$, where $a_1 \in \{0,1,2, \cdots ,9\}$. Among the a_1's for which this is an upper bound there is a smallest one we call m_1. Then $m_0.m_1 999 \cdots$ is the smallest upper bound of E that has the form $a_0.a_1 999 \cdots$.

We use induction to define a function $g : N \rightarrow R_+$, where $g(i) = m_0.m_1 m_2 \cdots m_i 999 \cdots$, the smallest upper bound of E of the form $a_0.a_1 a_2 \cdots a_i 999 \cdots$. We have already defined $g(1) = m_0.m_1 999 \cdots$.

---

[1] The reader can verify that, if there is a least upper bound, it is unique. We can therefore refer to *the* least upper bound.
[2] See previous footnote.

We must now define $g(i+1)$ in terms of $g(i) = m_0.m_1m_2 \cdots m_i999 \cdots$. Consider the set of all upper bounds of E that have the form $m_0.m_1m_2 \cdots m_ia_{i+1}999 \cdots$ with $a_{i+1} \in \{0,1,2, \cdots ,9\}$. Among the a_{i+1} that appear there is a smallest one, which we call m_{i+1}. We then define $g(i+1) = m_0.m_1m_2 \cdots m_im_{i+1}999 \cdots$.

We have thus defined a real number $m = m_0.m_1m_2m_3 \cdots$. We want to show that m is the least upper bound of E.

If $x \in E$, where $x = x_0.x_1x_2x_3 \cdots$, and $x > m$, there is an $i \in N \cup \{0\}$ such that $x_n = m_n$ for $n < i$ and $x_i > m_i$. Then

$$x = m_0.m_1m_2 \cdots m_{i-1}x_ix_{i+1} \cdots > m_0.m_1m_2 \cdots m_{i-1}m_i99 \cdots .$$

But this is a contradiction. Therefore $x \leq m$ for all $x \in E$ and m is an upper bound for E. Consider any $r < m$. Then $r = m_0.m_1m_2 \cdots m_{i-1}r_ir_{i+1} \cdots$, where $r_i < m_i$ for some $i \in N \cup \{0\}$. Then $r' = m_0.m_1m_2 \cdots m_{i-1}r_i99 \cdots$ is not an upper bound of E. Hence r is not an upper bound, and so m is the least upper bound. •

The next theorem gives a similar result for greatest lower bounds.

THEOREM   6.6

Every nonempty set of positive real numbers that is bounded below has a greatest lower bound.

Proof

Let S be a set of positive real numbers that is bounded below. Let L be the set of all positive real numbers that are lower bounds for S. Since S is bounded below, L is not empty. Any element of S is an upper bound for L. Theorem 6.5 shows that L has a least upper bound l. We shall show that l is the greatest lower bound of S. There is no $s \in S$ such that $s < l$, for, if there were, s would be an upper bound for L and l would not be the least upper bound. Therefore l is a lower bound for S. If $r \in R_+$ is a lower bound for S, then $r \in L$ and hence $r \leq l$. Therefore l is the greatest lower bound of S. •

In introducing the real numbers, we hoped to obtain a set containing a subset that behaves[3] like the rational numbers and in which we can solve additional problems. We must now see how such a set is contained in the reals.

We have seen that any rational number can be associated with a repeating decimal simply by carrying out division in the decimal notation. We have also seen that we can replace a decimal with a repeating zero by a decimal with a repeating nine.

We shall refer to a positive real number that has the form of a repeating decimal as a *positive real rational*. We now see that there is a natural identification between the positive rationals and the positive real rationals.

---

[3] The phrase "behaves like" will be given a precise meaning when we study isomorphism in Chapters 8 and 9.

We shall preserve the distinction between rationals and real rationals until we have defined addition and multiplication. Thereafter we shall identify the two sets and deliberately confuse the terminology by saying that the rationals are *embedded in the reals*. This is similar to what we did in agreeing to make no distinction between the natural numbers and the positive integers.

THEOREM 6.7

Between any two distinct positive real numbers there is a real rational number.

Proof

Let a and b be the two positive real numbers. If $a < b$, then there is an index n such that $a_i = b_i$ for $0 \leq i \leq n - 1$ and $a_n < b_n$. Then $a_0.a_1a_2 \cdots a_n < b_0.b_1b_2 \cdots b_n$. Let i be the smallest index $i > n$ such that $b_i \neq 0$. This is possible, because b has an infinite number of digits different from 0. Then $b_0.b_1b_2 \cdots b_nb_{n+1} \cdots b_{i-1}q_i00 \cdots$, where $q_i = b_i - 1$, is a real rational number and $a = a_0.a_1 \cdots a_n < b_0.b_1 \cdots b_{i-1}q_i00 \cdots < b_0.b_1 \cdots b_n \cdots = b$. ●

We sometimes express this property by saying that the positive real rational numbers are dense in the positive reals. After we have introduced addition for positive real numbers, the reader will be able to show that Theorem 6.7 implies that we can find a positive real rational number differing from a given positive real number by an amount as small as we please.

6.11   Addition of positive real numbers

Let $a = a_0.a_1a_2a_3 \cdots$ and $b = b_0.b_1b_2b_3 \cdots$ be two positive real numbers. The terminating decimals $a_0.a_1a_2 \cdots a_n$ and $b_0.b_1b_2 \cdots b_n$ represent rational numbers $a(n)$ and $b(n)$, respectively. Let s_n be the real rational number associated with $a(n) + b(n)$, that is, s_n is a repeating decimal with an infinite number of digits different from 0. Since $a(n) \leq a_0 + 1$ and $b(n) \leq b_0 + 1$, we have $a(n) + b(n) \leq a_0 + b_0 + 2 = (a_0 + b_0 + 1).999 \cdots$, and hence the set of real rational numbers $\{s_n | n \in N\}$ is bounded above by $(a_0 + b_0 + 1).999 \cdots$. Theorem 6.5 shows that this set has a least upper bound.

We define the *sum of the positive real numbers* a and b by $a + b = \text{lub}\,\{s_n\}$. The following theorems give some important properties of addition.

THEOREM 6.8

The addition of positive real numbers is commutative, that is, $a + b = b + a$, and associative, that is, $(a + b) + c = a + (b + c)$.

Proof

By the commutative law for rational numbers we have $a_0.a_1a_2 \cdots a_n + b_0.b_1b_2 \cdots b_n = b_0.b_1b_2 \cdots b_n + a_0.a_1a_2 \cdots a_n$. Therefore the sets $\{s_n\}$ and $\{s_n'\}$ used to define $a + b$ and $b + a$ are the same. Then $a + b =$ lub $\{s_n\}$ = lub $\{s_n'\}$ = $b + a$. The proof of the associative law is similar and is omitted. •

THEOREM   6.9

The function $s_a : R_+ \to R_+$, where $s_a(x) = x + a$ is an increasing function.

Proof

Choose $x \in R_+$, $y \in R_+$ with $x < y$. Then $x = x_0.x_1x_2x_3 \cdots$ and $y = y_0.y_1y_2y_3 \cdots$ with $x_k = y_k$ for $k < i$ and $x_i < y_i$. Choose j, the smallest natural number such that $y_{i+j} \neq 0$. We saw in the proof of Theorem 6.7 that this is possible. Now let

$$t = x_0.x_1x_2 \cdots x_{i-1}y_i0 \cdots 09 \cdots ,$$

where 9 is the digit in position $i + j + 1$. It is clear that $x < t < y$. If s_n is the real number associated with $a(n) + x(n)$, then $a + x =$ lub $\{s_n\}$. But $a(n) + x(n) < a(n) + t(n)$ for $n \geq i$. Therefore $a + x < a + t$. Also $a(n) + t(n) < a(n) + y(n)$ for $n \geq i + j + 1$. Therefore $a + t < a + y$. This completes the proof that $a + x < a + y$, and hence s_a is an increasing function. •

Since an increasing function must be injective, the following corollary is obvious.

Corollary 1

The function $s_a : R_+ \to R_+$, where $s_a(x) = x$, is injective.

As usual, the fact that s_a is injective provides us with the cancellation law stated in Corollary 2.

Corollary 2

The addition of positive real numbers obeys the cancellation law, that is, if $a + x = a + y$, then $x = y$ for any positive real numbers a, x, y.

6.12   Multiplication of positive real numbers

Let $a = a_0.a_1a_2a_3 \cdots$ and $b = b_0.b_1b_2b_3 \cdots$ be two positive real numbers. We have seen that $a_0.a_1a_2 \cdots a_n$ and $b_0.b_1b_2 \cdots b_n$ represent rational numbers $a(n)$ and $b(n)$, respectively. Let p_n be the real rational number associated with the product $a(n)b(n)$. Then $\{p_n|n \in N\}$ is bounded above by $(a_0b_0 + a_0).999 \cdot \cdot \cdot$, and hence has a least upper bound.

We define the *product of positive real numbers* a and b by $ab = \text{lub } \{p_n\}$.

Some important properties of multiplication are given in the following theorem.

THEOREM   6.10

The multiplication of positive real numbers is commutative $(ab = ba)$, associative $[(ab)c = a(bc)]$, and distributive over addition $[a(b + c) = (ab + ac)]$.

We omit the proofs.

We shall also omit the proof of the fact that, for each $a \in R_+$, the function $p_a:R_+ \to R_+$, where $p_a(x) = ax$ is an increasing function, that is, if $x < y$ then $ax < ay$.

We can now use several of our results to prove the Archimedean property for the positive real numbers.

THEOREM   6.11

The positive real numbers have the Archimedean property, that is, if $q \in R_+$ and $r \in R_+$, then there is $n \in N$ such that $nq > r$.

Proof

We use Theorem 6.6 to obtain real rational numbers $\bar{q}$ and $\bar{r}$ such that $0 < \bar{q} < q$ and $r < \bar{r}$. By Theorem 6.2 there is $n \in N$ such that $n\bar{q} > \bar{r}$. Therefore $nq > n\bar{q} > \bar{r} > r$. •

6.13   Order for the real numbers

In Section 6.8 we obtained the real numbers by associating with each $a \in R_+$ a symbol $(-a)$ that we called a negative real number. Then R was taken as the set consisting of the positive reals, 0, and the negative reals. We shall now consider the problem of extending the concepts of order, addition, and multiplication from the positive reals to the set of all real numbers.

We can define a relation $<$ on R. This is not the same as the relation $<$ on R_+, because the domains and codomains are different, but the reader can see that no confusion will arise from using the same notation in both cases. Our definition follows:

1. If a, b are positive real numbers, then $a < b$ as elements in R if and only if $a < b$ as elements in R_+.

2. $0 < a$ for any positive real number a.

3. $(-a) < 0$ for any negative real number $(-a)$.

4. $(-a) < b$ for any negative real number $(-a)$ and any positive real number b.

5. If $(-a)$ and $(-b)$ are negative real numbers, then $(-a) < (-b)$ if and only if $b < a$.

The reader can provide a proof for the following theorem.

THEOREM 6.12

The relation $\leq$ is a linear order on R.

By referring to the proof of Theorem 6.5, the reader can prove that every nonempty set of negative real numbers has a least upper bound, since it is bounded above by 0, and that every nonempty set of negative real numbers bounded below has a greatest lower bound. From these results along with Theorems 6.5 and 6.6 we can prove:

THEOREM 6.13

1. Every nonempty set of real numbers that is bounded above has a least upper bound.

2. Every nonempty set of real numbers that is bounded below has a greatest lower bound.

The reader can also generalize Theorem 6.7 as follows:

THEOREM 6.14

Between any two distinct real numbers there is a real rational number.

6.14   Operations on the real numbers

We can define addition and multiplication for the real numbers in the same way we defined the operations for the integers.

For addition we define:

1. $a + b$ is defined as before for $a \in R_+$, $b \in R_+$.
2. $a + 0 = a = 0 + a$ for $a \in R_+$;
   $(-a) + 0 = (-a) = 0 + (-a)$;
   $0 + 0 = 0$.
3. $(-a) + (-b) = (-(a + b))$.
4. $a + (-b) = (-b) + a$
$$= \begin{cases} a - b \text{ (solution of } a + x = b) & \text{if } a > b, \\ 0 & \text{if } a = b, \\ (-(b - a)) & \text{if } a < b. \end{cases}$$

Addition defined in this way satisfies the commutative, associative, and cancellation laws.

For multiplication we define:

1. ab as before for $a \in R_+$, $b \in R_+$;
2. $a0 = 0 = 0a$, $(-a)0 = 0 = 0(-0)$, $00 = 0$;
3. $(-a)(-b) = ab$;
4. $a(-b) = (-a)b = (-ab)$.

Multiplication defined in this way is commutative and associative. It also obeys the cancellation law provided the number being cancelled is not 0. Addition and multiplication are related to each other by the distributive laws.

Instead of $(-a)$ we shall usually write $-a$.

We can now see that for each $x \in R$ there is a $y \in R$ such that $x + y = 0$. To see this, we observe that for $x > 0$ we can choose $y = -x$ and then $x + (-x) = 0$ by the definition of addition. If $x < 0$, we choose $y > 0$ such that $(-y) = x$. Then $x + y = (-y) + y = 0$. We shall write[4] $-x$ for the real number y that satisfies $x + y = 0$. We shall call $-x$ the negative of x. We have used the symbol "$-$" and the word "negative" in two different senses. This should not lead to confusion.

By the difference of two real numbers a and b we mean the real number x such that $b + x = a$. It is easily verified that $x = a + (-b)$ satisfies this equation. We shall write $a + (-b)$ as $a - b$. The following results are easily verified:

$$a - (-b) = a + b,$$
$$(-a) - (-b) = b - a,$$
$$-(-b) = b.$$

Theorem 6.9 shows a connection between addition and order for the positive real numbers. A similar result holds for the set of all real numbers. If $a \in R$, then the function $s_a : R \to R$, where $s_a(x) = x + a$, is an increasing function. We shall omit the proof of this result, but make use of it in the following theorem.

THEOREM 6.15

If a and b are real numbers then $a < b$ if and only if there is $x > 0$ such that $a + x = b$.

Proof

1. Assume $a < b$. We know there is $x \in R$ such that $a + x = b$; in fact, $x = b - a$. If $x \le 0$ then $a + x \le a + 0$, that is, $b \le a$, a contradiction. Therefore $x > 0$.

---

[4] The careful reader may realize that we should prove the uniqueness of 0 before we introduce $-x$. The proof is given in a more general context in Chapter 8.

2. Assume $a + x = b$ and $x > 0$. Then $b = a + x > a + 0 = a$, that is, $a < b$.

We shall state without proof the important fact that, for each real number $a \neq 0$, there is a real number, which we denote by a^{-1} or $1/a$, such that $aa^{-1} = 1$. •

Our discussion of the real numbers is incomplete, but we shall terminate it at this point by giving a summary of the main properties of the reals. The proofs of some of these properties have been given, others have been omitted. These properties of the real numbers are essential for the study of the calculus.

The real-number system is a set with an order structure in which addition and multiplication can be performed.

Addition is the function $s : R \times R \to R$, where $s(x,y) = x + y$ such that

1. The *associative* law holds.
2. The *commutative* law holds.
3. There is $0 \in R$, called the *zero*, such that $x + 0 = x$ for all $x \in R$.
4. For each $x \in R$ there is a *negative*, denoted by $-x$, such that $x - x = 0$.

Multiplication is a function $p : R \times R \to R$, where $p(x,y) = xy$, such that

1. The *associative* law holds.
2. The *commutative* law holds.
3. There is $1 \in R$, called the *unit*, such that $x \cdot 1 = x$ for all $x \in R$.
4. For each $x \in R$, $x \neq 0$ there is an *inverse*, denoted by $x^{-1} \in R$, such that $x \cdot x^{-1} = 1$.

Addition and multiplication are related by the *distributive* laws.

There is a *linear order* denoted by $\leq$ such that:

1. There is a subset, called the *real rationals*, that can be identified with the rational numbers. This subset is dense in R.
2. Any subset of R that is bounded above has a *least upper bound;* any subset of R that is bounded below has a *greatest lower bound.*

Addition and *order* are related as follows:

1. For each $a \in R$ the function $s_a : R \to R$, where $s_a(x) = x + a$, is an *increasing function.*
2. The *Archimedean property* holds for the real numbers. As a result there are no infinitely large or infinitely small real numbers.

Multiplication and *order* are related by the fact that, for $a \in R$, the function $p_a : R \to R$, where $p_a(x) = ax$, is an increasing function if $a > 0$, a constant function if $a = 0$, a decreasing function if $a < 0$.

EXERCISES

6.24. Prove that $\sqrt{3}$ is an irrational number.

6.25. Why can the proof that $\sqrt{2}$ is irrational not be used to prove that $\sqrt{9}$ is irrational?

6.26. Prove that the product of a rational and an irrational number is always irrational.

6.27. Prove that, if a set has a least upper bound, then the least upper bound is unique.

6.28. If $x \in R_+$, prove that for given $k \in N$ there is a real rational a within $1/10^k$ of x.

6.29. Prove the commutative law for multiplication of positive real numbers.

6.30. Prove the analogue of Theorem 6.9 for multiplication.

6.31. Prove Theorem 6.12.

6.32. Prove that every set of negative real numbers has a least upper bound.

6.33. Prove that every set of negative real numbers that is bounded below has a greatest lower bound.

6.34. Prove Theorem 6.13.

6.35. Prove Theorem 6.14.

6.36. Prove the commutative law for the addition of real numbers. (You may assume the law for positive real numbers.)

6.37. In the system of real numbers prove
   (a) $a(b(cd)) = (ab)(cd)$.
   (b) $a(b(cd)) = ((ab)c)d$.

6.38. In the system of real numbers prove
   (a) $a(b + c + d) = ab + ac + ad$.
   (b) $a(b_1 + b_2 + \cdots + b_n) = ab_1 + ab_2 + \cdots + ab_n$.

6.39. If a and b are real numbers, prove that $1/ab = (1/a)(1/b)$.

6.40. Prove the commutative law for the multiplication of real numbers. (You may assume the law for positive real numbers.)

6.41. If a and b are real numbers, prove that $ab = 0$ if and only if $a = 0$ or $b = 0$ (or both).

6.42. If a, b, c are real numbers and $a < b$ and $c < 0$, prove that $ac > bc$.

6.43. If a, b, c, d are real numbers and $a < b$ and $c < d$, prove that $a + c < b + d$.

6.44. If a is a real number and $a < 0$, prove that $-a > 0$.

6.45. If a, b are real numbers and $ab > 0$, prove that either $a > 0$ and $b > 0$ or $a < 0$ and $b < 0$.

6.46. If a is a nonzero real number, prove that $a^2 > 0$.

6.47. If a is a real number, prove that $a > 0$ if and only if $1/a > 0$.

6.48. If a, b are real numbers and $a > b > 0$, prove that $1/a < 1/b$.

7

Complex Numbers

7.1 Insufficiency of the reals

An equation of the form $ax + b = 0$ is called a *linear equation*. Such an equation can always be solved in the system of rational numbers, provided the coefficients are rational. An equation of the form $ax^2 + bx + c = 0$ is called a *quadratic equation*. The quadratic equation $x^2 - 2 = 0$ shows the insufficiency of the rational numbers. An equation $x^2 - a^2 = 0$, where a is a real number, has the solutions $x = a$ and $x = -a$ in the set of real numbers. What about $x^2 + a^2 = 0$ and, in particular, $x^2 + 1 = 0$?

We have seen that $a^2 \geq 0$ for all real a. Also $1 > 0$ and hence $a^2 + 1 > 0$ for all real a. Thus the equation $x^2 + 1 = 0$ cannot be solved in the system of real numbers. We recall that analogous shortcomings of other number systems motivated our extension of these systems. Insolubility of $x + a = b$ in the natural numbers led to the introduction of the integers; insolubility of $ax = b$ in the integers led to the introduction of the rationals. We now want to extend the real numbers to a system in which we can solve the general quadratic equation $ax^2 + bx + c = 0$. To do this we again make use of the concept of ordered pairs.

7.2 The set of complex numbers

Consider the Cartesian product $R \times R$, that is, the set of all ordered pairs (a,b), where a and b are real numbers. We use the usual definition for equality: $(a,b) = (c,d)$ if and only if $a = c$ and $b = d$. For the present discussion, we shall write $R \times R$ as C.

We define a function $s: C \times C \to C$, called addition. The value $s((a,b),(c,d))$ is defined as $(a + c, b + d)$ and is written $(a,b) + (c,d)$. We also define a function $p: C \times C \rightarrow C$, called multiplication. The value $p((a,b),(c,d))$ is defined as $(ac - bd, ad + bc)$ and is written $(a,b)(c,d)$.

The set C, with the foregoing operations of addition and multiplication, is called the system of *complex numbers*.

Now consider the subset of ordered pairs $(a,0)$. Then $(a,0) = (c,0)$ if and only if $a = c$; $(a,0) + (c,0) = (a + c,0)$ and $(a,0)(c,0) = (ac,0)$. We observe that these properties are exactly the same as the properties of real numbers, except for the notation we have chosen. This means that we can identify the real number a with the ordered pair $(a,0)$. We have already seen examples of this process of identification in the case of integers and rational integers and in the case of rationals and real rationals. When we speak of $a \in R$ being identified with $(a,0) \in C$, we mean that there is a bijective function $f: R \rightarrow R'$ such that $f(a) = (a,0)$, where $R' = \{(a,0) | a \in R\}$. In view of this, we may say that the real numbers are embedded in the set of complex numbers.

We also observe that $(0,1)^2 = (0,1)(0,1) = (-1,0)$, and hence $(0,1)^2 + (1,0) = (0,0)$. Thus the equation $x^2 + 1 = 0$ has a solution in C.

The reader can verify that the addition and multiplication of complex numbers satisfy the associative, commutative, cancellation, and distributive laws.

We can now define subtraction of complex numbers. By $(a,b) - (c,d)$ we mean a complex number (x,y) such that $(x,y) + (c,d) = (a,b)$, that is, $(x + c, y + d) = (a,b)$ and therefore $x = a - c$, $y = b - d$. Thus $(a,b) - (c,d) = (a - c, b - d)$, which can also be written $(a,b) + (-c,-d)$.

We can also define division. By $(a,b)/(c,d)$ we mean a complex number (x,y) such that $(x,y)(c,d) = (a,b)$. We shall not attempt to express (x,y) in terms of a, b, c, d until we have introduced a more convenient notation in the next section.

7.3 The symbol *i*

We can simplify the handling of complex numbers by adopting certain conventions of notation. We have already identified the real number a with the complex number $(a,0)$. We can denote this complex number by a without causing confusion. We shall also denote the complex number $(0,1)$ by i. We have seen that $(0,1)^2 = (-1,0)$; that is, $i^2 = -1$.

The properties of addition and multiplication enable us to write any complex number (a,b) in the form

$$(a,b) = (a,0) + (0,1)(b,0).$$

But we have agreed to denote $(a,0)$ and $(b,0)$ by a and b, respectively, and $(0,1)$ by i. We have thus represented the complex number (a,b) by $a + ib$. One advantage of this notation is that addition and multiplication can now be carried out without referring to the definitions in terms of ordered pairs. The various properties of addition and multiplication together with the fact that $i^2 = -1$ are all that is required. Thus we have

$$(a + ib) + (c + id) = a + c + i(b + d),$$
$$(a + ib)(c + id) = ac + i^2bd + i(ad + bc),$$
$$= ac - bd + i(ad + bc).$$

The complex number $0 + ib$ is usually written ib; $0 + i1$ is written i. These are sometimes called *imaginary numbers* or *pure imaginary numbers*. In the complex number $a + ib$ we call a the *real part* and b the *imaginary part*.

The word *imaginary* is unfortunate, but it has the weight of history supporting it. It probably reflects the fact that when quadratic equations applied to problems in geometry had nonreal roots they could not be represented in the existing geometric framework. The name tends to raise a psychological block against the acceptance of complex numbers. Actually complex numbers are no more artificial than real numbers. In fact, the step from real numbers to complex numbers is easier than the step from rationals to reals. We shall see that complex numbers can be used to describe geometric concepts; in fact, they provide a most natural interpretation of the geometry of the plane.

We shall terminate our development of number systems here. Our system is now complete in the sense that we can solve any polynomial equation. This is stated precisely as d'Alembert's theorem, or the *fundamental theorem of algebra*. The proof, first given by Gauss, is beyond the scope of the methods we have available. The statement of the theorem is:

The equation

$$a_n x^n + a_{n-1} x^{n-1} + \cdots + a_1 x + a_0 = 0,$$

where $a_n, a_{n-1}, \cdots, a_0$ are complex numbers, has a complex solution $x = b + ic$.

7.4 Conjugates and division

With the complex number $a + ib$ we associate $a + i(-b)$, which we write $a - ib$. We call this number the *complex conjugate* (or simply *conjugate*) of $a + ib$. If we write $z = a + ib$, we often use $\bar{z}$ to represent $a - ib$. Using this notation, the reader can verify the following results by direct computation.

$$z + \bar{z} = 2a \qquad \text{(a real number)},$$
$$z - \bar{z} = i2b \qquad \text{(a pure imaginary number)},$$
$$z\bar{z} = a^2 + b^2 \qquad \text{(a real number)}.$$

We now return to the problem of performing division with complex numbers. For the given complex numbers $a + ib$ and $c + id$, we want to find a complex number $x + iy$ such that $x + iy = (a + ib)/(c + id)$, that is, such that $(x + iy)(c + id) = a + ib$. To do this we could carry out the multiplication and use the definition of equality to obtain equations that can be solved for x and y. If we carried this out we would see that division is possible provided $c + id$ is not zero.

Although the method mentioned above will provide us with formulas for x and y, it is easier to handle division as follows: To obtain the complex number equal to $(a + ib)/(c + id)$, we multiply this ratio by $(c - id)/(c - id)$, which is obtained from the conjugate of the denominator and is clearly equal to 1. The reader can justify the multiplication of ratios to obtain

$$\frac{a + ib}{c + id} = \frac{1}{c^2 + d^2} \{(ac + bd) + i(bc - ad)\}$$
$$= \frac{ac + bd}{c^2 + d^2} + i\frac{bc - ad}{c^2 + d^2}.$$

It is not intended that this result should be memorized. The student should instead learn to apply the method as shown in Example 7.1. We refer to this method as *realization of the denominator*, that is, making the denominator real.

EXAMPLE 7.1

Find the quotient $\dfrac{1 + 2i}{2 - i}$.

Solution

We realize the denominator as follows:

$$\frac{1 + 2i}{2 - i} = \frac{1 + 2i}{2 - i} \cdot \frac{2 + i}{2 + i} = \frac{(2 - 2) + i(4 + 1)}{4 + 1} = \frac{0 + 5i}{5} = i.$$

7.5   Geometric interpretation

Complex numbers and the simplest operations on them have a convenient geometric representation. The complex number $a + ib$ can be represented in the xy plane either by the point (a,b) or by a directed line from the origin to this point. We note that the result of moving along this directed line is the same as moving a distance a parallel to the x axis, followed by a distance b parallel to the y axis. This representation of a complex number is sometimes referred to as the *Argand diagram.*[1]

Figure 7.1 represents the addition $(a + ib) + (c + id) = (a + c) + i(b + d)$. We represent $a + ib$ by a directed line segment from $(0,0)$ to (a,b) and $c + id$ by a directed line segment from $(0,0)$ to (c,d). To add the two numbers, we draw from (a,b) a line parallel to and of the same length as the line for $c + id$. This line ends at $(a + c, b + d)$, and the directed line from $(0,0)$ to $(a + c, b + d)$ represents the sum.

Consider the complex number $a + ib$ represented in the xy plane (or complex plane) by a directed line from $(0,0)$ to (a,b) as in Figure 7.2.

---

[1] Named for the French mathematician J. R. Argand (1768–1822).

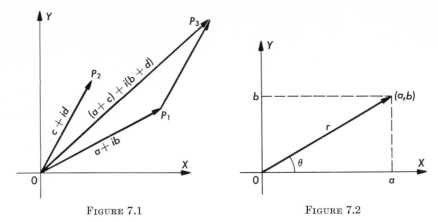

FIGURE 7.1   FIGURE 7.2

The length of this line is $\sqrt{a^2 + b^2}$. We write this $|a + ib|$ or r and call it the *modulus of the complex number*. We let θ represent the angle this line makes with the positive x axis and call it the *amplitude* or *argument of the complex* number.

From these definitions it is clear that the modulus r of a complex number is uniquely determined. The amplitude, however, is not uniquely determined. Since $r(\cos \theta + i \sin \theta) = r[\cos (\theta + 2k\pi) + i \sin (\theta + 2k\pi)]$ for any $k \in Z$, we see that any of the values $\theta + 2k\pi$ can be used as the amplitude. For the complex number 0 we have $r = 0$, and any value of θ can be considered the amplitude. In the next section we shall see a situation in which we must write the amplitude in the general form $\theta + 2k\pi$.

From elementary trigonometry we see that $a = r \cos \theta$, $b = r \sin \theta$. Therefore $a + ib = r(\cos \theta + i \sin \theta)$. We call $a + ib$ the *rectangular form* of the complex number and $r(\cos \theta + i \sin \theta)$ the *polar* or *mod-amplitude form*. It is important to have both representations and to be able to change readily from one to the other, because each form has advantages for certain problems. To transform a complex number from $r(\cos \theta + i \sin \theta)$ to $a + ib$, we use $r^2 = a^2 + b^2$, $\theta = \arctan b/a$.

There are two inequalities involving the modulus that are of considerable importance:

$$|z_1 + z_2| \leq |z_1| + |z_2|,$$
$$|z_3 + z_4| \geq |z_3| - |z_4|.$$

If we refer to Figure 7.1 and let $z_1 = a + ib$, $z_2 = c + id$, we see that the first of these is equivalent to the familiar property for the triangle: $OP_3 \leq OP_1 + P_1P_3$. For this reason it is referred to as the *triangle inequality*.

To prove the second inequality, we set $z_1 = z_3 + z_4$, $z_2 = -z_4$. Then $z_1 + z_2 = z_3$ and hence

$$|z_3| \leq |z_3 + z_4| + |-z_4|.$$

The reader can show that $|-z_4| = |z_4|$. Therefore, $|z_3| \leq |z_3 + z_4| + |z_4|$; hence $|z_3 + z_4| \geq |z_3| - |z_4|$.

Since the real numbers are embedded in the complex numbers, these inequalities are also true for real numbers. For real numbers we usually speak of the absolute value instead of the modulus and the definition is equivalent to

$$|x| = \begin{cases} x & \text{if } x \geq 0, \\ -x & \text{if } x < 0. \end{cases}$$

To obtain a rule for the multiplication of two complex numbers in polar form, we make use of two formulas with which the student is familiar from his study of trigonometry. These are

$$\cos \theta_1 \cos \theta_2 - \sin \theta_1 \sin \theta_2 = \cos (\theta_1 + \theta_2),$$
$$\cos \theta_1 \sin \theta_2 + \sin \theta_1 \cos \theta_2 = \sin (\theta_1 + \theta_2).$$

We can now multiply as follows:

$$r_1(\cos \theta_1 + i \sin \theta_1) \cdot r_2(\cos \theta_2 + i \sin \theta_2)$$
$$= (r_1 \cos \theta_1 + ir_1 \sin \theta_1)(r_2 \cos \theta_2 + ir_2 \sin \theta_2)$$
$$= (r_1r_2 \cos \theta_1 \cos \theta_2 - r_1r_2 \sin \theta_1 \sin \theta_2)$$
$$\qquad\qquad + i(r_1r_2 \cos \theta_1 \sin \theta_2 + r_1r_2 \sin \theta_1 \cos \theta_2)$$
$$= r_1r_2 \cos (\theta_1 + \theta_2) + ir_1r_2 \sin (\theta_1 + \theta_2)$$
$$= r_1r_2\{\cos (\theta_1 + \theta_2) + i \sin (\theta_1 + \theta_2)\}.$$

This gives us the following rule: *To multiply two complex numbers in polar form, multiply the moduli and add the arguments.* This has a simple geometric interpretation as seen in Figure 7.3.

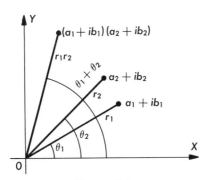

FIGURE 7.3

There is also a simple rule for division in terms of the polar form. We observe that

$$\frac{r_1(\cos \theta_1 + i \sin \theta_1)}{r_2(\cos \theta_2 + i \sin \theta_2)} = \frac{r_1(\cos \theta_1 + i \sin \theta_1)}{r_2(\cos \theta_2 + i \sin \theta_2)} \cdot \frac{r_2(\cos \theta_2 - i \sin \theta_2)}{r_2(\cos \theta_2 - i \sin \theta_2)}$$
$$= \frac{r_1r_2\{\cos \theta_1 \cos \theta_2 + \sin \theta_1 \sin \theta_2 + i(\sin \theta_1 \cos \theta_2 - \cos \theta_1 \sin \theta_2)\}}{r_2^2(\cos^2 \theta_2 + \sin^2 \theta_2)}$$
$$= \frac{r_1}{r_2} \{\cos (\theta_1 - \theta_2) + i \sin (\theta_1 - \theta_2)\}.$$

This gives the following rule: *To divide two complex numbers in polar form, divide the moduli and subtract the arguments.*

EXAMPLE   7.2

We shall calculate the sum and product of $z_1 = 1 + i\sqrt{3}$ and $z_2 = 2\sqrt{3} + i2$. In polar form these are[2] $z_1 = 2(\cos \pi/3 + i \sin \pi/3)$ and $z_2 = 4(\cos \pi/6 + i \sin \pi/6)$. Then $z_1 z_2 = (2)(4)(\cos (\pi/3 + \pi/6) + i \sin (\pi/3 + \pi/6)) = 8(\cos \pi/2 + i \sin \pi/2) = 8i$ and $z_1/z_2 = (2/4)(\cos (\pi/3 - \pi/6) + i \sin (\pi/3 - \pi/6)) = (1/2)(\cos \pi/6 + i \sin \pi/6) = \sqrt{3}/4 + (1/4)i$.

7.6   Powers and roots

The mod-amplitude notation is convenient for finding the square, cube, or any positive integer power of a complex number. Consider the square of $r(\cos \theta + i \sin \theta)$. Then $r_1 = r_2$, $\theta_1 = \theta_2$, and hence $\{r(\cos \theta + i \sin \theta)\}^2 = r^2(\cos 2\theta + i \sin 2\theta)$. The general expression for a power of a complex number is given by the following theorem.

THEOREM   7.1 (DE MOIVRE'S THEOREM)

If n is a positive integer, then $\{r(\cos \theta + i \sin \theta)\}^n = r^n(\cos n\theta + i \sin n\theta)$. The theorem can be proved by induction. The proof is left as an exercise.

EXAMPLE   7.3

Calculate $(4 - 4i)^5$.

Solution

Since $r = \sqrt{16 + 16} = 4\sqrt{2}$, $\cos \theta = 4/r = 1/\sqrt{2}$ and $\sin \theta = -4/r = -1/\sqrt{2}$, we have $\theta = 7\pi/4$ and hence $4 - 4i = 4\sqrt{2}(\cos 7\pi/4 + i \sin 7\pi/4)$. Therefore,

$$(4 - 4i)^5 = (4\sqrt{2})^5 \left(\cos \frac{35\pi}{4} + i \sin \frac{35\pi}{4} \right)$$

$$= (4\sqrt{2})^5 \left(\cos \frac{3\pi}{4} + i \sin \frac{3\pi}{4} \right)$$

$$= (4\sqrt{2})^5 \left(-\frac{1}{\sqrt{2}} + i \frac{1}{\sqrt{2}} \right)$$

$$= -4096 + 4096i.$$

---

[2] We shall use radian measure for all angles.

De Moivre's theorem also gives a means of extracting roots. Every non-zero complex number has n distinct nth roots for any $n \in N$. To obtain all of them we must write the amplitude not simply as θ but in its general form $\theta + 2k\pi$. We shall illustrate the method by an example.

EXAMPLE 7.4

Find the cube roots of $4 + i4\sqrt{3}$.

Solution

Since $r = \sqrt{4^2 + 3(4)^2} = 8$, $\cos \theta = 4/r = \frac{1}{2}$ and $\sin \theta = 4\sqrt{3}/r = \sqrt{3}/2$, we have $4 + i4\sqrt{3} = 8(\cos \pi/3 + i \sin \pi/3)$. We want ρ, φ so that

$$\{\rho(\cos \varphi + i \sin \varphi)\}^3 = 8 \left\{ \cos \left(\frac{\pi}{3} + 2k\pi \right) + i \sin \left(\frac{\pi}{3} + 2k\pi \right) \right\}.$$

That is, we want $\rho^3 = 8$, $3\varphi = \pi/3 + 2k\pi$. Therefore $\rho = 2$, $\varphi = \pi/9 + 2k\pi/3$. For $k = 0$, we have the root $2(\cos \pi/9 + i \sin \pi/9)$; for $k = 1$, the root $2(\cos 7\pi/9 + i \sin 7\pi/9)$; and for $k = 2$, the root $2(\cos 13\pi/9 + i \sin 13\pi/9)$. This gives three distinct cube roots. If we tried $k = 3$ we would get $2(\cos 19\pi/9 + i \sin 19\pi/9) = 2(\cos \pi/9 + i \sin \pi/9)$, which we already had from $k = 0$.

These three roots are represented geometrically by three equally spaced points on the circumference of a circle of radius 2 with center at the origin, as in Figure 7.4.

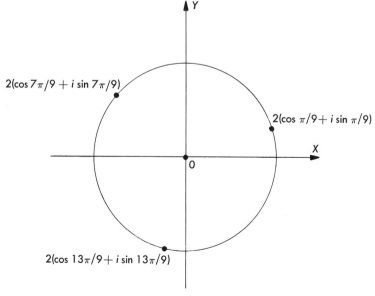

FIGURE 7.4

EXAMPLE 7.5

Find all the nth roots of 1.

Solution

We have $1 = 1(1 + i0) = 1(\cos 2k\pi + i \sin 2k\pi)$. We want ρ, φ such that $\rho^n(\cos n\varphi + i \sin n\varphi) = 1$, that is, $\rho = 1$ and $\varphi = 2k\pi/n$. Thus the nth roots of 1 are $\cos (2k\pi/n) + i \sin (2k\pi/n)$ for $k = 0,1,2, \cdot \cdot \cdot ,n - 1$. These n roots are represented by n points equally spaced about the circle of radius 1 with center at the origin (called *the unit circle*), with one point on the positive real axis. That is, they are the vertices of a regular polygon of n sides inscribed in the unit circle with one vertex at the point 1. For $n = 7$ the points are represented in Figure 7.5.

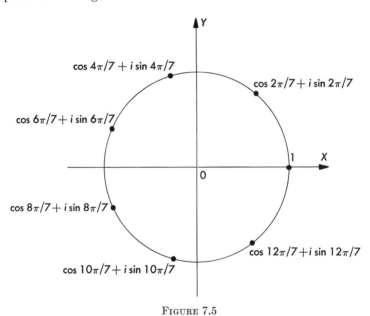

Figure 7.5

EXERCISES

7.1. Using the ordered-pair notation, prove the associative law for the addition of complex numbers.

7.2. Prove the commutative law for the addition of complex numbers.

7.3. Prove the commutative law for the multiplication of complex numbers.

7.4. Prove the associative law for the multiplication of complex numbers.

7.5. Prove the distributive law for complex numbers.

7.6. Prove that the conjugate of the product of any two complex numbers is equal to the product of their conjugates.

7.7. If $z = a + ib$, prove that

(a) $z + \bar{z} = 2a$.
(b) $z - \bar{z} = i2b$.
(c) $z\bar{z} = a^2 + b^2$.

7.8. If a, b, c, d, e, f are complex numbers and $a/b = e$ and $c/d = f$, prove that $ac/bd = ef$.

7.9. Carry out the following divisions:

(a) $\dfrac{1 + i}{2 - i}$,   (b) $\dfrac{2 - 3i}{i}$,   (c) $\dfrac{3 + 4i}{1 + 2i}$.

7.10. For what complex numbers z is the negative $(-z)$ equal to the reciprocal $(1/z)$?

7.11. Prove that $|z| = |-z|$ for all $z \in C$.

7.12. Prove that $|z| = |\bar{z}| = \sqrt{z\bar{z}}$ for all $z \in C$.

7.13. Under what conditions is $|z_1| + |z_2| = |z_1 + z_2|$?

7.14. Under what conditions is $|z_1| - |z_2| = |z_1 + z_2|$?

7.15. Give geometric interpretations of the following:

(a) $|z_1 - z_2| = 2$.
(b) $|z - 2| + |z + 2| = 4$.
(c) $|z + 3i| - |z - 3i| = 9$.

7.16. If $z + 1/z$ is real, show that either $|z| = 1$ or z is real.

7.17. Show that the values of z for which $(z + 1)/(z + i) = 1$ lie on a straight line in the Argand plane.

7.18. Let A be a set of numbers and define $x \, \rho \, y$ for $x \in A$, $y \in A$ if and only if $x^3 = y^3$. Prove that ρ is a function if $A = R$ but not if $A = C$.

7.19. Show on the Argand diagram the points $z = x + iy$ that satisfy $|z - 2i| = |z - 3|$.

7.20. For complex numbers a and b, we define a relation as follows: $a \, \rho \, b$ if and only if their arguments differ by an integer multiple of $\pi/2$. Prove that ρ is an equivalence relation on the set of complex numbers. How is an equivalence class represented on the Argand diagram?

7.21. We define a relation on the complex numbers as follows: $z_1 \, \rho \, z_2$ if and only if $|z_1| = |z_2|$. Prove that this is an equivalence relation. Describe the representation of an equivalence class on the Argand diagram.

7.22. We define a relation on the complex numbers as $z_1 \, \rho \, z_2$ if and only if $[|z_1|] = [|z_2|]$, where $[|z_1|]$ denotes the integer n such that $n \le |z_1| < n + 1$ (see Example 2.2). Prove that this is an equivalence relation on the complex numbers. Describe the representation of an equivalence class on the Argand diagram.

7.23. Write the following in polar form:

(a) 1.
(b) i.
(c) $2 - 3i$.

(d) $2 - 2i$.
(e) $3\sqrt{3} + 3i$.
(f) -3.

7.24. Write the following in rectangular form:

(a) $3(\cos \pi + i \sin \pi)$.
(b) $5(\cos 5\pi/4 + i \sin 5\pi/4)$.
(c) $2(\cos \pi/4 + i \sin \pi/4)$.
(d) $(\frac{1}{4})(\cos 5\pi/6 + i \sin 5\pi/6)$.

(e) $15(\cos 0 + i \sin 0)$.

(f) $12(\cos 3\pi/2 + i \sin 3\pi/2)$.

7.25. Perform the following multiplications:

(a) $[2(\cos \pi/6 + i \sin \pi/6)][3(\cos \pi/3 + i \sin \pi/3)]$.

(b) $[4(\cos 5\pi/4 + i \sin 5\pi/4)][2(\cos \pi/6 + i \sin \pi/6)]$.

(c) $[2(\cos \pi/2 + i \sin \pi/2)][3(\cos \pi/3 + i \sin \pi/3)][4(\cos \pi/6 + i \sin \pi/6)]$.

7.26. Perform the following divisions:

(a) $[4(\cos 3\pi/2 + i \sin 3\pi/2)]/[2(\cos \pi/6 + i \sin \pi/6)]$.

(b) $[3(\cos 4\pi/3 + i \sin 4\pi/3)]/[2(\cos \pi/4 + i \sin \pi/4)]$.

(c) $[6(\cos \pi/6 + i \sin \pi/6)]/[3(\cos 2\pi/3 + i \sin 2\pi/3)]$.

7.27. Use finite induction to prove De Moivre's theorem for positive integer powers.

7.28. Calculate the following powers

(a) $(2 - 2i)^3$.

(b) $(1 + i\sqrt{3})^4$.

(c) $(i)^3$.

(d) $(-i)^3$.

7.29. Prove that $(\frac{1}{2} + i\sqrt{3}/2)^{20} = -\frac{1}{2} + i\sqrt{3}/2$.

7.30. Prove that $\bar{z}^n$ is conjugate to z^n.

7.31. Write $(\cos \theta + i \sin \theta)^5$ in two ways and hence find expressions for $\cos 5\theta$ and $\sin 5\theta$ in terms of powers of $\cos \theta$ and $\sin \theta$.

7.32. Simplify the expression $(1 - i)^4 + (\sqrt{3} + i)^9$.

7.33. Find the following roots:

(a) All fourth roots of 16.

(b) All cube roots of $2 + 2\sqrt{3}\, i$.

(c) The square roots of i.

(d) All sixth roots of 1.

7.34. Find the following roots and represent them on the Argand diagram:

(a) All cube roots of $4\sqrt{2}\,(1 + i)$.

(b) All cube roots of 8.

(c) All eighth roots of $256i$.

(d) All cube roots of i.

(e) All fourth roots of -1.

7.35. Find all the roots of the following equations:

(a) $x^2 + 2 = 0$.

(b) $x^5 - i = 0$.

(c) $x^5 + 3x = 0$.

7.36. Find a complex number k such that k^n, $n = 1,2,3, \cdots ,20$ are roots of $x^{20} - 1 = 0$.

7.37. Factor the following expressions:

(a) $x^6 + 64$.

(b) $32x^5 + 1$.

7.38. Represent the roots of $x^5 - 32 = 0$ on the Argand diagram.

7.39. Find all the complex numbers z such that $z^6 - 2z^3 + 4 = 0$.

7.40. Find all the roots of $z^4 + 3z^2 + 2 = 0$.

7.41. (a) Find all the roots of $x^3 = (\sqrt{2}/2)(-1 + i)$.

(b) Using the geometric interpretation of multiplication of complex numbers obtain the product of each of these roots by $(\sqrt{2}/2)(1 + i)$.

8
Groups

8.1   Algebraic systems

In the last three chapters certain words appeared repeatedly in our study of the various number systems. We were concerned with a set, say A, and two operations $A \times A \to A$, called addition and multiplication. We spoke of various laws—associative, commutative, and distributive—satisfied by these operations. To the reader who is beginning to get the "feel" of mathematical thinking, this repetition of certain concepts should raise the question of whether it would be profitable to study the consequences of these laws without considering other special properties of the number systems. Such a study may have the advantage that it allows us to discuss the properties of several number systems at once. There is also another advantage, for we discover that there are systems other than the number systems that can be included in our general study. Many examples of these were first introduced as convenient tools for describing physical and geometrical problems. The general study we are about to introduce is referred to as *abstract algebra*. It has varied examples and applications, and its importance in modern mathematics can hardly be overemphasized.

In dealing with such systems, which we call *algebraic systems*, we shall make use of the theory of sets from Part I. In each algebraic system we shall proceed as we did for the number systems, that is, we shall work with a set and one or more functions, or operations. We shall restrict ourselves to *binary operations*, that is, if the set is A we have a function, or operation, whose domain is $A \times A$ and whose codomain is A. For the present we shall use the notation $a \circ b$ to represent the value $f(a,b)$ of the function; other notation will be introduced later.

Most algebraic systems that we shall study are defined as a set with one or two binary operations. The conditions that these operations must satisfy are called the axioms of the system. In a particular example we shall describe the operations explicitly and then examine them to see whether they have the required properties.

8.2 Definition and properties of groups

It is natural to start our study of algebraic systems by considering a set G with a single binary operation that satisfies certain of the laws that we saw hold for the number systems.

The first algebraic system we shall study is a *group*. A group consists of a nonempty set $G = \{a,b,c, \cdot \cdot \cdot\}$ and a binary operation $G \times G \to G$ (whose values we denote by $a \circ b$) such that the following axioms are satisfied:

1. $a \circ (b \circ c) = (a \circ b) \circ c$, that is, the *associative law* holds.
2. There exists an element $e \in G$ (called the *identity element*) such that $a \circ e = a = e \circ a$ for all $a \in G$.
3. For each $a \in G$ there is an element $a^{-1} \in G$ (called the *inverse element* of a) such that $a \circ a^{-1} = e = a^{-1} \circ a$.

The axioms for a group are frequently given as including a statement such as: "The set is *closed* under the operation," which is explained as: If a and b are elements of G, then $a \circ b$ is an element of G. We have avoided the necessity for such a statement by giving a precise description of the domain $G \times G$ and the codomain G of the binary operation.

We shall use the letter G to represent the group as well as the set. This will ordinarily cause no confusion. But the same set can be a group with respect to two different operations (see Example 8.1). When this double use of the letter G is likely to cause confusion, we can indicate the operation as well as the set, for example, $(G, \circ)$.

In Section 3.10 we introduced a table to describe the graph of a function $A \times B \to C$, where A and B are finite sets. This idea is useful for describing the operation in a group G, where the set G is finite. For $x \in G$ and $y \in G$, we find $x \circ y$ by looking for x in the left-hand column and y in the top row. Then $x \circ y$ is read from the cell in the table in the same row as x and the same column as y.

EXAMPLE 8.1

Consider the set $G = \{a,b,c\}$ and the two multiplication tables of Table 8.1. These tables represent different operations on G, since $f(b,b) = c$ but

Table 8.1

f	a	b	c		g	a	b	c
a	a	b	c		a	b	c	a
b	b	c	a		b	c	a	b
c	c	a	b		c	a	b	c

$g(b,b) = a$. It is left to the reader to verify that each operation makes G into a group. We shall see later that from one point of view these two groups can be considered the same. When we want to distinguish between them we could write $(G,\circ)$ for one and $(G,\square)$ for the other, or (G,f) for one and (G,g) for the other.

EXAMPLE   8.2

Consider the set Z of integers and the addition operation. We know that $+ : Z \times Z \to Z$.

1. The associative law holds, that is $(a + b) + c = a + (b + c)$.
2. The integer 0 is an identity element, that is, $a + 0 = a = 0 + a$ for all $a \in Z$.
3. The integer $-a$ is an inverse element of $a \in Z$, that is, $a + (-a) = 0 = -a + a$.

From these properties we see that the integers with the operation of addition form a group. This group is referred to as the *additive group of the integers*.

If we recall our knowledge of the addition of integers, we may observe that there is one property, the commutative law, which has not been used in proving that the system forms a group. In many examples of groups, the commutative law holds and this leads us to define a special type of group.

DEFINITION

A group in which the commutative law $a \circ b = b \circ a$ holds is called a *commutative* or *Abelian*[1] group.

We frequently use the notation $a \cdot b$ or ab instead of $a \circ b$ to represent the value of the group operation for the pair (a,b). We call ab the product of a and b and refer to this notation as the multiplicative notation. It is not necessarily the same operation as multiplication in any of the number systems. In this notation we usually write a^{-1} for the inverse element of a.

In a non-Abelian group we must distinguish between ab and ba and must be careful in referring to these as the product of a and b or the product of b and a. For an Abelian group these distinctions are not necessary, because $ab = ba$.

It is convenient to introduce a power or exponential notation for the group operation. In the multiplicative notation we write a^1 for a and a^n for $a^{n-1}a$, where n is a positive integer. We write a^0 for the identity and a^{-n} for $(a^{-1})^n$. With these conventions, the laws of exponents that we developed for the number systems can be shown to hold, provided the exponents are integers.

---

[1] This name is given in honour of the Norwegian mathematician, N. H. Abel (1802–1829).

In the case of an Abelian group, we sometimes write $a + b$ for the value of the group operation for the pair (a,b) and speak of the *sum of a and b*. We call this the additive notation. The use of this notation *does not* mean that we are dealing with the addition of a number system. In the additive notation the inverse element of a is denoted by $-a$ and is sometimes called the negative[2] of a. The identity element is called the zero element and is written 0, even though it is not the zero of the number systems.

In the additive notation we do not use exponents, but write $1a$ for a, na for $(n-1)a + a$, $0a$ for the identity (zero), and $(-n)a$ for $n(-a)$, where n is a positive integer. Laws similar to the laws of exponents hold in this case.

EXAMPLE   8.3

Since the addition of integers is commutative, the additive group of the integers is an Abelian group.

EXAMPLE   8.4

Consider the set Q_0 of nonzero rational numbers and the operation of multiplication. We know that $ab \in Q_0$ for all a, b in Q_0; that is, multiplication is a function $Q_0 \times Q_0 \to Q_0$. We saw in Chapter 6 that the multiplication of rational numbers satisfies the associative and commutative laws. The rational number $1 = p/p$ is an identity element and p/q is an inverse element of q/p. We thus see that the nonzero rational numbers under multiplication form an Abelian group that we call the *multiplicative group of the nonzero rationals*.

EXAMPLE   8.5

Consider the set C_0 of nonzero complex numbers and the operation of multiplication. Multiplication is a function $C_0 \times C_0 \to C_0$. In Chapter 7 we saw that the multiplication of complex numbers is associative and commutative. The complex number $1 + 0i$ is an identity element. For the complex number $a + ib$ the number $(a - ib)/(a^2 + b^2)$ can easily be shown to be an inverse element. We thus have an Abelian group, the *multiplicative group of nonzero complex numbers*.

There are other examples of groups among the number systems. We leave the proof of this as an exercise. In each case the group is Abelian. The reader may well ask two questions at this point: (1) does every set together with a binary operation form a group? and (2) are there any groups (or any interesting groups) that are not Abelian? Example 8.6 shows that a binary

---

[2] Our use of the word "negative" here does not imply that we can distinguish between positive and negative elements of the group. It is simply a convenient name for the additive inverse, suggested by the notation $-a$, which we read as "minus a."

operation does not always satisfy the axioms of a group. The answer to the second question will be deferred until the permutation group is discussed, since it is one of the most natural examples of a non-Abelian group.

EXAMPLE 8.6

The natural numbers under addition do not form a group. Addition is an associative, commutative, binary operation, but there is no identity element.

The multiplication of the natural numbers is an associative, commutative, binary operation. In this case 1 is an identity element, but there is no inverse element for the natural number $n \neq 1$. Therefore we do not have a group.

Thus we see that the natural numbers do not form a group under either addition or multiplication.

There are some important properties of a group that can easily be proved from the axioms. These are stated in the next theorems.

THEOREM 8.1

If G is any group and $a \in G$, the functions $r_a : G \to G$, where $r_a(x) = xa$ for $x \in G$, and $l_a : G \to G$, where $l_a(x) = ax$ for $x \in G$, are bijective.

Proof

We shall give the proof for r_a and leave the reader to supply a similar proof for l_a.

If $r_a(x) = r_a(y)$ for $x \in G$ and $y \in G$, then $xa = ya$. But a has an inverse element a^{-1}. Then $x = x(aa^{-1}) = (xa)a^{-1} = (ya)a^{-1} = y(aa^{-1}) = y$. Therefore r_a is injective.

For each $b \in G$ we have $r_a(ba^{-1}) = (ba^{-1})a = b(a^{-1}a) = b$. Therefore r_a is onto and hence is bijective. •

Since r_a and l_a are injective functions, the cancellation laws hold in any group. We state this as a corollary.

Corollary 1

In any group G the right cancellation law holds; that is, if $ba = ca$ for elements a, b, c of G, then $b = c$; and the left cancellation law holds; that is, if $ab = ac$ for elements a, b, c of G, then $b = c$.

Proof

In the notation of Theorem 8.1, $ba = ca$ is written $r_a(b) = r_a(c)$. But r_a is injective, therefore $b = c$. The left cancellation law can be proved similarly. •

THEOREM   8.2

Let G be any group with $a \in G$ and $b \in G$. Then the equations $ax = b$ and $ya = b$ have unique solutions $x \in G$ and $y \in G$.

Proof

If we write $ax = b$ in the notation of Theorem 8.1, we have $l_a(x) = b$. The function l_a is onto; therefore the equation has a solution. Also l_a is injective; therefore the solution is unique. A similar proof shows that $ya = b$ has a unique solution. •

THEOREM   8.3

In any group G the identity element is unique.

Proof

If e is an identity element, then $ae = a$ for any $a \in G$. But by Theorem 8.2 the equation $ax = a$ has a unique solution. Therefore the identity is unique. •

THEOREM   8.4

If G is any group then the inverse of any element $a \in G$ is unique.

Proof

If a^{-1} is an inverse of a, then $a^{-1}a = e$, where e is the identity. But Theorem 8.2 shows that the equation $xa = e$ has a unique solution. Therefore the inverse of a is unique. •

8.3   Permutation groups

In Section 3.5 we defined a permutation as a bijective function of a set onto itself. Let A be any set and let F be the set of all permutations on A. As an example let $A = \{1,2,3\}$. Then $F = \{f_1, f_2, \cdots, f_6\}$, where

$$f_1 = \begin{pmatrix} 1 & 2 & 3 \\ 1 & 2 & 3 \end{pmatrix},$$

$$f_2 = \begin{pmatrix} 1 & 2 & 3 \\ 1 & 3 & 2 \end{pmatrix},$$

$$f_3 = \begin{pmatrix} 1 & 2 & 3 \\ 2 & 1 & 3 \end{pmatrix},$$

$$f_4 = \begin{pmatrix} 1 & 2 & 3 \\ 2 & 3 & 1 \end{pmatrix},$$

$$f_5 = \begin{pmatrix} 1 & 2 & 3 \\ 3 & 1 & 2 \end{pmatrix},$$

$$f_6 = \begin{pmatrix} 1 & 2 & 3 \\ 3 & 2 & 1 \end{pmatrix}.$$

The composition of functions as defined in Section 3.8 is a binary operation $F \times F \to F$. For example, $f_2 f_3 = \begin{pmatrix} 1 & 2 & 3 \\ 3 & 1 & 2 \end{pmatrix}$. It should be emphasized again that by $f_2 f_3$, the product of f_2 and f_3, we mean the *composition* of f_3 and f_2, that is, the result of applying first f_3 and then f_2. This apparent reversal of the order of symbols is consistent with our usage in Chapter 3 but does not agree with many algebra texts. The reader is warned to be on his guard against confusion at this point.

Theorem 3.1 proved the associative law for composition. The identity map i_A is a permutation and is an identity element for the operation of composition. Also, if $f \in F$, then $f^{-1} \in F$, where f^{-1} is the inverse function of f and f^{-1} is an inverse element of f under the composition. We have thus shown that F forms a group under the composition operation. If A is a finite set with n elements, this group is denoted by S_n and is called the *symmetric group on n symbols*.

The symmetric group provides us with an example of a non-Abelian group, since, for $n > 2$, S_n is non-Abelian. In particular, from our example S_3, we see $f_2 f_3 = \begin{pmatrix} 1 & 2 & 3 \\ 3 & 1 & 2 \end{pmatrix}$ and $f_3 f_2 = \begin{pmatrix} 1 & 2 & 3 \\ 2 & 3 & 1 \end{pmatrix}$ so that $f_2 f_3 \neq f_3 f_2$.

8.4   Subgroups and cosets

For a given group G and a subset H we may have the property that $ab \in H$ whenever $a \in H$ and $b \in H$, that is, H is closed for the operation of the group. In addition, H may satisfy all the axioms of a group. It is subsets of this kind in which we shall be primarily interested.

If H is a subset of the set of elements of a group G and if H is a group under the operation of the group G restricted to H, we call H a *subgroup* of G.

It is not sufficient to say that H is a group. To have a subgroup it is necessary that the operation for H be a restriction of the operation for G.

EXAMPLE   8.7

The additive group of the integers $(Z, +)$ is a subgroup of the additive group of the rationals $(Q, +)$, since $Z \subset Q$, addition on Z is a restricted function of addition on Q and $(Z, +)$ is a group.

EXAMPLE   8.8

The multiplicative group of the nonzero rationals $(Q_0, \cdot)$, is not a subgroup of the additive group of the reals $(R, +)$. It is true that $(Q_0, \cdot)$ is a group and $Q_0 \subset R$, but multiplication on Q_0 is not a restricted function of addition on R.

To prove that a set with an operation is a group we ordinarily must check four properties: (1) the operation is a binary operation, that is, if a, b are in the set, so is ab; (2) the associative law holds; (3) there is an identity element; (4) each element has an inverse. To prove that a subset of a group is a subgroup it is not necessary to check all of these. The method of proof is stated in the following theorem.

THEOREM   8.5

In order for a nonempty subset H of a group G to be a subgroup, it is necessary and sufficient that $ab^{-1} \in H$ whenever $a \in H$ and $b \in H$.

Proof

1. *Necessity proof:* Suppose H is a subgroup. Let e be the identity in G and $\bar{e}$ the identity in H. For any $a \in H$ we have $ae = a = a\bar{e}$ and by cancellation $e = \bar{e}$, that is, $e \in H$. For $b \in H$, let b^{-1} be the inverse in G and $\bar{b}^{-1}$ the inverse in H. Then $b\bar{b}^{-1} = e = bb^{-1}$ and by cancellation $\bar{b}^{-1} = b^{-1}$, that is, $b^{-1} \in H$.

Then for $a \in H$, $b \in H$ it is clear that $ab^{-1} \in H$.

2. *Sufficiency proof:* Suppose that $ab^{-1} \in H$ whenever $a \in H$ and $b \in H$. Since H is nonempty, there is some $a \in H$. Then $aa^{-1} = e \in H$. Also for any $b \in H$ we have $eb^{-1} = b^{-1} \in H$. We thus have an identity element in H and an inverse for each element of H. The associative law holds in G and hence in H. It remains to prove that H is closed under the operation. For any $a \in H$ and $b \in H$ we have $b^{-1} \in H$ and hence $a(b^{-1})^{-1} \in H$. But $b^{-1}b = e$ and, since the inverse of b^{-1} is unique, $(b^{-1})^{-1} = b$. Therefore $ab \in H$. This completes the proof that H is a subgroup. •

If G is a group with identity element e, then G and $\{e\}$ both satisfy the definition of a subgroup. A subgroup other than G or $\{e\}$ is called a *proper subgroup*.

It is clear that any subgroup of an Abelian group is itself Abelian.

EXAMPLE   8.9

We return to the symmetric group S_3, the group of all permutations on a set of three elements, for an example of a subgroup (see Section 8.3). Consider the set $\{f_1, f_4, f_5\}$. We can verify that $f_4 f_5^{-1} = f_4 f_4 = f_5$, etc., and by Theorem 8.5 we have a subgroup. This subgroup is usually denoted by A_3 and is called the *alternating group* on three symbols. Clearly, A_3 is a proper subgroup of S_3. There is a similar subgroup A_n consisting of $n!/2$ elements for each symmetric group S_n.

If G is a group, H a subgroup, and a an element of G, we write aH for the set $\{x|x = ah, h \in H\}$ and call aH a *left coset* of H. Similarly, $Ha = \{x|x = ha, h \in H\}$ is called a *right coset* of H.

EXAMPLE   8.10

In the previous example we saw that $A_3 = \{f_1, f_4, f_5\}$ is a subgroup of S_3. The coset $f_4 A_3$ is the set $\{f_4 f_1, f_4 f_4, f_4 f_5\} = \{f_4, f_5, f_1\} = A_3$, $f_2 A_3 = \{f_2 f_1, f_2 f_4, f_2 f_5\} = \{f_2, f_3, f_6\}$, $f_3 A_3 = \{f_3, f_6, f_2\}$, $f_5 A_3 = \{f_5, f_1, f_4\}$.

This example suggests certain properties of cosets that are generally true and that enable us to construct the equivalence classes of the next section. In particular, for $f \in A_3$, we have $f A_3 = A_3$ and, if $f_i A_3 \neq f_j A_3$, then $f_i A_3 \cap f_j A_3 = \varnothing$.

In this example we also observe that the two left cosets have the same number of elements. We shall now show that this is true in general.

THEOREM   8.6

Let G be any group and H any subgroup of G. Then any two left (right) cosets of H have the same cardinal number.

Proof

Let $l_a : G \to G$ be the bijective function defined in Theorem 8.1. The restricted function $l_a | H : H \to G$ has as its range the coset aH. Then the reduced function (see VII in Section 3.7) is a bijective function with domain H and codomain aH. Therefore card $H = $ card aH and hence card $aH = $ card bH for any elements a, b in G. The proof for right cosets is similar. •

8.5   Equivalence relations in a group

A subgroup H of a group G can be used to define an equivalence relation on the set G. For $a \in G$ and $b \in G$, we say that a is congruent to b on the right modulo H if $ab^{-1} \in H$. We write this as $a \equiv b(\mathrm{mod}_r H)$. It is clear that $a \equiv a(\mathrm{mod}_r H)$, since $aa^{-1} = e \in H$ where e is the identity element. Therefore the congruence relation is reflexive. If $a \equiv b(\mathrm{mod}_r H)$, then $ab^{-1} \in H$. But $ba^{-1} = (ab^{-1})^{-1}$ (the proof is left as an exercise) and hence $ba^{-1} \in H$. Therefore $b \equiv a(\mathrm{mod}_r H)$ and the congruence relation is symmetric. If $a \equiv b(\mathrm{mod}_r H)$ and $b \equiv c(\mathrm{mod}_r H)$, then $ab^{-1} \in H$ and $bc^{-1} \in H$. Therefore

$ac^{-1} = (ab^{-1})(bc^{-1}) \in H$, $a \equiv c(\bmod_r H)$, and the congruence relation is transitive. This completes the proof that the congruence relation is an equivalence relation.

THEOREM 8.7

The equivalence classes with respect to right congruence modulo a subgroup H are the right cosets of H.

Proof

Let a be any element of G. Then it is sufficient to prove that $C_a = Ha$, where C_a is the equivalence class containing a.

Pick $x \in C_a$. Then $x \equiv a(\bmod_r H)$ and therefore xa^{-1} is an element of H; that is, $xa^{-1} = h$ for some $h \in H$. Then $x = ha$ and x is in the coset Ha. Therefore $C_a \subset Ha$.

Pick $x \in Ha$. Then $x = ha$ for some $h \in H$, $xa^{-1} = h \in H$, and hence $x \equiv a(\bmod_r H)$. Therefore x is an element of C_a and $Ha \subset C_a$.

This completes the proof that $C_a = Ha$. •

The following corollary is an immediate consequence of the theorem.

Corollary 1

If G is any group and H is any subgroup, then either $Ha = Hb$ or $Ha \cap Hb = \varnothing$.

Before stating the next result we introduce two new definitions.

A group is called a *finite group* if its set of elements is a finite set.

By the *order of a finite group* we mean the number of elements in the group.

Corollary 2

If G is any finite group and H is any subgroup, then the order of H divides the order of G.

Proof

Corollary 1 shows that each element of G is in exactly one coset of H. Theorem 8.6 shows that each of these cosets contains the same number of elements. Therefore the order of G is the product of the number of cosets and the number of elements in any coset. But $H = He$ is a coset. Therefore the order of G is a multiple of the order of H. ○

The number of cosets of a subgroup is called the *index of the subgroup*. It is clear that in the case of a finite group the index is the quotient of the orders of the group and the subgroup.

The reader can supply the proof for results similar to Theorem 8.7 and Corollary 1 in the case of left cosets.

In the commutative case there is no need to distinguish between left and right cosets, since $aH = Ha$. Even for a non-Abelian group it may be that, for some subgroup H of G, we have $aH = Ha$ for all $a \in G$. Such a subgroup is called a *normal subgroup* of G.

EXAMPLE 8.11

In our example of $A_3 = \{f_1, f_4, f_5\}$ as a subgroup of S_3, we can verify that $f_1 A_3 = f_4 A_3 = f_5 A_3 = \{f_1, f_4, f_5\}$ and that $A_3 f_1 = A_3 f_4 = A_3 f_5 = \{f_1, f_4, f_5\}$. Also $f_2 A_3 = f_3 A_3 = f_6 A_3 = \{f_2, f_3, f_6\}$ and $A_3 f_2 = A_3 f_3 = A_3 f_6 = \{f_2, f_3, f_6\}$. Therefore A_3 is a normal subgroup of S_3.

EXAMPLE 8.12

Let Z be the additive group of integers. Let $H = \{x | x = 3k, k \in Z\}$. Then H is a subgroup, since for $a \in H$ and $b \in H$ we have $a = 3k_1$, $b = 3k_2$, $-b = -3k_2$, and $a - b = 3k_1 - 3k_2 = 3(k_1 - k_2) \in H$.

For $m \in Z$ and $n \in Z$, we say $m \equiv n (\bmod\ H)$ if $m - n \in H$, that is, if $m - n = 3k$, $k \in Z$. The equivalence relation determined by H is the same as the congruence of integers studied in Example 2.2. From this we can see that the cosets are[3]

$$H + 0 = 0 + H = H,$$
$$H + 1 = 1 + H = \{x | x = 3k + 1, k \in Z\},$$
$$H + 2 = 2 + H = \{x | x = 3k + 2, k \in Z\}.$$

This example can be put in a more general form in which $H = \{x | x = nk, k \in Z\}$ for any fixed $n \in N$. Again H is a subgroup, and the equivalence relation it determines is the congruence of integers modulo n. In this case the cosets are

$$H + 0, H + 1, H + 2, \cdots, H + (n - 1).$$

EXAMPLE 8.13

Let C_0 be the multiplicative group of the nonzero complex numbers. Let $H = \{z | z \in C_0, |z| = 1\}$, that is, H is the set of complex numbers represented by points on the unit circle. For $a \in H$ and $b \in H$, we have $|a| = 1$, $|b^{-1}| = 1$, $|ab^{-1}| = |a| \, |b^{-1}| = 1$, and so H is a subgroup of C_0.

For $z_0 \in C_0$ and $z_1 \in C_0$, we have $z_0 \equiv z_1 (\bmod\ H)$ if $z_0 z_1^{-1} \in H$, that is, if $|z_0 z_1^{-1}| = 1$. But $|z_0 z_1^{-1}| = |z_0| \, |z_1^{-1}| = |z_0| \, |z_1|^{-1}$, and if $|z_0 z_1^{-1}| = 1$, then $|z_0| = |z_1|$. Therefore two complex numbers are congruent modulo H if and only if they have the same modulus. From this we see that the equivalence classes are represented by circles with center at the origin.

---

[3] In the additive notation, cosets are written $a + H$ instead of aH.

EXAMPLE   8.14

By means of De Moivre's theorem (Theorem 7.1) we can find all the nth roots of unity, that is, all the complex numbers z such that $z^n = 1$. Let D_n represent this set of nth roots of unity. It is a subset of the complex numbers. We want to show that it is a subgroup of the multiplicative group of nonzero complex numbers. For $z_1 \in D_n$ and $z_2 \in D_n$ we have $z_1{}^n = z_2{}^n = 1$. Also $(z_1 z_2{}^{-1})^n = z_1{}^n z_2{}^{-n} = 1$ and hence D_n is a subgroup. Since the multiplicative group of complex numbers is Abelian, D_n is also Abelian. For $u \in C_0$ and $v \in C_0$ we have $u \equiv v (\bmod\ D_n)$ if and only if $uv^{-1} \in D_n$, that is, $(uv^{-1})^n = 1$. But this means that $u^n = v^n$; therefore a coset of D_n is a set of complex numbers that have the same nth power. From this we see that the coset containing u is represented by n points equally spaced about the circumference of a circle of radius $|u|$.

8.6   Groups of translations and rotations

In Example 3.13 we saw a function that we referred to as a translation. In general we refer to a function $f: R \times R \to R \times R$, where $f(x,y) = (x + a, y + b)$, as a translation of the plane $R \times R$. There is a translation for each ordered pair of real numbers (a,b).

Let T represent the set of all translations of the plane $R \times R$. Let f, g be two elements of T, say, $f(x,y) = (x + a, y + b)$ and $g(x,y) = (x + c, y + d)$. Then $(g \cdot f)(x,y) = g(f(x,y)) = g(x + a, y + b) = (x + a + c, y + b + d)$. Similarly, $(f \cdot g)(x,y) = (x + c + a, y + d + b)$. Thus the composition of functions defines an operation $T \times T \to T$ and Theorem 3.1 shows that this operation is associative. It is left to the reader to verify that the identity function $i_{R \times R}$ is a translation and acts as an identity element in the composition and also that the function $f^{-1}: R \times R \to R \times R$, where $f^{-1}(x,y) = (x - a, y - b)$ acts as an inverse element of $f(x,y) = (x + a, y + b)$ in the composition. We thus see that the set T of translations of $R \times R$ together with the operation of composition forms an Abelian group, called the *group of translations of the plane.*

Groups of translations also exist for the straight line R and the three-dimensional space $R \times R \times R$. The details are left for the reader to supply.[4]

A different transformation of a plane onto itself can be determined as follows: Select any point of the plane and denote it by P. Then, using P as center; rotate the plane through an angle θ. If θ is positive the rotation is in the counterclockwise direction; if θ is negative the rotation is clockwise; if $\theta = 0$ the plane is not moved. Geometric intuition assures us that this is a bijective map of the plane onto itself. Consider the set G of all rotations of the plane about a fixed point P. If r_1 is a rotation through an angle θ_1 and r_2 a rotation through an angle θ_2, we define $r_1 r_2$ as a rotation through an angle

---

[4] Translations in three-dimensional space are important for the definition of a vector in Chapter 10.

$\theta_1 + \theta_2$. This multiplication of rotations is a binary operation $G \times G \to G$. Since it is in fact the composition of the functions r_2 and r_1, we know that it is associative. Rotation through the angle 0 is the identity element for this operation, and rotation through $-\theta$ is the inverse for rotation through an angle θ. From this we see that G is a group under this operation. Since rotation through $\theta_1 + \theta_2$ is the same as rotation through $\theta_2 + \theta_1$, we see that the group is Abelian. This group G is a subgroup of the *group of rotations of the plane*.

Consider now the set of functions of the plane onto itself consisting of all translations, rotations, reflections in a line, and composites of a finite number of translations, rotations, and reflections. This set forms a group under the operation of composition. It is clear that we have a binary operation. The composition of functions is always associative. The identity function is the identity element. To find the inverse of the composite of a finite number of translations and rotations, we take the composite of their inverses in the opposite order. This group is called the *Euclidean group of the plane*.

8.7   Cyclic groups

Consider a group G and an element $a \in G$. What is the smallest subgroup H of G containing a? It is clear that H must contain all positive integral powers a^n, for otherwise H is not closed. Also $a^0 \in H$, since a^0 is the identity. Since $a^n \in H$, the inverse a^{-n} must be in H. Thus if $A = \{x | x = a^n, n \in Z\}$, we have $A \subset H$. If we can show that A is a subgroup, we have proved $A = H$. If $x \in A$ and $y \in A$, then $x = a^n$, $y = a^m$, and $xy^{-1} = a^n a^{-m} = a^{n-m} \in A$. Therefore A is a subgroup.

We have shown that in any group G the set of integral powers of a forms a subgroup. This subgroup is called the *cyclic subgroup of G generated by a*.

EXAMPLE   8.15

In the additive group of integers the even integers form the cyclic subgroup generated by 2; the multiples of 5 form the cyclic subgroup generated by 5.

THEOREM   8.8

Any subgroup of the additive group of integers is cyclic.

Proof

The subgroup $\{0\}$ is the cyclic subgroup generated by 0. It is now sufficient to give the proof for the subgroup $H \neq \{0\}$. If a is an element of H, then $-a$ is also an element of H. Therefore H contains both positive and negative integers. By Theorem 5.7 we see that there is a smallest positive integer in H; denote it by m. Let a be any element of H. If a is positive, then Theorem 5.9 shows that $a = k_1 m + b_1$ where $k_1 \in N$ and $0 \le b_1 < m$. Since a and $k_1 m$ are elements of H, so is $b_1 = a - k_1 m$. If $b_1 \ne 0$, this contradicts the choice of m as the smallest positive integer in H. Therefore $b_1 = 0$ and $a = k_1 m$. If a is negative, then $-a = k_2 m + b_2$ with $k_2 \in N$ and $0 \le b_2 < m$. Again $b_2 = 0$ and $a = -k_2 m$. Therefore H is the cyclic subgroup generated by m. •

If a group G is equal to one of its cyclic subgroups we call G a cyclic group. That is, G is a *cyclic group generated by the element a* (or *with generator a*) if $G = \{x | x = a^m, m \in Z\}$.

EXAMPLE   8.16

The additive group of the integers is a cyclic group, generated either by 1 or by -1. From this we see that the generator of a cyclic group need not be unique.

EXAMPLE   8.17

Consider the set $\{0, b, c\}$ and the operation defined by Table 8.2. The reader can verify that this forms a group.

Table 8.2

	0	b	c
0	0	b	c
b	b	c	0
c	c	0	b

Since this group is commutative, we shall use the additive notation. We observe that this group is a cyclic group generated by b, since $0 = 0b$, $b = 1b$, $c = 2b$.

EXERCISES

8.1. Show that the following are groups. Are they Abelian?
   (a) Rational numbers under addition.
   (b) Real numbers under addition.
   (c) Nonzero real numbers under multiplication.
   (d) Complex numbers under addition.

8.2. Do the nonzero integers form a group under multiplication?

8.3. Prove that $(ab)^{-1} = b^{-1}a^{-1}$ for any elements a, b of a group.

8.4. Let A be any set with more than one element.
   (a) Is $\mathcal{F}(A, A)$ a group under the composition of functions?
   (b) What is the largest proper subset of $\mathcal{F}(A, A)$ that is a group under composition?

8.5. Let G be a group with identity element e. Prove that, if $x^2 = e$ for all $x \in G$, then G is Abelian.

8.6. Let G be a group with the operation written as multiplication. Prove that $a^m a^n = a^{m+n}$ and $(a^m)^n = a^{mn}$ for all $a \in G$, $m \in Z$, $n \in Z$.

8.7. Prove that each table in Table 8.1 defines a group operation.

8.8. Complete the proof of Theorem 8.1 by showing that l_a is bijective.

8.9. Complete the proof of Corollary 1 to Theorem 8.1 by proving the left cancellation law.

8.10. Complete the proof of Theorem 8.2 by showing that $ya = b$ has a unique solution.

8.11. Show that the nth roots of unity (i.e., the roots of $x^n = 1$) form an Abelian group under multiplication.

8.12. Do the roots of the equation $x^3 = (-1 + i)/\sqrt{2}$ form a group under multiplication?

8.13. Let A be any finite set and $f : A \times A \to A$ a function denoted by $f(a,b) = a \circ b$. Prove that, if f has the following properties, then $(A, \circ)$ is a group:

(a) The operation is associative.
(b) There is an identity element.
(c) The two cancellation laws hold.

[*Hint*: For finite A, if $g : A \to A$ is an injective function, then it is onto.]

8.14. Show that the set

$$\left\{ x \mid x = \frac{p}{q} \left(\frac{1}{2} + \frac{\sqrt{3}}{2} i \right)^n, \ p \in N, \ q \in N, \ n \in N \right\}$$

is a subgroup of the multiplicative group of nonzero complex numbers.

8.15. Let G be any group and a any element of G. The set $C_a = \{x \mid x \in G, ax = xa\}$ is called the *normalizer* of a. Prove that C_a is a subgroup of G.

8.16. Let G be any group and A any subset of G. The set $C_A = \{x \mid x \in G, ax = xa$ for all $a \in A\}$ is called the *centralizer* of A. Prove that C_A is a subgroup of G.

8.17. Let G be any group, A any subset of G, and a any element of A. Prove that $C_A \subset C_a$ where C_A and C_a are defined as in Exercises 8.15 and 8.16.

8.18. Let G be any group. The set $C = \{x \mid x \in G, ax = xa$ for all $a \in G\}$ is called the *center* of G. Prove that C is a subgroup of G.

8.19. Let G be any group and A any subset of G. Prove that $C \subset C_A$, where C, C_A are as defined in Exercises 8.16 and 8.18.

8.20. Supply the details for the proof that A_3 is a subgroup of S_3 (see Section 8.4).

8.21. Find the center of the group S_3. (The center is defined in Exercise 8.18.)

8.22. Find all the subgroups of S_3.

8.23. Give the proof of Theorem 8.6 for the case of right cosets.

8.24. State and prove analogues for Theorem 8.7 and Corollary 1 dealing with left cosets.

8.25. Prove that if a subgroup has only two cosets, then it is a normal subgroup.

8.26. Let H be the subgroup of C_0 consisting of the roots of the equation $x^6 = 1$. Describe the coset of H that contains $\sqrt{3} + i$. Represent it on the complex plane.

8.27. Let C_0 be the multiplicative group of nonzero complex numbers and R_+ the set of positive real numbers.

(a) Prove that R_+ is a subgroup.
(b) Describe the cosets of R_+ and represent them in the complex plane.

8.28. Replace R_+ in Exercise 8.26 by R_0, the set of nonzero real numbers. Describe the cosets of R_0 in C_0.

8.29. Replace R_+ in Exercise 8.26 by R and describe the cosets.

8.30. Prove that the identity function $i_{R\times R}$ is a translation of $R \times R$ and show that it is the identity element in the group of translations.

8.31. Prove that the translation $f^{-1}(x,y) = (x - a, y - b)$ is the inverse element of $f(x,y) = (x + a, y + b)$ in the group of translations of $R \times R$.

8.32. Define a translation on the line R. Prove that these translations form a group under composition.

8.33. Define a translation on the three-dimensional space $R \times R \times R$. Prove that these translations form a group under the composition of maps.

8.34. Consider the translation $t_{m,n}$ of $R \times R$ where m, n are integers and $t_{m,n}(x,y) = (x + m, y + n)$. Prove that the set of all such translations is a group.

8.35. Prove that every cyclic group is Abelian.

8.36. Let S be the set of subgroups of the additive group of the integers. For $H \in S$ and $K \in S$ we define $H \leq K$ if H is a subgroup of K. What are the largest and smallest elements with respect to this order?

8.37. Let S_1 be the set of *proper* subgroups of the additive group of the integers· An order on S_1 is defined as in Exercise 8.36.

(a) Are there maximal and minimal elements of S_1 for this order? If so, what are they?

(b) The Hasse diagram for S_1 has an infinite number of points. Draw enough of this diagram to show that you understand its form.

8.38. Let G be a group, B a set, and $f:G \to B$ a bijective function. A binary operation is defined on B as follows: $f(g_1)f(g_2) = f(g_1g_2)$ for $g_1 \in G$, $g_2 \in G$. Prove that B together with this binary operation forms a group.

8.8   The group of the square

In this section we shall consider the various types of symmetry possessed by a square and shall use these symmetries to construct an example of a group. Consider a square drawn on a plane with one edge horizontal. For convenience we number the vertices 1, 2, 3, 4 as shown in Figure 8.1. Suppose this square

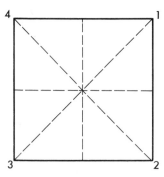

FIGURE 8.1

is cut out of the plane. In how many ways can it be put back in the plane so as to fill the opening left when it was removed? We call each way in which the square can be replaced in the plane a *rigid motion* or a *symmetry* of the square. We shall now enumerate all such symmetries. It is clear that each symmetry performs a permutation on the set $\{1,2,3,4\}$ representing the vertices. We shall use the permutation notation to describe the symmetries. We shall see, however, that not all permutations of this set represent symmetries of the square.

We shall include among the symmetries the identity permutation, that is, the rigid motion that leaves the square unchanged. We denote this by

$$I = \begin{pmatrix} 1 & 2 & 3 & 4 \\ 1 & 2 & 3 & 4 \end{pmatrix}.$$

It is clear that rotating the square through a right angle counterclockwise about its center gives a symmetry. We denote this by

$$R_1 = \begin{pmatrix} 1 & 2 & 3 & 4 \\ 4 & 1 & 2 & 3 \end{pmatrix}.$$

We also see that counterclockwise rotations through two or three right angles are symmetries. These are denoted by

$$R_2 = \begin{pmatrix} 1 & 2 & 3 & 4 \\ 3 & 4 & 1 & 2 \end{pmatrix},$$
$$R_3 = \begin{pmatrix} 1 & 2 & 3 & 4 \\ 2 & 3 & 4 & 1 \end{pmatrix}.$$

We observe that clockwise rotations through one, two, or three right angles have the same effect as R_3, R_2, and R_1, respectively.

Instead of being rotated about the center, the square could be reflected in one of its lines of symmetry. In our model of the square cut out of the plane these reflections will "turn the square over," but it will retain its properties as a square. There are four lines of symmetry as shown in Figure 8.1—one horizontal, one vertical, one diagonal with positive slope, one diagonal with negative slope. We denote the effects of the corresponding rigid motions by H, V, D_+, D_-, respectively. Then

$$H = \begin{pmatrix} 1 & 2 & 3 & 4 \\ 2 & 1 & 4 & 3 \end{pmatrix},$$
$$V = \begin{pmatrix} 1 & 2 & 3 & 4 \\ 4 & 3 & 2 & 1 \end{pmatrix},$$
$$D_+ = \begin{pmatrix} 1 & 2 & 3 & 4 \\ 1 & 4 & 3 & 2 \end{pmatrix},$$
$$D_- = \begin{pmatrix} 1 & 2 & 3 & 4 \\ 3 & 2 & 1 & 4 \end{pmatrix}.$$

Are there any other symmetries of the square? To show that there are not, we might consider each of the remaining permutations on the set $\{1,2,3,4\}$ and show that they do not preserve the properties of the square. For example, consider the permutations

$$\begin{pmatrix} 1 & 2 & 3 & 4 \\ 2 & 1 & 3 & 4 \end{pmatrix} \quad \text{and} \quad \begin{pmatrix} 1 & 2 & 3 & 4 \\ 1 & 3 & 4 & 2 \end{pmatrix}.$$

If the first of these were applied to the vertices of the square it would interchange vertices 1 and 2 and leave the others unchanged. This would change the side 4, 1 into a diagonal and hence would not be a rigid motion of the square. The second of these permutations would change the side 2, 3 into a diagonal and so would not give a rigid motion of the square. All the other permutations can be disposed of in the same way.

The eight operations I, R_1, R_2, R_3, H, V, D_+, D_- form the set of symmetries of the square. Since each element of this set is a permutation of $\{1,2,3,4\}$, we can form the composite (or product as it is usually called in this context) of any two elements. We present the composites in Table 8.3. The composite R_1H, which is D_+, is found in the row labeled R_1 and the column labeled H.

Table 8.3

	I	R_1	R_2	R_3	H	V	D_+	D_-
I	I	R_1	R_2	R_3	H	V	D_+	D_-
R_1	R_1	R_2	R_3	I	D_+	D_-	V	H
R_2	R_2	R_3	I	R_1	V	H	D_-	D_+
R_3	R_3	I	R_1	R_2	D_-	D_+	H	V
H	H	D_-	V	D_+	I	R_2	R_3	R_1
V	V	D_+	H	D_-	R_2	I	R_1	R_3
D_+	D_+	H	D_-	V_+	R_1	R_3	I	R_2
D_-	D_-	V	D_+	H	R_3	R_1	R_2	I

Since each entry in the table is an element of the set of symmetries, it is clear that the product (or composition) is a binary operation. Since the product is in fact the composition of functions, it is associative. It is clear from the table that I is an identity element and that for each element there is an inverse element. This completes the proof that the set of symmetries forms a group, called the *group of the square*.

The group of the square is not commutative; in particular, $HR_3 \neq R_3H$.

The set $\{I, R_1, R_2, R_3\}$ is a subgroup of the group of the square. It is called the *group of rotations of the square*. It is the cyclic subgroup generated by R_1.

8.9 Homomorphism and isomorphism

We have seen that a group consists of a set G and a binary operation $g(x,y) = xy$. We have also emphasized that two different binary operations on the set may form different groups. If we consider groups on the sets G and G', we might ask what functions with domain G and codomain G' have an interesting connection with the binary operations on G and G'. In our study of ordered sets we found that the functions that preserved the order were of particular interest. Here we are interested in the functions that preserve the group operation. A function $f:G \to G'$ is said to *preserve the group operation* if, for $x \in G$, $y \in G$, we have $f(xy)$ equal to the value of the group operation in G' for the pair $(f(x),f(y))$. We shall see by examples that not all functions $G \to G'$ have this property.

We shall usually use the same notation ab (or $a + b$) for the binary operations in G and in G'. If there is danger of confusion, different symbols will be used and their specific meaning will be described.

DEFINITION

If G and G' are groups and $f:G \to G'$ a function such that $f(a)f(b) = f(ab)$ for all $a \in G$ and $b \in G$, we call f a *homomorphism* or a *group homomorphism* of G into G'.

EXAMPLE 8.18

A simple example of a homomorphism is the function $f:G \to G'$, where $f(x) = e'$ for all $x \in G$ and e' is the identity element of G'. This is referred to as the *trivial homomorphism*. In the case of Abelian groups it is sometimes called the *null homomorphism*. In order to see that f is a homomorphism, we need only observe that $f(x)f(y) = e'e' = e'$ and $f(xy) = e'$.

There is no other constant map $g:G \to G'$ with $g(x) = a'$ that is a homomorphism, for suppose g is a homomorphism. Then $g(xy) = a'$, $g(x)g(y) = a'a'$, and therefore $a' = a'a'$. But this shows $a' = e'$ and hence $g(x) = e'$ is the only constant homomorphism.

As a specific example consider $f:Z \to Z$, where Z is the additive group of integers and $f(x) = 0$. Then f is a homomorphism.

Also consider $g:Z \to Q_+$, where again Z is the additive group of integers and Q_+ is the group formed from the positive rationals by the usual multiplication. If $g(x) = 1$ for each $x \in Z$, then g is a homomorphism of Z into Q_+.

EXAMPLE 8.19

Let Q_0 be the group of nonzero rational numbers with the usual multiplication. Let $H = \{-1,1\}$ be the group whose table is shown in Table 8.4. The

Table 8.4

	1	−1
1	1	−1
−1	−1	1

reader can easily show by using the rule of signs for multiplication that the function $f:Q_0 \to H$, where $f(x) = 1$ if $x > 0$ and $f(x) = -1$ if $x < 0$, is a homomorphism.

EXAMPLE   8.20

Let Z be the additive group of integers and let $H = \{0,1\}$ be the group whose table is given in Table 8.5.

Table 8.5

	0	1
0	0	1
1	1	0

We define a function $f:Z \to H$ as follows: $f(2n) = 0$, $f(2n - 1) = 1$ for $n \in Z$. We observe that

$$f(2n_1) + f(2n_2) = 0,$$
$$f(2n_1 + 2n_2) = f(2(n_1 + n_2)) = 0,$$
$$f(2n_1) + f(2n_2 - 1) = 0 + 1 = 1,$$
$$f(2n_1 + 2n_2 - 1) = f(2(n_1 + n_2) - 1) = 1,$$
$$f(2n_1 - 1) + f(2n_2) = 1 + 0 = 1,$$
$$f(2n_2 - 1 + 2n_1) = f(2(n_2 + n_1) - 1) = 1,$$
$$f(2n_1 - 1) + f(2n_2 - 1) = 1 + 1 = 0,$$
$$f(2n_1 - 1 + 2n_2 - 1) = f(2(n_1 + n_2 - 1)) = 0.$$

From this we see that $f(a) + f(b) = f(a + b)$ for all $a \in G$ and $b \in G$. Therefore f is a homomorphism.

EXAMPLE   8.21

Let Z be the additive group of integers. Select some integer a and define a function $p_a:Z \to Z$, where $p_a(b) = ab$ for $b \in Z$. Then $p_a(b + c) = a(b + c)$ and $p_a(b) + p_a(c) = ab + ac$. By the distributive law for the integers we see that p_a is a homomorphism.

THEOREM   8.9

If f is a homomorphism of the group G into the group G', then $f(e) = e'$, where e is the identity element of G and e' is the identity element of G'. Also $f(a^{-1}) = (f(a))^{-1}$ for all $a \in G$.

Proof

Pick any $a \in G$. Since f is a homomorphism, we have $f(ae) = f(a)f(e)$. But $ae = a$ and therefore $f(ae) = f(a)$. Thus we have $f(a) = f(a)f(e)$. Since

e' is the identity element of G', we also have $f(a)e' = f(a)$ and hence $f(a)e' = f(a)f(e)$. Then by the left cancellation law we see that $f(e) = e'$.

For any $a \in G$ we have $e' = f(e) = f(aa^{-1}) = f(a)f(a^{-1})$. Similarly, $e' = f(a^{-1})f(a)$. Then $f(a^{-1}) = (f(a))^{-1}$, since the inverse of $f(a)$ is unique. •

THEOREM 8.10

Let G and G' be groups and $f: G \to G'$ a homomorphism. Then $f(G)$, the range of f, is a subgroup of G'.

Proof

Any two elements of $f(G)$ can be written $f(a)$ and $f(b)$ for some $a \in G$ and $b \in G$. Then $f(a)(f(b))^{-1} = f(a)f(b^{-1}) = f(ab^{-1})$. But $ab^{-1} \in G$; therefore $f(ab^{-1}) \in f(G)$ and, by Theorem 8.5, $f(G)$ is a subgroup of G'. •

EXAMPLE 8.22

If A and B are sets and B has more than one element, we have seen that there are always several functions $A \to B$. On the other hand, if A and B are groups there may be only one homomorphism of A into B. We have seen that there is always the trivial homomorphism, but this may be the only one. For example, consider the groups G_2 and G_3 whose tables are given in Table 8.6. If $g: G_2 \to G_3$ is a homomorphism, then $g(1) = e$, since if $g(1) = a$ then $e = g(0) = g(1 + 1) = g(1)g(1) = aa$, a contradiction, and if $g(1) = b$, then $e = g(1)g(1) = bb$, again a contradiction. Therefore there is only the trivial homomorphism of G_2 into G_3.

Table 8.6

	0	1
0	0	1
1	1	0

G_2

	e	a	b
e	e	a	b
a	a	b	e
b	b	e	a

G_3

Consider groups G and G' and the homomorphism $f: G \to G'$. We have seen that $f(e) = e'$, where e and e' are the identity elements of G and G', respectively. We also know that, if f is the trivial homomorphism, then $f(x) = e'$ for all $x \in G$. We now consider the subset of elements $x \in G$ such that $f(x) = e'$.

DEFINITION

For any group homomorphism $f: G \to G'$ we call the set $\{x | x \in G, f(x) = e'\}$ the *kernel of* f.

Theorem 8.11 gives an important property of the kernel of a homomorphism.

THEOREM   8.11

Let G and G' be groups and let $f: G \to G'$ be a group homomorphism. Then the kernel of f is a normal subgroup of G.

Proof

If x and y are in the kernel, then $f(x) = e'$ and $f(y) = e'$. We want to show that xy^{-1} is in the kernel, that is, $f(xy^{-1}) = e'$. But $f(xy^{-1}) = f(x)(f(y))^{-1} = e'(e')^{-1} = e'e' = e'$. Thus the kernel is a subgroup. For $a \in G$ and x in the kernel we have $f(a^{-1}xa) = (f(a))^{-1}e'f(a) = (f(a))^{-1}f(a) = e'$. Therefore $a^{-1}xa = y$ for some y in the kernel. Then $xa = ay$, and so the kernel is a normal subgroup. •

EXAMPLE   8.23

In the example $f: Z \to H$, where the group operation for H is given in Table 8.5 and $f(2n) = 0$, $f(2n - 1) = 1$, we see that $e' = 0$. Therefore the kernel of f is the subgroup of all even integers.

We now turn to the most important special form of a homomorphism.

DEFINITION

If a (group) homomorphism is a bijective function, it is called an *isomorphism* or a *group isomorphism*.

If $f: G \to G'$ is a group isomorphism, the groups G and G' are called *isomorphic*.

EXAMPLE   8.24

Let R_+ be the multiplicative group of the positive real numbers and let R be the additive group of all real numbers. Define the function $f: R_+ \to R$ by $f(x) = \log x$ for all $x \in R_+$. Since we have not given a precise definition of the logarithm, we cannot prove the following properties, but they are well-known from the use of logarithms in computation. We can find the antilogarithm of any real number and so we know that this function is onto R. We also know that the antilogarithm is unique and hence the function is injective. Furthermore, we know that $\log xy = \log x + \log y$, that is, $f(xy) = f(x) + f(y)$. This shows that the multiplicative group of the positive real numbers and the additive group of real numbers are isomorphic.

This example shows the importance of the concept of isomorphism. Addition is much easier to handle than multiplication. The use of the table or graph of the logarithm function reduces multiplication to addition. The construction of the table is not an easy matter, but once it is done it is very convenient. [The credit for discovering this useful computational tool belongs to the Scottish mathematician, Napier (1550–1617).]

EXAMPLE 8.25

An example closely related to the logarithm is provided by the function $g: R \to R_+$, where R, R_+ are as in the previous example and $g(x) = 10^x$ for $x \in R$. Again this function is bijective and, since $g(x)g(y) = 10^x 10^y = 10^{x+y} = g(x + y)$, we see that g is an isomorphism.

The student who is familiar with logarithms and exponential functions will observe that the function $g: R \to R_+$ is the *inverse* of $f: R_+ \to R$. Theorem 8.12 gives a general result for the inverse of an isomorphism.

THEOREM 8.12

The inverse map of a group isomorphism $f: G \to G'$ is an isomorphism.

Proof

An isomorphism is a bijective function, and therefore we know from our study of functions that it has an inverse function that is also bijective. We must now show that the inverse function preserves multiplication. Any two elements of G' can be written $f(a)$ and $f(b)$. Since $f^{-1}(f(a)f(b)) = f^{-1}(f(ab)) = ab$ and $f^{-1}(f(a))f^{-1}(f(b)) = ab$, we see that f^{-1} does preserve multiplication. •

EXAMPLE 8.26

Let Q be the additive group of rationals and let a be any nonzero rational number. Define $p_a: Q \to Q$ by $p_a(b) = ab$. This function preserves addition; the proof of this is similar to the proof for the similar example using integers. The function is onto; for $c \in Q$ (the codomain) we have $a^{-1}c \in Q$ (the domain) and $p_a(a^{-1}c) = c$. Also p_a is injective, for if $p_a(b) = p_a(c)$ then $ab = ac$ and $b = c$ by the cancellation law. Therefore p_a is an isomorphism. The reader should satisfy himself that, for the example $p_a: Z \to Z$, the function is a homomorphism but *not* an isomorphism unless $a = 1$.

8.10 Examples of groups of low order

From the point of view of group theory two groups that are isomorphic are essentially the same group; we simply describe the group in two ways.

For a given set G, we may ask how many of the functions $f: G \times G \to G$ satisfy the group axioms, that is, how many groups can be constructed on the set G. It may happen that two of the groups on the set G are isomorphic, that is, there is a bijective function $j: G \to G$ such that $j(f_1(x,y)) = f_2(j(x), j(y))$, where $f_1: G \times G \to G$ and $f_2: G \times G \to G$ both define groups on the set G.

We are chiefly interested in the number of nonisomorphic groups that can be defined on G. When we speak of the number of groups that can be formed on a given set we do not consider isomorphic groups distinct.

EXAMPLE 8.27

We want to find how many groups can be formed using the set $G = \{a,b,c\}$. We first observe that there are three possible choices for the identity element. Each choice allows us to begin the table of a group operation f_1, f_2, or f_3, as shown in Table 8.7.

Table 8.7

f_1	a	b	c		f_2	b	a	c		f_3	c	a	b
a	a	b	c		b	b	a	c		c	c	a	b
b	b				a	a				a	a		
c	c				c	c				b	b		

In the table for any group G the following is true: In each row and each column each element of G must appear exactly once. Suppose c does not appear in the row labeled b. Then $bx = c$ has no solution. But this is a contradiction and therefore c must appear. Suppose c appears twice. Then $bx = c$ has two solutions. This is also a contradiction and hence c appears only once.

Using this general rule we see that the tables for f_1, f_2, f_3 can be completed only as in Table 8.8. To prove that these determine groups, we consider the bijective function $g: A_3 \to G$, as in Exercise 8.38, where A_3 is the alternating group on three symbols. The details are left as an exercise.

Table 8.8

f_1	a	b	c		f_2	b	a	c		f_3	c	a	b
a	a	b	c		b	b	a	c		c	c	a	b
b	b	c	a		a	a	c	b		a	a	b	c
c	c	a	b		c	c	b	a		b	b	c	a

Therefore there are only three functions that can serve as group operations for $G = \{a,b,c\}$. We shall now show that these three groups are isomorphic. The function

$$j_{12} = \begin{pmatrix} a & b & c \\ b & a & c \end{pmatrix}$$

is an isomorphism of (G,f_1) onto (G,f_2). This isomorphism is not unique, for

$$k_{12} = \begin{pmatrix} a & b & c \\ b & c & a \end{pmatrix}$$

is also an isomorphism of (G,f_1) onto (G,f_2).

The functions

$$j_{13} = \begin{pmatrix} a & b & c \\ c & b & a \end{pmatrix} \quad \text{and} \quad k_{13} = \begin{pmatrix} a & b & c \\ c & a & b \end{pmatrix}$$

are isomorphisms of (G,f_1) onto (G,f_3).

The functions

$$j_{23} = \begin{pmatrix} a & b & c \\ a & c & b \end{pmatrix} \quad \text{and} \quad k_{23} = \begin{pmatrix} a & b & c \\ b & c & a \end{pmatrix}$$

are isomorphisms of (G,f_2) onto (G,f_3).

The reader is left to prove that each of these functions is an isomorphism.

We say that the group of order three is unique "up to isomorphism," or that there is only one group of order three.

EXAMPLE 8.28

We now ask how many groups there are of order four, that is, how many group structures we can impose on a set of four elements $\{a,b,c,d\}$. Arguments similar to those in the previous example show that there are only four group tables possible with a as the identity. The three shown in Table 8.9 are isomorphic (we leave the reader to work out the details), whereas the one in Table 8.10 is not isomorphic to the others, since in this group $x^2 = a$ for all x but this is not true in the others. The first table in Table 8.9 shows a cyclic group generated by the element c. The group in Table 8.10 is Abelian but not cyclic. It is called *Klein's four group*. Since the groups we get by taking any other element as the identity are isomorphic to these, we see that

Table 8.9

	a	b	c	d
a	a	b	c	d
b	b	a	d	c
c	c	d	b	a
d	d	c	a	b

	a	b	c	d
a	a	b	c	d
b	b	c	d	a
c	c	d	a	b
d	d	a	b	c

	a	b	c	d
a	a	b	c	d
b	b	d	a	c
c	c	a	d	b
d	d	c	b	a

Table 8.10

	a	b	c	d
a	a	b	c	d
b	b	a	d	c
c	c	d	a	b
d	d	c	b	a

there are only two groups of order four, the cyclic group and Klein's four-group. If we allow all possible choices for the identity, there are 12 different binary operations on $\{a,b,c,d\}$ that produce the cyclic group and 4 that produce the four-group.

8.11   Abstract groups and permutation groups

The study of groups started with permutation groups. J. L. Lagrange (1736–1813) and E. Galois (1811–1832), famous French mathematicians, used groups of permutations of roots of equations in trying to solve the famous problem of solving equations by radicals (extracting roots). The axiomatic approach came later. Theorem 8.13, due to the English mathematician Cayley (1821–1895), shows the equivalence of the two approaches.

THEOREM   8.13

A group G of order n is isomorphic to a permutation group on n symbols, that is, to a subgroup of the symmetric group S_n.

Proof

We denote the elements of G by $x_1, x_2, \cdots, x_n$ and consider the permutations

$$f_1 = \begin{pmatrix} x_1 & x_2 & x_3 & \cdots & x_n \\ x_1 x_1 & x_1 x_2 & x_1 x_3 & \cdots & x_1 x_n \end{pmatrix},$$

$$f_2 = \begin{pmatrix} x_1 & x_2 & & \cdots & x_n \\ x_2 x_1 & x_2 x_2 & & \cdots & x_2 x_n \end{pmatrix},$$

$$\cdots$$

$$f_n = \begin{pmatrix} x_1 & x_2 & & \cdots & x_n \\ x_n x_1 & x_n x_2 & & \cdots & x_n x_n \end{pmatrix}.$$

We want to show that $F = \{f_1, f_2, \cdots, f_n\}$ is a subgroup of the symmetric group, that is, we must show that $f_i f_j^{-1} \in F$ for all $f_i \in F$ and $f_j \in F$. If $x_k = x_j^{-1}$, then $f_k f_j$ is the identity and therefore $f_k = f_j^{-1}$. Also

$$f_i f_j^{-1} = f_i f_k = \begin{pmatrix} x_1 & x_2 & \cdots & x_n \\ x_i x_k x_1 & x_i x_k x_2 & \cdots & x_i x_k x_n \end{pmatrix} \in F,$$

since $x_i x_k \in G$. Therefore F is a subgroup of the symmetric group.

It remains to prove that G and F are isomorphic. Consider the mapping $g : G \to F$, where $g(x_i) = f_i$. This is clearly bijective and, since $g(x_i x_j) = f_i f_j$, it is an isomorphism.

F is called a regular *realization* of G. •

A similar result can be proved for infinite groups.

EXAMPLE   8.29

The two groups of order four are isomorphic to subgroups of S_4. Klein's four-group is isomorphic to the subgroup with elements

$$f_a = \begin{pmatrix} a & b & c & d \\ a & b & c & d \end{pmatrix},$$

$$f_b = \begin{pmatrix} a & b & c & d \\ b & a & d & c \end{pmatrix},$$

$$f_c = \begin{pmatrix} a & b & c & d \\ c & d & a & b \end{pmatrix},$$

$$f_d = \begin{pmatrix} a & b & c & d \\ d & c & b & a \end{pmatrix}.$$

The cyclic group with four elements (see first table in Table 8.9) is isomorphic to the subgroup with elements

$$f_a = \begin{pmatrix} a & b & c & d \\ a & b & c & d \end{pmatrix},$$

$$f_c = \begin{pmatrix} a & b & c & d \\ c & d & b & a \end{pmatrix},$$

$$f_b = \begin{pmatrix} a & b & c & d \\ b & a & d & c \end{pmatrix} = f_c{}^2,$$

$$f_d = \begin{pmatrix} a & b & c & d \\ d & c & a & b \end{pmatrix} = f_c{}^3.$$

EXERCISES

8.39. Prove that the group of rotations of the square is a subgroup of the group of the square.

8.40. Prove that $\{I, R_2, H, V\}$ is a subgroup of the group of the square. Find all its right and left cosets. Is it a normal subgroup?

8.41. Find all the subgroups of the group of the square.

8.42. Construct the table for the group of symmetries of an equilateral triangle. Is this group Abelian?

8.43. Prove that the group of symmetries of an equilateral triangle is isomorphic to the symmetric group S_3.

8.44. List all the subgroups of the group of symmetries of an equilateral triangle. Which are cyclic? Give all the possible generators for each cyclic subgroup.

8.45. Construct the table for the group of symmetries of a rectangle.

8.46. The group of symmetries of a rectangle has 16 subsets. List all of these and show which are subgroups.

8.47. Let A and B be subgroups of a group G. Prove that the subset $A \cap B$ is a subgroup of G.

8.48. If A and B are subgroups of the group G, is the subset $A \cup B$ always a subgroup of G? [*Hint:* Test this for various subgroups of the group of the square.]

8.49. Let B be any set of groups. If G_1 and G_2 are groups in B, we shall say that G_1 is related to G_2 if there is an isomorphism $f:G_1 \to G_2$. Is this an equivalence relation?

8.50. If G_1, G_2, and G_3 are groups and $f:G_1 \to G_2$, $h:G_2 \to G_3$ are isomorphisms, prove that the composite $h \cdot f$ is an isomorphism.

8.51. Use your knowledge of S_3 and A_3 to write down all the cosets of the subgroup of rotations of an equilateral triangle (see Exercise 8.43).

8.52. Consider the set of military commands "left turn," "right turn," "about turn," and "stand steady." If by the product of two commands we mean the result of giving one command followed by the other, show that this set forms an Abelian group. What other group have you studied that is isomorphic to it?

8.53. Set up a homomorphism of the group of a rectangle into the group of the square (see Exercise 8.45).

8.54. Prove that the group of translations of $R \times R$ (see Section 8.6) is isomorphic to the additive group of complex numbers.

8.55. Prove that the group of rotations of the plane about a fixed point (see Section 8.6) is isomorphic to the multiplicative group of complex numbers with modulus 1.

8.56. Let Q_+ be the multiplicative group of positive rationals. Prove that the function $f:Q_+ \to Q_+$, where $f(x) = 1/x$, is a group isomorphism.

8.57. What are the necessary and sufficient conditions on the group G in order for the function $f:G \to G$ where $f(a) = a^{-1}$ for all $a \in G$ to be an isomorphism?

8.58. Prove that a group homomorphism is an injective function if and only if its kernel contains only one element.

8.59. Let Z be the additive group of integers and let a be an integer different from 1. Show that the function $p_a:Z \to Z$, where $p_a(b) = ab$ for $b \in Z$, is not an isomorphism.

8.60. Let Q_0 be the multiplicative group of nonzero rationals, $H = \{-1,1\}$ the group whose table appears in Table 8.4. Show that the function $f:Q_0 \to H$, where

$$f(x) = \begin{cases} 1 & \text{if } x > 0, \\ -1 & \text{if } x < 0, \end{cases}$$

is a group homomorphism.

8.61. Show that the function $f:(R_0, \times) \to (R_0, \times)$, where $f(x) = x^m$ for $x \in R_0$ and m a fixed integer, is a group homomorphism.

8.62. Show that the function $f:(C_0, \times) \to (C_0, \times)$, where $f(x) = x^m$ for $x \in C_0$ and m a fixed integer, is a group homomorphism. Show that f is onto.

8.63. Show that the function $f:(Q_0, \times) \to (Q_0, \times)$, where $f(x) = x^3$ for $x \in Q_0$, is a homomorphism.

8.64. Show that the function $f:(R_+, \times) \to (R_+, \times)$, where $f(x) = x^3$, is an isomorphism.

8.65. Prove that each of the functions j_{mn} and k_{mn} that appear in the study of groups of order three in Section 8.10 is an isomorphism.

8.66. Prove that the three groups represented by Table 8.9 are isomorphic to each other.

8.67. Prove that the subgroup $\{I,R_2,H,V\}$ of the group of the square is isomorphic to Klein's four-group.

8.68. How many (nonisomorphic) groups are there of order 5?

8.69. Show that for any set G with n elements there are at least $n!$ functions $f:G \times G \to G$ such that (G,f) is a group. (*Note:* We do not require that the groups be nonisomorphic.)

8.70. Prove that the set $G = \{a,b,c\}$ with the operation f_1 as in Example 8.27 is a group and is isomorphic to the alternating group A_3.

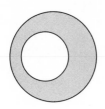

9

Rings and Fields

9.1 Definition and properties of rings

In each of the number systems studied in Chapters 5 to 7 there are two binary operations, addition and multiplication, connected by the distributive law. In Chapter 8 we saw that many number systems are groups under addition. We also saw that the distributive law ensures that a certain function defined in terms of multiplication is a homomorphism (see Section 8.9).

As mathematicians extended the scope of their study to include many entities other than number systems, it was realized that there are many examples of sets in which there are two binary operations that are similar to the operations for the number systems. In this way many arithmetic ideas, such as divisibility and decomposition into factors, were adapted to new systems.

In this section we shall study a set together with two binary operations.

Let A be a set on which two binary operations are defined:

$$\sigma : A \times A \to A,$$
$$\tau : A \times A \to A.$$

We find it convenient to denote the value $\sigma(a,b)$ by $a + b$ and the value $\tau(a,b)$ by $a \cdot b$ or ab, and refer to these as the *sum* and *product*, respectively. This notation and terminology *do not mean* that the operations are addition and multiplication in a number system.

DEFINITION

A set A is said to form a *ring* if there are two binary operations on A, called addition and multiplication, such that

1. Addition defines an Abelian group on the set A.
2. Multiplication is associative, that is, $a(bc) = (ab)c$.
3. The distributive laws hold, that is,

$$a(b + c) = ab + ac,$$
$$(b + c)a = ba + ca.$$

As we did for groups, we shall use A to represent both the set and the ring. When this notation is likely to cause confusion, we indicate the operations by writing $(A,+,\cdot)$. To single out the Abelian group determined by addition we write $(A,+)$.

Since the definition of a ring involves an Abelian group with respect to addition, we know that A must contain an additive identity or neutral element for addition. By analogy with number systems, we denote this identity by 0 and call it the *zero element*. The reader is warned, however, that the zero element of the ring need not be the same as the zero for the number systems. We also know that every $a \in A$ has an additive inverse, which we call the *negative of* a and denote by $-a$.

It is convenient to denote $a + a$ by $2a$, $a + a + a$ by $3a$, and so on. To do this in general we define na by induction as

$$1a = a, \qquad na = a + (n - 1)a.$$

It must be understood that a is an element of the ring and n is a natural number (which is not in general an element of the ring). It is also convenient to define $(-n)a$ for $n \in N$ to be $-(na)$, that is, the negative of na, and $0a$ to be the zero element of the ring. This last statement can be written $0a = 0$, where the symbol 0 is used in two different senses, once as an integer and once as the zero element of the ring. With these definitions it can be proved that $na + ma = (n + m)a$ for all $a \in A$ and all $n \in Z$ and $m \in Z$.

For multiplication we shall use similar notation a^n defined by

$$a^1 = a, \qquad a^n = a^{n-1}a,$$

where $a \in A$ and $n \in N$. It can be shown that $a^n a^m = a^{n+m}$. For rings in general we cannot extend this notation to a nonpositive integer n. We shall see, however, that in some special cases such notation is useful.

The definition of a ring does not require the existence of an element e such that $ae = ea = a$ for all a in the ring. If such an element exists it is called a *unity element* or *identity element*.

DEFINITION

A ring that has a unity or identity element is called a *ring with identity*.

THEOREM   9.1

The identity element of a ring, if it exists, is unique.

Proof

Suppose there are two identity elements e and e' in the ring. Since e is an identity, we have $e' = ee'$. Since e' is an identity, we have $e = ee'$. Therefore $e' = ee' = e$. ●

The reader may feel that this theorem is unnecessary, since we have a similar result for groups. We point out, however, that multiplication in a ring need not determine a group, so it is not automatic that the group result will hold.

In a ring with identity it is customary to denote the identity by e or 1. With the latter notation there is danger of confusion as to whether $1a$ is the product of two ring elements or whether 1 is an integer as in na. It is also convenient to define $a^0 = e$ for all elements a in the ring.

DEFINITION

A ring in which multiplication satisfies the commutative law, that is, $ab = ba$, is called a *commutative ring* (not an Abelian ring, although this would agree with our terminology for groups).

EXAMPLE   9.1

The reader can easily verify that the integers with the usual operations of addition and multiplication form a commutative ring with identity.

EXAMPLE   9.2

Any Abelian group can be made into a ring by defining a multiplication $ab = 0$ for all a, b in the group, where 0 is the zero element of the group. This is sometimes referred to as the *trivial multiplication*. This ring has few interesting properties.

Let A be any ring and let a be any element of A. Define the functions $h_a : A \to A$ and $k_a : A \to A$, where $h_a(x) = ax$ and $k_a(x) = xa$ for all $x \in A$. By the distributive law we see that $h_a(x + y) = a(x + y) = ax + ay = h_a(x) + h_a(y)$. Therefore h_a is a homomorphism of the group $(A, +)$ into $(A, +)$. Similarly, k_a is a homomorphism of $(A, +)$ into $(A, +)$. If A is a ring with the trivial multiplication, $ab = 0$, then all h_a and k_a are the null homomorphism.

From our study of homomorphism for groups we know that $h_a(0) = 0$, $k_a(0) = 0$, $h_a(-x) = -h_a(x)$, and $k_a(-x) = -k_a(x)$. From these we have the following properties of any ring A:

$$a0 = 0, \ 0a = 0 \qquad \text{for any } a \in A,$$
$$a(-x) = -(ax), \ (-x)a = -(xa) \qquad \text{for any } a \in A, \ x \in A.$$

In view of the first of these results we do not need to include 0 in the table giving the multiplication for the ring.

A set A may form a ring with respect to two different pairs of operations. It may even occur that addition is the same for two rings on the same set, but multiplication is different.

EXAMPLE   9.3

Consider the set $A = \{a,b,c\}$ and the tables given in Table 9.1. It is clear that $(A,+)$ is one of the groups in the examples of Section 8.2. It is also clear that $(A,+,\times)$ is a ring. The reader can verify that $(A,+,\cdot)$ is a ring. Clearly these are not the same ring.

Table 9.1

+	a	b	c
a	a	b	c
b	b	c	a
c	c	a	b

·	b	c
b	b	c
c	c	b

×	b	c
b	a	a
c	a	a

EXAMPLE   9.4

The group $(Z,+)$ can be made into a ring in at least two different ways, one by the usual multiplication for the integers, the other by means of the trivial multiplication $ab = 0$.

The following definition and theorem are concerned with elements of the ring that have inverses under multiplication.

DEFINITION

An element a in a ring A with identity is called an *invertible element* if there is an element $a^{-1} \in A$ such that $aa^{-1} = e = a^{-1}a$. The element a^{-1} is called the *inverse* of a.

THEOREM   9.2

If an element of a ring with identity has an inverse, then the inverse is unique.

Proof

Suppose $\bar{a}$ and a^{-1} are both inverses of a. Then $\bar{a} = \bar{a}(aa^{-1}) = (\bar{a}a)a^{-1} = a^{-1}$. •

9.2   Subrings

In Chapter 8 we considered subsets of a group that were themselves groups under the restricted operation. We shall now consider a similar idea for rings. Let A be a ring and B be a subset of A. If B forms a ring under the operations of A restricted to B, we call B a *subring* of A.

It is clear that, if B is a subring of A, then $(B,+)$ is a subgroup of $(A,+)$. This fact is used in the proof of Theorem 9.3.

THEOREM   9.3

In order for the nonempty subset B of the ring A to be a subring it is necessary and sufficient for $a - b$ and ab to be elements of B whenever a and b are elements of B.

Proof

It is clear from Theorem 8.5 that $(B,+)$ is a subgroup of $(A,+)$, therefore $(B,+)$ is an Abelian group. Since ab is an element of B whenever a and b are elements of B, it is clear that multiplication restricted to B is a binary operation for B. The associative law for multiplication and the distributive law hold in B, since they hold in A. This completes the proof that B is a subring of A. The necessity of the conditions is obvious. •

9.3   Equivalence relations in rings

If we followed the pattern of Chapter 8, we should now attempt to define an equivalence relation in a ring in terms of a subring. If we did so we should discover that, to obtain results parallel to those for groups, we should need a special type of subring. Rather than attempt such a general study, we shall turn to an important example of an equivalence relation in the ring of integers.

In our study of the theory of sets (see Section 2.3) we defined a relation on Z as follows: $a \, \rho \, b \, (a \equiv b(\mathrm{mod}\ n))$ if $a - b = kn$ for some $k \in Z$. This is called the *congruence* relation. We proved that this was an equivalence relation. In the study of groups (see Section 8.5) we saw that this same equivalence relation could be defined in terms of the cyclic subgroup of Z generated by n. The equivalence classes of this relation are often referred to as *residue classes modulo n*. We write $Z/(n)$ to represent the set of residue classes modulo n.

We want to construct a ring from the set $Z/(n)$. To do this we must define two binary operations on the set. As a first step we prove a theorem that relates the operations of addition and multiplication for the integers with the congruence relation.

THEOREM   9.4

If $a \equiv a_1 \pmod n$ and $b \equiv b_1 \pmod n$, then $a + b \equiv a_1 + b_1 \pmod n$ and $ab \equiv a_1 b_1 \pmod n$.

Proof

Since $a \equiv a_1 \pmod n$ and $b \equiv b_1 \pmod n$, we have $a - a_1 = k_1 n$, $b - b_1 = k_2 n$. Then $a + b - (a_1 + b_1) = a - a_1 + b - b_1 = (k_1 + k_2)n$, and therefore $a + b \equiv a_1 + b_1 \pmod n$.

Also $ab - a_1 b_1 = a(b - b_1) + (a - a_1)b_1 = ak_2 n + k_1 n b_1 = (ak_2 + k_1 b_1)n$, and therefore $ab \equiv a_1 b_1 \pmod n$. •

From this theorem we see that, if we select a representative of each of two residue classes and add these integers, the sum belongs to the same residue class no matter what representatives we chose. The same is true for multiplication. We can define two binary operations $Z/(n) \times Z/(n) \to Z/(n)$ as follows:

To add two residue classes, choose one representative from each, add these representatives as integers, and take the residue class to which the sum belongs as the sum of the two residue classes.

To multiply two residue classes, choose one representative from each, multiply these representatives as integers, and take the residue class to which the product belongs as the product of the residue classes.

In working with $Z/(n)$ we usually write a representative instead of a residue class. We prefer to choose the smallest nonnegative integer in each class as its representative. Thus $Z/(5)$ is represented by $\{0,1,2,3,4\}$. The addition and multiplication tables for $Z/(5)$ are given in Table 9.2. The set $Z/(n)$ is often referred to as the set of integers modulo n.

Table 9.2

+	0	1	2	3	4		×	0	1	2	3	4
0	0	1	2	3	4		0	0	0	0	0	0
1	1	2	3	4	0		1	0	1	2	3	4
2	2	3	4	0	1		2	0	2	4	1	3
3	3	4	0	1	2		3	0	3	1	4	2
4	4	0	1	2	3		4	0	4	3	2	1

We now have two binary operations on $Z/(n)$. Do we have a ring? It is clear from the definitions of addition and multiplication that the associative, commutative, and distributive laws hold. The class containing the integer 0 is a zero element for addition. The class containing $-a$ serves as a negative or additive inverse of the class containing a. Also the class containing 1 acts as an identity for multiplication. Therefore $Z/(n)$ forms a commutative ring with identity.

9.4   A set of functions as a ring

We have seen that we can construct a group from the permutations on any set by using composition as the group operation. We shall now show two other ways of defining operations on a set of functions. These operations enable us to construct a ring from certain sets of functions.

Let E be any set and A be any ring. We have already used the notation $\mathfrak{F}(E,A)$ to denote the set of all functions with E as domain and A as codomain. If f, g are two functions in $\mathfrak{F}(E,A)$, we can define their sum and product as follows:

$$f + g : E \to A \qquad \text{where } (f + g)(x) = f(x) + g(x) \text{ for all } x \in E;$$
$$fg : E \to A \qquad \text{where } (fg)(x) = f(x)g(x) \text{ for all } x \in E.$$

The reader is warned to beware of confusing this with the composite function. We sometimes refer to these operations as the *pointwise* sum and product of f and g.

We observe that the function $g(x) = 0$ for all $x \in E$, where 0 is the zero element of A, serves as a zero for the addition of functions. The function $h(x) = -f(x)$ for all $x \in E$ is a negative or additive inverse of $f(x)$. The reader can now verify that the set $\mathfrak{F}(E,A)$ together with these two operations forms a ring. If A is commutative, then $\mathfrak{F}(E,A)$ is commutative. If A has an identity e, then $\mathfrak{F}(E,A)$ has an identity $f(x) = e$ for all $x \in E$.

We shall introduce polynomials as a subset of $\mathfrak{F}(R,R)$, where R is the ring of real numbers and addition and multiplication of polynomials are defined as above. We shall use a similar method to introduce matrices, but with a different multiplication.

EXAMPLE   9.5

Consider the ring $\mathfrak{F}(R,R)$, that is, the ring of all real-valued functions of a real variable with addition and multiplication defined as above.

Let

$$f(x) = \begin{cases} 0 & \text{if } x \leq 0 \\ x & \text{if } x > 0 \end{cases}$$

$$g(x) = \begin{cases} x & \text{if } x < 0 \\ 0 & \text{if } x \geq 0. \end{cases}$$

Then $(fg)(x) = 0$ for all $x \in R$. We know that, in the rings of the number systems, a product of two numbers can be zero only if one of the numbers is zero. But here for $\mathfrak{F}(R,R)$ we have two functions, neither of which is the zero function, but whose product is the zero function. This property is sometimes expressed by saying that $\mathfrak{F}(R,R)$ has *divisors of zero*, or that $\mathfrak{F}(R,R)$ has nontrivial or nonzero divisors of zero to emphasize the fact that neither factor is zero. Whenever we speak of divisors of zero we mean nontrivial divisors.

9.5   Polynomials

We have seen that the set of functions $\mathfrak{F}(R,R)$ forms a ring. The same is true for $\mathfrak{F}(C,C)$. In this section we shall restrict ourselves to the subset of $\mathfrak{F}(R,R)$ consisting of the functions called real polynomial functions. The reader can verify that our results can also be obtained for the complex polynomials as a subset of $\mathfrak{F}(C,C)$.

A function $f:R \to R$, where $f(x) = a_n x^n + a_{n-1} x^{n-1} + \cdots + a_1 x + a_0$ for $a_i \in R$, $n \in N$, is called a polynomial function. If $a_n \neq 0$, we say that $f(x)$ is *a polynomial of degree n*. We include the constant function $f(x) = 0$ as a polynomial and refer to it as the *zero polynomial*.

The reader will already be familiar with rules for adding and multiplying polynomials. These rules are obtained from the definitions of $f(x) + g(x)$ and $f(x)g(x)$ in $\mathfrak{F}(R,R)$ by means of the laws of arithmetic for real numbers. We shall not prove this in general, but shall illustrate it by two examples.

EXAMPLE   9.6

$$(x^2 + 3x + 2) + (3x^3 + 2x + 1) = x^2 + 3x + 2 + 3x^3 + 2x + 1$$
$$\text{(associative law)}$$
$$= 3x^3 + x^2 + 3x + 2x + 2 + 1$$
$$\text{(commutative law)}$$
$$= 3x^3 + x^2 + (3 + 2)x + 2 + 1$$
$$\text{(distributive law)}$$
$$= 3x^3 + x^2 + 5x + 3.$$

EXAMPLE   9.7

$$(x^2 + 2x + 1)(x^2 + 3x - 2) = (x^2 + 2x + 1)x^2 + (x^2 + 2x + 1)3x$$
$$+ (x^2 + 2x + 1)(-2) \quad \text{(distributive law)}$$
$$= x^4 + 2x^3 + x^2 + 3x^3 + 6x^2 + 3x$$
$$- 2x^2 - 4x - 2 \quad \text{(commutative and}$$
$$\text{distributive laws)}$$
$$= x^4 + 2x^3 + 3x^3 + x^2 + 6x^2 - 2x^2$$
$$+ 3x - 4x - 2 \quad \text{(commutative law)}$$
$$= x^4 + 5x^3 + 5x^2 - x - 2$$
$$\text{(distributive law)}.$$

The sum and the product of two polynomials are themselves polynomials. If $f(x)$ and $g(x)$ are polynomials, then $f(x) + (-g(x)) = f(x) + (-1)g(x)$ is a polynomial, and hence the set of polynomials forms a subgroup of the additive group of $\mathfrak{F}(R,R)$. Also the product of any two polynomials is a polynomial and so the set of polynomials forms a subring of $\mathfrak{F}(R,R)$. The commutative law holds for multiplication and the polynomial $f(x) = 1$ is a multiplicative identity. We thus see that the polynomials with real coefficients or the polynomial functions over the real numbers form a commutative ring with identity. The relationship between $\mathfrak{F}(R,R)$ and the ring of polynomials is discussed further in the exercises.

9.6   Matrices

As we have already said we shall consider matrices as functions and define addition as it was defined in Section 9.4. Our definition of multiplication of matrices may seem strange at first, but it is a natural definition in view of the use that is made of matrices in linear algebra (systems of equations, linear transformations, etc.).

DEFINITION

An $m \times n$ *matrix* is a function with domain $S \times T$, and codomain a ring E, where $S = \{1,2, \cdots ,m\}$, $T = \{1,2, \cdots ,n\}$.

We shall immediately restrict our attention to matrices in which the codomain consists of either the real or the complex numbers.

It is often convenient to give the graph of the matrix function in terms of a table of m rows, one for each element of S, and n columns, one for each element of T. In the case of matrices it is not customary to label the rows and columns with elements of S and T. We adopt the convention that the element in the ith row and the jth column, which is often denoted by a_{ij}, is the value of the function for the element $(i,j) \in S \times T$.

For example, a 3×3 matrix is usually written

$$\begin{bmatrix} a_{11} & a_{12} & a_{13} \\ a_{21} & a_{22} & a_{23} \\ a_{31} & a_{32} & a_{33} \end{bmatrix}.$$

This is often abbreviated to $[a_{ij}]$.

We shall usually use capital letters to denote matrices although this is not the notation we generally use for functions.

The sum of matrices is defined as in Section 9.4. Let A, B be two $m \times n$ matrices, that is, $A : S \times T \to E$ and $B : S \times T \to E$. Let $A(i,j) = a_{ij}$ and $B(i,j) = b_{ij}$. Then we define $A + B : S \times T \to E$ as $(A + B)(i,j) = a_{ij} + b_{ij}$. If we write this definition out in terms of a table for the 3×3 case we have the following:

$$\begin{bmatrix} a_{11} & a_{12} & a_{13} \\ a_{21} & a_{22} & a_{23} \\ a_{31} & a_{32} & a_{33} \end{bmatrix} + \begin{bmatrix} b_{11} & b_{12} & b_{13} \\ b_{21} & b_{22} & b_{23} \\ b_{31} & b_{32} & b_{33} \end{bmatrix} = \begin{bmatrix} a_{11} + b_{11} & a_{12} + b_{12} & a_{13} + b_{13} \\ a_{21} + b_{21} & a_{22} + b_{22} & a_{23} + b_{23} \\ a_{31} + b_{31} & a_{32} + b_{32} & a_{33} + b_{33} \end{bmatrix}.$$

EXAMPLE 9.8

$$\begin{bmatrix} 1 & 2 & 1 \\ 3 & 0 & 2 \\ 0 & 1 & 1 \end{bmatrix} + \begin{bmatrix} 2 & 0 & 1 \\ 1 & 1 & 0 \\ 3 & 0 & 1 \end{bmatrix} = \begin{bmatrix} 1+2 & 2+0 & 1+1 \\ 3+1 & 0+1 & 2+0 \\ 0+3 & 1+0 & 1+1 \end{bmatrix} = \begin{bmatrix} 3 & 2 & 2 \\ 4 & 1 & 2 \\ 3 & 1 & 2 \end{bmatrix}.$$

From what has been said in Section 9.4 it is clear that the $m \times n$ matrices form an Abelian group under addition.

We shall now restrict our attention to 3×3 matrices. The reader is advised to carry through the same ideas for the 2×2 case. It is possible to proceed in much greater generality, but we shall forego this generality in the interests of simplicity.

The product of two 3×3 matrices $A = [a_{ij}]$ and $B = [b_{ij}]$ is a 3×3 matrix that can be found by the method of *row-by-column multiplication,* so called because each element of the product is obtained by multiplying the elements of a row of A by the corresponding elements of a column of B. More precisely, $AB = [c_{ij}]$, where $c_{ij} = a_{i1}b_{1j} + a_{i2}b_{2j} + a_{i3}b_{3j}$. If we write out all the details of this multiplication we see that

$$\begin{bmatrix} a_{11} & a_{12} & a_{13} \\ a_{21} & a_{22} & a_{23} \\ a_{31} & a_{32} & a_{33} \end{bmatrix} \begin{bmatrix} b_{11} & b_{12} & b_{13} \\ b_{21} & b_{22} & b_{23} \\ b_{31} & b_{32} & b_{33} \end{bmatrix}$$
$$= \begin{bmatrix} a_{11}b_{11} + a_{12}b_{21} + a_{13}b_{31} & a_{11}b_{12} + a_{12}b_{22} + a_{13}b_{32} & a_{11}b_{13} + a_{12}b_{23} + a_{13}b_{33} \\ a_{21}b_{11} + a_{22}b_{21} + a_{23}b_{31} & a_{21}b_{12} + a_{22}b_{22} + a_{23}b_{32} & a_{21}b_{13} + a_{22}b_{23} + a_{23}b_{33} \\ a_{31}b_{11} + a_{32}b_{21} + a_{33}b_{31} & a_{31}b_{12} + a_{32}b_{22} + a_{33}b_{32} & a_{31}b_{13} + a_{32}b_{23} + a_{33}b_{33} \end{bmatrix}.$$

EXAMPLE 9.9

$$\begin{bmatrix} 1 & 0 & 2 \\ 2 & 1 & 1 \\ 2 & 3 & 0 \end{bmatrix} \begin{bmatrix} 1 & 1 & 2 \\ 2 & 1 & 0 \\ 3 & 0 & 1 \end{bmatrix}$$
$$= \begin{bmatrix} 1(1) + 0(2) + 2(3) & 1(1) + 0(1) + 2(0) & 1(2) + 0(0) + 2(1) \\ 2(1) + 1(2) + 1(3) & 2(1) + 1(1) + 1(0) & 2(2) + 1(0) + 1(1) \\ 2(1) + 3(2) + 0(3) & 2(1) + 3(1) + 0(0) & 2(2) + 3(0) + 0(1) \end{bmatrix}$$
$$= \begin{bmatrix} 7 & 1 & 4 \\ 7 & 3 & 5 \\ 8 & 5 & 4 \end{bmatrix}.$$

If $A = [a_{ij}]$, $B = [b_{ij}]$, and $C = [c_{ij}]$ are 3×3 matrices, then $(AB)C = A(BC)$, that is, the associative law holds for multiplication. We can prove this as follows: $AB = [d_{ij}]$, where $d_{ij} = a_{i1}b_{1j} + a_{i2}b_{2j} + a_{i3}b_{3j}$. $(AB)C = [e_{ij}]$, where $e_{ij} = d_{i1}c_{1j} + d_{i2}c_{2j} + d_{i3}c_{3j}$. Also $BC = [f_{ij}]$, where $f_{ij} = b_{i1}c_{1j} + b_{i2}c_{2j} + b_{i3}c_{3j}$, and $A(BC) = [g_{ij}]$, where $g_{ij} = a_{i1}f_{1j} + a_{i2}f_{2j} + a_{i3}f_{3j}$. By substituting the values for d_{ij} into e_{ij} and the values for f_{ij} into g_{ij} the reader can verify that $e_{ij} = g_{ij}$ and hence $(AB)C = A(BC)$.

The proof of the distributive laws is similar but somewhat shorter. We shall prove only the left distributive law and leave the reader to give the similar proof for the right distributive law. Let A, B, C be 3×3 matrices as before. Then $B + C = [b_{ij} + c_{ij}]$ and $A(B + C) = [d_{ij}]$, where $d_{ij} = a_{i1}(b_{1j} + c_{1j}) + a_{i2}(b_{2j} + c_{2j}) + a_{i3}(b_{3j} + c_{3j}) = a_{i1}b_{1j} + a_{i2}b_{2j} + a_{i3}b_{3j} + a_{i1}c_{1j} + a_{i2}c_{2j} + a_{i3}c_{3j}$. But $a_{i1}b_{1j} + a_{i2}b_{2j} + a_{i3}b_{3j}$ is the i, j element of the product AB, and $a_{i1}c_{1j} + a_{i2}c_{2j} + a_{i3}c_{3j}$ is the i, j element of the product AC. Therefore $A(B + C) = AB + AC$.

This completes the proof that the set of all 3×3 matrices whose elements are real (or complex) numbers forms a ring. We can also show that the matrix

$$I = \begin{bmatrix} 1 & 0 & 0 \\ 0 & 1 & 0 \\ 0 & 0 & 1 \end{bmatrix}$$

acts as the identity element under multiplication. Therefore the 3×3 matrices form a ring with identity. This ring is not commutative, as we see from the following computation:

$$\begin{bmatrix} 1 & 0 & 1 \\ 0 & 1 & 0 \\ 0 & 0 & 1 \end{bmatrix} \begin{bmatrix} 1 & 0 & 0 \\ 0 & 1 & 0 \\ 1 & 0 & 1 \end{bmatrix} = \begin{bmatrix} 2 & 0 & 1 \\ 0 & 1 & 0 \\ 1 & 0 & 1 \end{bmatrix},$$

$$\begin{bmatrix} 1 & 0 & 0 \\ 0 & 1 & 0 \\ 1 & 0 & 1 \end{bmatrix} \begin{bmatrix} 1 & 0 & 1 \\ 0 & 1 & 0 \\ 0 & 0 & 1 \end{bmatrix} = \begin{bmatrix} 1 & 0 & 1 \\ 0 & 1 & 0 \\ 1 & 0 & 2 \end{bmatrix}.$$

The ring of 3×3 matrices contains divisors of zero; for example,

$$\begin{bmatrix} 1 & 0 & 0 \\ 0 & 3 & 0 \\ 0 & 0 & 0 \end{bmatrix} \begin{bmatrix} 0 & 0 & 0 \\ 0 & 0 & 0 \\ 3 & 1 & 5 \end{bmatrix} = \begin{bmatrix} 0 & 0 & 0 \\ 0 & 0 & 0 \\ 0 & 0 & 0 \end{bmatrix}.$$

We shall delve no further into the properties of matrices but shall remark that they are of great importance both in theoretical mathematics and in practical computation.

9.7   Homomorphism and isomorphism

In our study of groups we saw that there were certain functions that preserved the group operation and that these functions were of special interest to us. The question now arises of whether there are functions that preserve both the ring operations and, if so, whether there are any interesting and useful examples.

DEFINITION

A function $f: A \rightarrow A'$, where A and A' are rings, is called a *homomorphism* or *ring homomorphism* if $f(a + b) = f(a) + f(b)$ and $f(ab) = f(a)f(b)$.

It is clear that any ring homomorphism of $(A, +, \cdot)$ into $(A', +, \cdot)$ is also a group homomorphism of $(A, +)$ into $(A', +)$. This fact will be useful to us in our study of ring homomorphisms. In particular, we have the following theorem.

THEOREM   9.5

If $f: A \rightarrow A'$ is a ring homomorphism, then $f(0) = 0'$ and $f(-a) = -f(a)$, where 0, $0'$ are the zeros in A and A', respectively.

EXAMPLE   9.10

If A and A' are rings, then $f: A \rightarrow A'$, where $f(x) = 0'$ for all $x \in A$, and $0'$ is the zero element in A' is a homomorphism. To see this we observe that $f(x) + f(y) = 0' + 0' = 0' = f(x + y)$ and $f(x)f(y) = 0'0' = 0' = f(xy)$. As for groups this is referred to as the *trivial* or *null homomorphism*. It is the only constant function that can be a ring homomorphism.

THEOREM   9.6

The range of a ring homomorphism is a ring, that is, if $f: A \rightarrow A'$ is a ring homomorphism, then $f(A)$ is a subring of A'.

Proof

Let x, y be any elements of $f(A)$. Then $x = f(a)$ and $y = f(b)$ for some $a \in A, b \in A$. We know that $f(A)$ is a subgroup of $(A', +)$. Therefore $x - y$ is an element of $f(A)$. Also $xy = f(a)f(b) = f(ab)$ is an element of $f(A)$. It is clear that $f(A) \neq \varnothing$; therefore, by Theorem 9.3, $f(A)$ is a subring of A'. •

We know that a group homomorphism preserves the identity element, that is, $f: G \rightarrow G'$ maps the identity element of G onto the identity element of G'. We also know that a ring homomorphism preserves the zero element. It is reasonable to ask whether, for rings A and A' with identity elements e and e', respectively, we have $f(e) = e'$ for every ring homomorphism $f: A \rightarrow A'$. We see immediately that this need not be true for the trivial homomorphism. Theorem 9.7 shows a closely related property.

THEOREM   9.7

Let A be a ring with identity element e; let B be a ring and let $f: A \rightarrow B$ be a ring homomorphism. Then the ring $f(A)$ has an identity element.

Proof

It is sufficient to show that $x'f(e) = f(e)x' = x'$ for all $x' \in f(A)$. But $x' = f(a)$ for some $a \in A$. Therefore $x'f(e) = f(a)f(e) = f(ae) = f(a) = x'$ and, similarly, $f(e)x' = x'$. •

It is worth pointing out that this result is still true if f is the trivial homomorphism. In that case $f(A) = \{0\}$, $f(e) = 0$, and $f(a) = f(e)f(a) = 0$.

It is important that the reader understand that this theorem does not state that B has an identity element, but only that the subring $f(A)$ has an identity. The element $f(e)$ is always an identity for $f(A)$, but it need not be an identity for B.

EXAMPLE   9.11

Let Z be the ring of integers and let A be any ring with identity e. Consider the function $g:Z \rightarrow A$ such that $g(n) = ne$. Since $g(n + m) = ne + me = g(n) + g(m)$, we see that g preserves addition. The reader can prove by induction that $(mn)e = (me)(ne)$ for $m \in Z$, $n \in Z$, e the identity in A. Therefore $g(nm) = g(n)g(m)$ and g is a homomorphism. Since $g(1) = e$, we see that $g(Z)$ has the identity e.

As for groups, we consider the set of elements whose value under a homomorphism is the zero element. This set is given a name in the following definition.

DEFINITION

Let A and A' be rings and let $f:A \rightarrow A'$ be a ring homomorphism. The set $\{x|x \in A, f(x) = 0'\}$, where $0'$ is the zero element of A', is called the *kernel* of f.

It is obvious that if f is the trivial homomorphism then A is the kernel.

In the case of groups we saw that the kernel was a subgroup. We shall now prove that the kernel of a ring homomorphism is a subring.

THEOREM   9.8

If A and A' are rings and if $f:A \rightarrow A'$ is a ring homomorphism, then the kernel of f is a subring of A.

Proof

Theorem 8.11 shows that the kernel is a subgroup of $(A,+)$, and hence that $a - b$ is an element of the kernel whenever a and b are elements of the kernel. Let a and b be elements of the kernel, that is, $f(a) = 0'$ and $f(b) = 0'$, where $0'$ is the zero element of A'. Therefore $f(ab) = f(a)f(b) = 0'$, and ab is an element of the kernel. The kernel is not empty since $f(0) = 0'$. Then Theorem 9.3 shows that the kernel is a subring of A. •

An additional property of the kernel will be found in the exercises.

EXAMPLE   9.12

Let Z be the ring of integers and $Z/(n)$ the ring of integers (residue classes) modulo n. Consider the function $f: Z \to Z/(n)$, where $f(n) = C_n$, the residue class containing n. Theorem 9.4 shows that this function preserves addition and multiplication and hence is a homomorphism. The identity in $f(Z)$ is $f(1) = C_1$ and the kernel is the set $\{m | m \in Z, m = kn$ for some $k \in Z\}$.

An important case of a ring homomorphism is introduced in the following definition.

DEFINITION

A homomorphism that is bijective is called an *isomorphism*, or a *ring isomorphism*.

If A and A' are rings and $f: A \to A'$ is an isomorphism, we say that A and A' are *isomorphic*.

EXAMPLE   9.13

Let A be the set of matrices of the form

$$\begin{bmatrix} m & 0 & 0 \\ 0 & m & 0 \\ 0 & 0 & m \end{bmatrix}$$

for some $m \in Z$. The reader can verify that A is a ring. Then the function $f: Z \to A$, where

$$f(m) = \begin{bmatrix} m & 0 & 0 \\ 0 & m & 0 \\ 0 & 0 & m \end{bmatrix},$$

is an isomorphism. We saw in an earlier exercise that this is a homomorphism and it is clear that it is bijective.

EXAMPLE   9.14

Let C be the ring of complex numbers and let M be the set of 2×2 matrices of the form

$$\begin{bmatrix} a & b \\ -b & a \end{bmatrix},$$

where a and b are real numbers. The reader can verify that this is a subring of the ring of all 2×2 matrices with real elements. Consider the function $f:C \to M$, where

$$f(a + ib) = \begin{bmatrix} a & b \\ -b & a \end{bmatrix}.$$

We observe that

$$f(a + ib) + f(c + id) = \begin{bmatrix} a & b \\ -b & a \end{bmatrix} + \begin{bmatrix} c & d \\ -d & c \end{bmatrix} = \begin{bmatrix} a + c & b + d \\ -(b + d) & a + c \end{bmatrix}$$
$$= f((a + ib) + (c + id)),$$

and

$$f(a + ib)f(c + id) = \begin{bmatrix} a & b \\ -b & a \end{bmatrix}\begin{bmatrix} c & d \\ -d & c \end{bmatrix} = \begin{bmatrix} ac - bd & ad + bc \\ -(bc + ad) & -bd + ac \end{bmatrix}$$
$$= f((a + ib)(c + id)).$$

Therefore f is a homomorphism. If $f(a + ib) = f(c + id)$, then

$$\begin{bmatrix} a & b \\ -b & a \end{bmatrix} = \begin{bmatrix} c & d \\ -d & c \end{bmatrix},$$

and hence $a = c$ and $b = d$. Therefore f is injective. Finally, for each matrix

$$\begin{bmatrix} a & b \\ -b & a \end{bmatrix} \in M,$$

we have $a + ib \in C$ such that

$$f(a + ib) = \begin{bmatrix} a & b \\ -b & a \end{bmatrix}.$$

Therefore f maps C onto M. This completes the proof that f is an isomorphism.

9.8   Divisibility

Let a, b be elements of a commutative ring A. We say that a *divides* b or b *is divisible by* a if there is an element $x \in A$ such that $ax = b$. We write $a|b$ to express this property. If there is no such $x \in A$ we say that a does not divide b and we write $a \nmid b$.

Theorem 5.9 is the division algorithm for natural numbers; for natural numbers a, b we have either $a = bq$ or $a = bq + r$, where q, r are natural numbers and $r < b$. It is clear that a similar result holds for Z: For integers a, b with $b \neq 0$, we have $a = bq + r$, where q and r are integers and $|r| < |b|$. We shall now show that a similar theorem holds for the ring of polynomials with real (or complex) coefficients.

THEOREM 9.9 (DIVISION ALGORITHM FOR POLYNOMIALS)

Let f and $h \neq 0$ be two polynomials with real coefficients. Then there exist unique polynomials q and r such that $f = hq + r$, where either $r = 0$ or else the degree of r is less than the degree of h.

Proof

Consider the set $A = \{z|z = f - hq, q \text{ a polynomial}\}$. If $0 \in A$, then $f = hq$ for some q and the existence of q and r is proved with $r = 0$.

Suppose $0 \notin A$. The degrees of the polynomials in A form a subset of the nonnegative integers. Let r be a polynomial in A with smallest degree. Then $f - hq = r$ for some polynomial q. Suppose $h = a_n x^n + a_{n-1} x^{n-1} + \cdots + a_0$, where $a_n \neq 0$ and $r = b_m x^m + b_{m-1} x^{m-1} + \cdots + b_0$, where $b_m \neq 0$. If $n > m$ we have found suitable q and r. Suppose $n \leq m$. Then $f - (q + (b_m/a_n)x^{m-n})h = f - hq - (b_m/a_n)x^{m-n}h = r - (b_m/a_n)x^{m-n}h$ has degree less than the degree of r. But this contradicts our choice of r as a polynomial in A with the least degree. Therefore $n > m$, and the existence part of the theorem is proved.

To prove the uniqueness of q and r, we suppose that q_1, r_1 and q_2, r_2 both satisfy the conditions; that is, $f = hq_1 + r_1$, where the degree of r_1 is less than the degree of h, and $f = hq_2 + r_2$, where the degree of r_2 is less than the degree of h. Then $r_1 - r_2 = (f - hq_1) - (f - hq_2) = h(q_2 - q_1)$. If $q_2 \neq q_1$, the degree of $h(q_2 - q_1)$ is not less than the degree of h. But the degree of $r_1 - r_2$ is less than the degree of h. Therefore $q_2 = q_1$ and hence $r_1 = r_2$. Therefore q and r are unique. •

As in the natural numbers, q is called the *quotient* and r is called the *remainder*.

There are two useful corollaries of this theorem.

Corollary 1 (Remainder Theorem)

If a polynomial f is divided by the polynomial $x - a$, the remainder is $f(a)$.

Proof

By the division algorithm $f = (x - a)q + r$, where the degree of r is less than the degree of $(x - a)$. Therefore r is a constant. If we set $x = a$, we have $f(a) = (a - a)q(a) + r$ and $r = f(a)$. •

Corollary 2 (Factor Theorem)

A polynomial f is divisible by $x - a$ if and only if $f(a) = 0$.

Proof

By the remainder theorem we have $f = (x - a)c + f(a)$. Then $f(a) = 0$ if and only if $x - a$ divides f. •

The close similarity between the division algorithm for integers and for polynomials suggests the possibility of studying a class of rings of which the integers and polynomials are examples. We shall now define such a class of rings.

DEFINITION

Let A be a commutative ring for which there is a function $g : A - \{0\} \to N \cup \{0\}$ such that:

1. For $a \neq 0$ and $b \neq 0$ we have $ab \neq 0$, that is, A has no nontrivial divisors of zero.

2. For all $a \in A - \{0\}$, $b \in A - \{0\}$, we have $g(ab) \geq g(a)$.

3. There is a division algorithm, that is, for a, $b \neq 0$ in A, there exist q and r in A such that $a = bq + r$ and either $r = 0$ or $g(r) < g(b)$.

A ring for which these properties hold is called a *Euclidean ring*.

For the ring Z we can define $g(n) = |n|$. Thus Z is a Euclidean ring. The ring of polynomials with real coefficients is a Euclidean ring with $g(f)$ defined as the degree of f.

We shall make use of this concept of a Euclidean ring in studying the greatest common divisor of elements in a ring. Our definition is in terms of any ring, but our proofs will give a device for finding the greatest common divisor and for this we make use of the properties of a Euclidean ring. These proofs provide a good example of the power of the abstract method. By working with a Euclidean ring we get a result that can be applied immediately to any Euclidean ring, in particular to integers and polynomials. Without the idea of Euclidean ring, we would have to go through essentially the same proof for each example.

DEFINITION

An element d of a ring A is called a *greatest common divisor* of elements a and b in A if $d|a$ and $d|b$ and if, whenever $c|a$ and $c|b$, it is also true that $c|d$.

We abbreviate this by writing *d is a g.c.d. of a and b* or by the notation[1] $d = (a,b)$.

We shall now provide a means of calculating the greatest common divisor.

---

[1] This notation must not be confused with an ordered pair.

THEOREM   9.10 (EUCLIDEAN ALGORITHM)

For any two nonzero elements of a Euclidean ring, there is a method of computing their greatest common divisor.

Proof

Let a and b be the two elements. Since the ring is Euclidean, we have $a = q_1 b + r_1$, where $r_1 = 0$ or $g(r_1) < g(b)$.

Similarly, $b = q_2 r_1 + r_2$ with $r_2 = 0$ or $g(r_2) < g(r_1)$, $r_1 = q_3 r_2 + r_3$ with $r_3 = 0$ or $g(r_3) < g(r_2)$, etc.

Since $g(r_1) > g(r_2) > g(r_3) > \cdots$, we must have $r_n = 0$ for some n. Then $r_{n-2} = q_n r_{n-1}$. From this we see that $r_{n-1} | r_{n-2}$. Also $r_{n-3} = q_{n-1} r_{n-2} + r_{n-1}$, and hence $r_{n-1} | r_{n-3}$. We can continue in this way to prove $r_{n-1} | r_{n-4}$, $\cdots$, $r_{n-1} | r_2$, $r_{n-1} | r_1$, $r_{n-1} | b$, $r_{n-1} | a$. Therefore r_{n-1} is a common divisor of a and b.

Suppose that $c | a$ and $c | b$. Since $a = q_1 b + r_1$, we see that $c | r_1$. Similarly, we can show that $c | r_2$, $c | r_3$, $\cdots$, $c | r_{n-1}$.

This completes the proof that r_{n-1} is a greatest common divisor of a and b. •

Theorem 9.11 expresses the greatest common divisor in a form that is convenient for some purposes.

THEOREM   9.11

Let d be a greatest common divisor of elements a, b of a Euclidean ring. Then there are elements m, n such that $d = ma + nb$.

Proof

As a first step we show that the particular g.c.d. produced by the Euclidean algorithm can be represented in the required form. We have

$$
\begin{aligned}
r_{n-1} &= r_{n-3} - q_{n-1} r_{n-2} \\
&= r_{n-3} - q_{n-1}(r_{n-4} - q_{n-2} r_{n-3}) \\
&= -q_{n-1} r_{n-4} + (1 + q_{n-1} q_{n-2}) r_{n-3} \\
&\qquad \cdots \\
&= m_1 r_1 + n_1 r_2 \\
&= m_1 r_1 + n_1 (b - q_2 r_1) \\
&= n_1 b + (m_1 - n_1 q_2) r_1 \\
&= n_1 b + (m_1 - n_1 q_2)(a - q_1 b) \\
&= (m_1 - n_1 q_2) a + (n_1 - m_1 q_1 + n_1 q_1 q_2) b \\
&= ma + nb.
\end{aligned}
$$

Now consider any g.c.d., say d. Then $r_{n-1}|d$, that is, $d = kr_{n-1}$. Therefore $d = (km)a + (kn)b$, the required form. •

9.9   Fields

We have seen that the rational numbers, the real numbers, and the complex numbers are commutative rings with identity. But each has an additional property that is not included in the properties of a commutative ring with identity; namely, each nonzero element has a multiplicative inverse. We now consider rings that have this property.

DEFINITION

A commutative ring with identity containing at least two elements in which each nonzero element has a multiplicative inverse is called a *field*.

We have seen that some, but not all, rings have (nonzero) divisors of zero. The following theorem shows that this is impossible in a field.

THEOREM   9.12

There are no divisors of zero in a field.

Proof

Let F be any field with $a \in F$, $b \in F$. If $ab = 0$ and $a \neq 0$, then $b = a^{-1}ab = a^{-1}0 = 0$. Therefore there are no zero divisors in F. •

A field can obviously be defined as a set together with two binary operations, called addition and multiplication, such that the set forms an Abelian group under addition, the nonzero elements form an Abelian group under multiplication, and the distributive law holds.

Since the nonzero elements of a field form a group, Theorem 8.4 implies that the multiplicative inverse of any element is unique.

EXAMPLE   9.15

The reader is already familiar with the fact that $Z/(5)$ forms a commutative ring with identity. From the multiplication table for $Z/(5)$ (see Table 9.2) it is clear that each nonzero element has a multiplicative inverse. Therefore $Z/(5)$ is a field.

Is $Z/(n)$ always a field? If $n = n_1 n_2$, then $n_1 \times n_2 \equiv 0 (\mod n)$ and $Z/(n)$ has zero divisors. Thus the only possible fields of this form are $Z/(p)$, where p is a prime. This proves the first part of Theorem 9.13.

THEOREM   9.13

The ring $Z/(p)$ is a field if and only if p is a prime.

Proof

We need only show that, if p is a prime, every nonzero element of $Z/(p)$ has an inverse. Let a be a representative of the nonzero equivalence class C_a. Since p is a prime, the greatest common divisor of p and a is 1. Therefore, by Theorem 9.11, $ma + np = 1$ for some integers m and n. Then $ma + np$ is a representative of the identity element C_1. But $ma + np \equiv ma(\mathrm{mod}\ p)$; therefore $C_1 = C_{ma} = C_m C_a$ and hence C_m is the inverse of C_a. $\bullet$

In a field F we can always solve the equation $ax = b$ provided $a \neq 0$. If $b \neq 0$, the result follows from the fact that the nonzero elements form a multiplicative group. If $b = 0$ then $x = 0$ is a solution. Furthermore, the solution is unique.

EXERCISES

9.1. Which of the following number systems are rings: N, Z, Q, R, C?

9.2. By a complex integer we mean a complex number $n + im$ with $n \in Z$, $m \in Z$. Prove that the set of complex integers forms a ring (with the usual operations for complex numbers). Is this ring commutative? Does it have an identity?

9.3. Prove that the subset of real numbers $\{x | x = n + m\sqrt{2}, n \in Z, m \in Z\}$ forms a ring with the usual operations for real numbers. Is it commutative? Does it have an identity?

9.4. The sets $A = \{x | x = n + m\sqrt{2}, n \in Z, m \in Z\}$ and $B = \{y | y = j + k\sqrt{3}, j \in Z, k \in Z\}$ both form rings (see Exercise 9.3). Is $A \cup B$ a ring with the usual operations for real numbers?

9.5. Let A be any ring. Prove that $na + ma = (n + m)a$ for all $a \in A$, $n \in Z$, $m \in Z$.

9.6. Let A be any ring. Prove that $a^{n+m} = a^n a^m$ for all $a \in A$, $n \in N$, $m \in N$.

9.7. Let A be a ring with identity element. Show that the set of invertible elements forms a group under the ring multiplication.

9.8. Show that $(A, +, \cdot)$, with the operations as in Table 9.1, is a ring. Is it commutative? Does it have an identity?

9.9. Let E be any set. Is $(\mathcal{P}(E), \cup, \cap)$ a ring?

9.10. Let E be any set. Define two operations:

$$\oplus : \mathcal{P}(E) \times \mathcal{P}(E) \to \mathcal{P}(E), \text{ where } A \oplus B = (A - B) \cup (B - A);$$
$$\odot : \mathcal{P}(E) \times \mathcal{P}(E) \to \mathcal{P}(E), \text{ where } A \odot B = A \cap B.$$

Is $(\mathcal{P}(E), \oplus, \odot)$ a ring?

9.11. Prove that in any ring $-(-a) = a$ for any a in the ring.

9.12. Prove that in any ring $(-a)(-b) = ab$ for any a and b in the ring.

9.13. Let E be any ring and let A and B be subrings. Prove that $A \cap B$ is a subring.

9.14. Show that for any given $n \in N$ there is at least one ring (and hence a group) with n elements.

9.15. Perform the following operations

(a) $8 + 3 \pmod 9$.

(b) $7 + 12 \pmod{31}$.

(c) $8 + 19 \pmod{15}$.

(d) $2 \times 4 \pmod 2$.

(e) $3 \times 9 \pmod{10}$.

(f) $2 \times 15 \pmod{20}$.

9.16. Construct the addition and multiplication tables for $Z/(6)$. Does this ring have divisors of zero?

9.17. In the set $Z/(5) \times Z/(5)$ define two operations as follows:

$$(a,b) + (c,d) = (a + c, b + d).$$
$$(a,b)(c,d) = (ac, bd).$$

Prove that this forms a ring. Does it have divisors of zero?

9.18. Complete the proof from Section 9.4 that $\mathfrak{F}(E,A)$ forms a ring.

9.19. Describe the smallest subring of $\mathfrak{F}(R,R)$ that contains the constant function $f(x) = 1$ and the identity function $i_R(x) = x$.

9.20. Complete the proof from Section 9.6 that $(AB)C = A(BC)$ for matrices A, B, C; that is, prove $e_{ij} = g_{ij}$.

9.21. Prove that the matrix

$$I = \begin{bmatrix} 1 & 0 & 0 \\ 0 & 1 & 0 \\ 0 & 0 & 1 \end{bmatrix}$$

is the identity in the ring of 3×3 matrices.

9.22. Perform the following matrix additions:

(a) $\begin{bmatrix} 1 & 3 \\ 6 & 0 \end{bmatrix} + \begin{bmatrix} 2 & 1 \\ 4 & 2 \end{bmatrix}$.

(b) $\begin{bmatrix} 1 & 3 & 1 \\ 2 & 0 & 4 \\ 6 & 1 & 7 \end{bmatrix} + \begin{bmatrix} 1 & 4 & 1 \\ 2 & 8 & 2 \\ 7 & 1 & 4 \end{bmatrix}$.

(c) $\begin{bmatrix} 3 & 1 \\ 1 & 2 \end{bmatrix} + \begin{bmatrix} 2 & 1 \\ 2 & 0 \end{bmatrix}$.

(d) $\begin{bmatrix} 1 & 3 & 1 \\ 2 & 6 & 1 \\ 5 & 1 & 4 \end{bmatrix} + \begin{bmatrix} 0 & -1 & 3 \\ -1 & 2 & 5 \\ 1 & -2 & 0 \end{bmatrix}$.

9.23. Let $A = [a_{ij}]$, $B = [b_{ij}]$ be 3×3 matrices. Find a 3×3 matrix C such that $A + C = B$.

9.24. Perform the following matrix multiplications:

(a) $\begin{bmatrix} 1 & 2 & 1 \\ 3 & 2 & 1 \\ 1 & 4 & 0 \end{bmatrix} \begin{bmatrix} 2 & 1 & 1 \\ 3 & 2 & 0 \\ 4 & 1 & 2 \end{bmatrix}$.

(b) $\begin{bmatrix} 1 & 2 \\ 7 & 1 \end{bmatrix} \begin{bmatrix} 5 & 4 \\ 1 & 3 \end{bmatrix}$.

(c) $\begin{bmatrix} 1 & -1 & 2 \\ 4 & 1 & 0 \\ 3 & 2 & 1 \end{bmatrix} \begin{bmatrix} 1 & 4 & 2 \\ -1 & 3 & -4 \\ 2 & 1 & 1 \end{bmatrix}.$

(d) $\begin{bmatrix} 1 & 0 \\ 2 & 0 \end{bmatrix} \begin{bmatrix} 0 & 0 \\ 3 & 1 \end{bmatrix}.$

(e) $\begin{bmatrix} 1 & 3 & 2 \\ 2 & 1 & 0 \\ 0 & 1 & 3 \end{bmatrix} \begin{bmatrix} 3 & 0 & 2 \\ 1 & 1 & 2 \\ 2 & 0 & 1 \end{bmatrix}.$

9.25. Find A^2, A^3, A^4, A^n, where

$$A = \begin{bmatrix} 1 & 0 \\ 2 & 3 \end{bmatrix}.$$

9.26. Does the ring of 3×3 matrices with real elements have divisors of zero?

9.27. Find the multiplicative inverses for

(a) $\begin{bmatrix} 0 & 1 \\ 2 & 0 \end{bmatrix}.$ (b) $\begin{bmatrix} 1 & 0 & 0 \\ 0 & 0 & 2 \\ 0 & 3 & 0 \end{bmatrix}.$ (c) $\begin{bmatrix} 2 & 0 & 0 \\ 3 & 0 & 1 \\ 1 & 2 & 3 \end{bmatrix}.$

9.28. Does the matrix

$$\begin{bmatrix} 2 & 0 & 0 \\ 3 & 0 & 1 \\ 1 & 0 & 3 \end{bmatrix}$$

have a multiplicative inverse?

9.29. The matrix

$$\begin{bmatrix} k & 0 & 0 \\ 0 & k & 0 \\ 0 & 0 & k \end{bmatrix}$$

is called a 3×3 scalar matrix. Let $A = [a_{ij}]$ be any 3×3 matrix. Describe in words the effect on A of multiplying by a scalar matrix (a) on the left, (b) on the right.

9.30. Prove that a 3×3 scalar matrix (see Exercise 9.29) commutes in multiplication with any 3×3 matrix.

9.31. Prove that the set of 2×2 matrices of the form

$$\begin{bmatrix} a & b \\ -b & a \end{bmatrix}$$

for $a \in R$, $b \in R$ forms a ring.

9.32. Prove that the set of 3×3 scalar matrices (see Exercise 9.29) forms a ring.

9.33. Prove that the homomorphic image (the range of the homomorphism) of a commutative ring is commutative.

9.34. Let A be a ring with identity e, let A' be a ring, and let $f: A \rightarrow A'$ be a ring homomorphism. If f is a function onto A', prove that A' has an identity e', and that $f(e) = e'$.

9.35. Let A be any ring and a any element of A. Let e be the identity element of A. Prove that $na = (ne)a$ for any $n \in N$.

9.36. Let A be a ring with identity e. Prove that $(mn)e = (me)(ne)$ for any integers m and n.

9.37. Prove that a ring homomorphism is injective if and only if its kernel is $\{0\}$.

9.38. Let A and A' be rings and let K be the kernel of the homomorphism $f: A \to A'$. Prove that xa is an element of K for any $x \in A$ and any $a \in K$.

9.39. Let C be the ring of complex numbers. Prove that the function $f: C \to C$, where $f(a + ib) = a - ib$, is a ring isomorphism.

9.40. Let A be the ring in Exercise 9.17. Prove that the function $f: A \to Z/(5)$, where $f(a,b) = a$, is a ring homomorphism.

9.41. Let A be an additive Abelian group. Let $\mathcal{3C}$ be the set of all homomorphisms of A into itself. Let f, g be homomorphisms in $\mathcal{3C}$. Define $f + g: A \to A$ as $(f + g)(x) = f(x) + g(x)$ and $fg: A \to A$ as $(fg)(x) = f(g(x))$. Prove that, with these two operations, $\mathcal{3C}$ forms a ring with identity.

9.42. Let A be any ring. Let $\mathcal{3C}$ be the ring of homomorphisms of $(A,+)$ into itself as in Exercise 9.41. Define $f_a \in \mathcal{3C}$, where $f_a(x) = xa$ for all $x \in A$. Show that the function $\varphi: A \to \mathcal{3C}$, where $\varphi(a) = f_a$ is a ring homomorphism. Prove that A is isomorphic to $f(A)$.

9.43. Write out the tables for all distinct (nonisomorphic) rings with (a) 2 elements, (b) 3 elements, (c) 4 elements.

9.44. Let Z be the set of integers. Define $a \oplus b = a + b - 1$ and $a \otimes b = ab - (a + b) + 2$. Prove that $(Z, \oplus, \otimes)$ is a commutative ring with identity. Prove that the function $f: Z \to Z$, where $f(n) = n + 1$, is an isomorphism of $(Z, +, \cdot)$ onto $(Z, \oplus, \otimes)$.

9.45. Find the g.c.d. for each of the following pairs of integers and express it in the form $d = mx + ny$:

    (a) 15, 27.
    (b) 8, 36.
    (c) 11, 13.
    (d) 18, 30.

9.46. Find the g.c.d. for each of the following pairs of polynomials and express it in the form

$$d(x) = m(x)f(x) + n(x)g(x).$$

    (a) $x^4 - 5x^3 + 8x^2 - 4x$ and $x^3 - 4x^2 + 5x - 2$.
    (b) $x^4 - 4x^3 + 5x^2 - 2x$ and $x^3 - x^2 - 5x - 3$.
    (c) $x^4 - 5x^2 + 4$ and $x^3 - 4x^2 + 5x - 2$.

9.47. Factor the following polynomials into linear factors

    (a) $x^6 - 26x^4 + 169x^2 - 144$.
    (b) $x^4 - 2x^3 - 8x^2 + 18x - 9$.
    (c) $x^6 - 14x^4 + 49x^2 - 36$.

9.48. Prove that the two definitions of a field given in Section 9.9 are equivalent.

9.49. (a) Define a subfield by analogy with the definition of subring given in Section 9.2.

    (b) Let F be any field and S a subset of F. Prove that S is a subfield of F if and only if the following conditions are satisfied:

    (1) S has at least two elements.
    (2) For $a \in S$ and $b \in S$ we have $a - b \in S$.
    (3) For $a \in S - \{0\}$ and $b \in S - \{0\}$, we have $ab^{-1} \in S - \{0\}$.

9.50. Let F be any field. Let A be a nonempty subset of F such that, for $x \in F$ and $a \in A$, we have $xa \in A$. Prove that $A = \{0\}$ or $A = F$.

Part Three

ANALYTIC GEOMETRY

10
Vector Algebra

10.1   Introduction

Two French mathematicians, René Descartes (1596–1650) and P. deFermat (1601–1665), are credited with the first systematic use of coordinates in geometry and hence the first translation of a geometric problem into an algebraic problem. At the beginning they used only positive coordinates. Sir Isaac Newton (1643–1727) in his *Enumeratio linearum tertii ordinis* introduced negative coordinates. This analytic method was amazingly successful for handling geometric problems and it required less skill and imagination than earlier geometric methods. Late in the eighteenth century mathematicians began to think that the geometric figures were not essential and began to write geometry books without diagrams. This prepared the way for a new conception of space. Studies began to appear of spaces and geometries that could not be visualized in the space where man's first ideas of geometry were found.

In the nineteenth century it became apparent that a new algebraic system, a new generalization of the number systems, would give a convenient representation for geometric and physical problems. The elements of this new system are called *vectors*. The student has already met these in high school as a device for representing forces.

There are two ways in which vectors could be introduced. We could define a vector as a 1×3 matrix or as an ordered triple of real numbers. This approach has the advantage that all the properties of vectors can be developed from the properties of real numbers. It has the disadvantage, however, that it does not provide us with a means of justifying the use of vectors in the framework of geometry, which the reader already knows, either axiomatically or intuitively. We shall introduce vectors in terms of directed line segments. This approach has intuitive appeal, especially for geometric applications. Since we shall be concerned with solid geometry, we shall have to consider a few axioms, definitions, and properties that we require in addition to the ideas of plane geometry with which we assume the reader is familiar. We shall not study solid geometry in detail, but list these few important facts in the next section.

10.2   Solid geometry

In the study of solid geometry we are concerned with the undefined concepts *point*, *line*, and *plane*. The relations among these are given by a list of axioms. Although we do not assume that the reader has a thorough knowledge of the axiomatic development of plane geometry, we shall present here only the few axioms, definitions, and important properties that are needed to extend the study of plane geometry to solid geometry.

A1. Any three points that do not lie on the same line determine a plane.

A2. If a line has two of its points lying in a plane, then the entire line lies in the plane.

A3. If two planes have a point in common, then they have at least one line in common.

A4. There are at least four points that do not lie on the same plane.

Two lines that lie in the same plane are called *coplanar*. Two lines are called *parallel* if they are coplanar and do not intersect, that is, if they are coplanar and are parallel in the sense of plane geometry.

It can be proved that, if lines l_1 and l_2 are parallel and lines l_2 and l_3 are parallel, then l_1 and l_3 are parallel. We call this result the "transitivity of the parallel relation." We shall not give a proof, although it is of fundamental importance in our study of vectors.

A line l is said to be *parallel to a plane* p if p contains a line l_1 that is parallel to l. It can be shown that, for a given line l and a given plane p, either l lies in p or l is parallel to p or l meets p in exactly one point.

Consider two distinct lines l_1 and l_2 that intersect in the point[1] P. If we choose P_1 on l_1 and P_2 on l_2 both different from P, then the points P, P_1, P_2 determine a plane (axiom A1) and l_1, l_2 lie in the plane (axiom A2). It can be proved that there is a line through P that is perpendicular to both l_1 and l_2 and also that this line is perpendicular to any line through P which lies in the plane. We say that this line is *perpendicular to the plane*.

Consider a function t with our geometric space as domain and codomain. Let A, B be points in the space. If the line determined by A, B is parallel to or equal to the line determined by $t(A)$, $t(B)$ and the line determined by A, $t(A)$ is parallel to or equal to the line determined by B, $t(B)$ for all points A and B, then we say that the function t is a translation of the space. It can

---

[1] Since points are elements of the set (space), the conventions of Part I would require that they be represented by small letters. We prefer to follow the practice of elementary geometry and represent points by capitals.

be proved, using the transitivity of the parallel relation, that the set of all translations of space forms a group under the composition of functions.

With these few facts of solid geometry at our disposal we can turn to the question of defining a vector. Other geometric facts will be mentioned as they are needed.

10.3   The vector concept

Let A and B be points in space. They determine a line and we can speak of the line segment between A and B. Furthermore, the ordered pair (A,B) determines a *directed line segment* AB with initial point A and terminal point B.

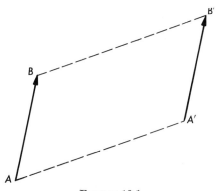

FIGURE 10.1

We define a relation between directed segments as follows. For directed segments AB and $A'B'$ we have $AB \, \rho \, A'B'$ if and only if there is a translation t such that $t(A) = A'$ and $t(B) = B'$. Since the set of translations forms a group, this is an equivalence relation. The reader can supply the details of this proof.

The following description of this relation may assist the reader's intuition. If A, B, A', B' do not lie on the same line, then $AB \, \rho \, A'B'$ if and only if the quadrilateral $AA'B'B$ is a parallelogram (with the vertices arranged around the perimeter in this order). This is illustrated in Figure 10.1. If A, B, A', B' are on the same line, then $AB \, \rho \, A'B'$ if and only if AB and $A'B'$ have the same length and point in the same direction.

Two directed segments related in either of these ways are sometimes called *equipollent* and the relation is called the *equipolence* relation. These terms are borrowed from French; they are not yet in general use in English.

An equivalence class for this relation is called a *vector*. We often indicate a vector by means of one of its representatives, that is, by a directed segment. We treated rational numbers in a similar way (see Chapter 6). When we spoke of the rational number $3/7$ we in fact meant the equivalence class (or rational number) one of whose representatives is $\frac{3}{7}$. The same class (that is, the same rational number) could have been represented by $\frac{6}{14}$, etc. With this understanding of a directed segment as a representative of a vector we often draw an arrow as the directed segment and use it to indicate the vector.

In printed work it is customary to use boldface type, **a**, **b**, **v**, $\cdots$ to represent vectors. In handwritten or typewritten material they may be indicated by underlining, $\underline{a}$, $\underline{b}$, $\underline{v}$, $\cdots$, by overscoring, $\bar{a}$, $\bar{b}$, $\bar{v}$, $\cdots$, or by an arrow over the letter, $\vec{a}$, $\vec{b}$, $\vec{v}$, $\cdots$. We shall sometimes indicate a vector by a directed segment representing it, AB. If the directed segment AB is a representative of the vector **a**, we sometimes write **a** $= AB$, although this is an abuse of our notation for segments and equivalence classes. If we also have CD as a representative of **a**, we shall write $AB = CD$ to mean that the segments are equivalent (equipollent), but not necessarily equal. We similarly abuse our notation for rational numbers when we write $\frac{3}{5} = \frac{6}{10}$ to mean that the two fractions are in the same equivalence class.

Consider a vector **a** with representative AB and any point P. We assert without proof that there is always one and only one translation t such that $t(A) = P$. If we denote $t(B)$ by P_1, then PP_1 is a representative of **a**. It follows that at any point P there is one and only one directed segment PP_1 representing a given vector **a**.

10.4   Addition of vectors

We shall now define an operation between vectors which we call the *addition of vectors*. The set of all vectors forms an Abelian group with respect to this addition.

Let **a** and **b** be two vectors. We want to define a vector **a** + **b**. Choose a directed segment AB such that $AB = $ **a**. We have observed that there is exactly one directed segment BC such that $BC = $ **b**. Then **a** + **b** is defined as the vector represented by the directed segment AC (see Figure 10.2).

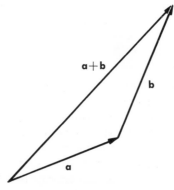

FIGURE 10.2

If this is to be a suitable definition for addition, we must show that the sum $\mathbf{a} + \mathbf{b}$ is unique, that it is independent of the choice of representatives of $\mathbf{a}$ and $\mathbf{b}$. If we had chosen representatives $A'B'$ and $B'C'$ as in Figure 10.3 we would have translations t_1 such that $t_1(A) = A'$ and $t_1(B) = B'$ and t_2 such that $t_2(B) = B'$ and $t_2(C) = C'$. Since $t_1(B) = t_2(B)$, we have $t_1 = t_2$ and hence $t_1(C) = C'$. Therefore AC and $A'C'$ represent the same vector $\mathbf{a} + \mathbf{b}$.

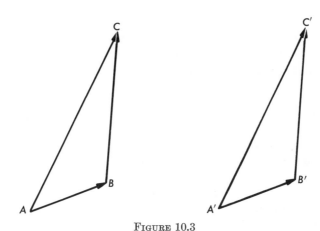

FIGURE 10.3

We shall now show that the set of vectors together with this addition forms an Abelian group. It is clear that addition is a binary operation, since our definition associates with each pair of vectors $\mathbf{a}$ and $\mathbf{b}$ a vector $\mathbf{a} + \mathbf{b}$.

It is easily seen from Figure 10.4 that $\mathbf{a} + (\mathbf{b} + \mathbf{c}) = (\mathbf{a} + \mathbf{b}) + \mathbf{c}$, that is, that the associative law holds.

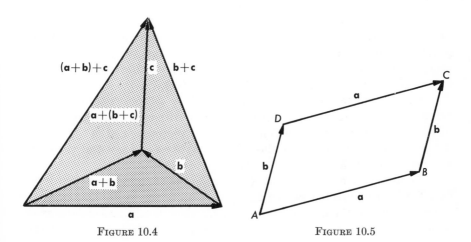

FIGURE 10.4   FIGURE 10.5

Since a directed segment is determined by an ordered pair of points, we can speak of the directed segment AA with the two points coinciding. All such segments are equivalent according to the definition of equivalence in terms of a translation. The equivalence class of these segments is called the *zero vector* and is denoted **0**. It is clear that $\mathbf{a} + \mathbf{0} = \mathbf{a}$ and $\mathbf{0} + \mathbf{a} = \mathbf{a}$ for any vector **a**.

Associated with each vector **a** we define a vector $-\mathbf{a}$. If $AB = \mathbf{a}$, then $-\mathbf{a} = BA$. Then $AB + BA = AA = \mathbf{0}$ and hence $\mathbf{a} + (-\mathbf{a}) = \mathbf{0}$. Similarly, $(-\mathbf{a}) + \mathbf{a} = \mathbf{0}$, and $-\mathbf{a}$ is an inverse of **a** under addition.

Finally we can see from Figure 10.5 that $\mathbf{a} + \mathbf{b} = \mathbf{b} + \mathbf{a}$, since AB and DC are equivalent and, similarly, AD and BC are equivalent.

This completes the proof that the set of all vectors, which we denote by V, is an Abelian group under addition.

EXAMPLE 10.1

What is the necessary and sufficient condition in order that the vectors **a**, **b**, **c** may be represented by the sides AB, BC, CA, respectively, of triangle ABC?

If we let $\mathbf{a} = AB$, $\mathbf{b} = BC$, $\mathbf{c} = CD$, we want the necessary and sufficient conditions for $D = A$. If $D = A$, then $AB + BC + CD = AA$ and hence $\mathbf{a} + \mathbf{b} + \mathbf{c} = \mathbf{0}$. Conversely, if $\mathbf{a} + \mathbf{b} + \mathbf{c} = \mathbf{0}$, then $AD = AB + BC + CD = AA$, and hence $A = D$. Thus **a**, **b**, **c** can be represented by the sides of the triangle if and only if $\mathbf{a} + \mathbf{b} + \mathbf{c} = \mathbf{0}$.

10.5   Multiplication of a vector by a scalar

Besides the addition operation under which the set of vectors forms an Abelian group, we shall now introduce a new operation that we call the multiplication of a vector by a scalar. The term scalar is traditionally used to refer to a real number. It originated in the early applications of vectors to physics to distinguish between those physical quantities that could be measured by a single number on a scale (scalars) and those that required two or more numbers for their representation (vectors).

This new operation is a function $f: R \times V \to V$ whose definition will be completed by giving the value $f(x,\mathbf{a})$ associated with each pair consisting of a real number x and a vector **a**. This value is a vector, since the codomain is the set of all vectors. We write the value $f(x,\mathbf{a})$ as $x\mathbf{a}$ and say that the vector **a** is *multiplied by the scalar x*.

We use our geometric knowledge as a means of defining $x\mathbf{a}$. If **a** is represented by the directed segment AB, then $x\mathbf{a}$ is the vector one of whose representatives is the directed segment AC, which is $|x|$ times as long as the segment AB, lies along the same line as AB, and is such that, if $x > 0$, then

C and B are on the same side of A, and, if $x < 0$, then A is between C and B (see Figure 10.6).

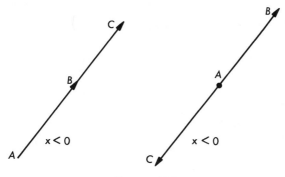

FIGURE 10.6

The following distributive laws hold as a consequence of the geometric nature of the definition:

$$(x + y)\mathbf{a} = x\mathbf{a} + y\mathbf{a}.$$
$$x(\mathbf{a} + \mathbf{b}) = x\mathbf{a} + x\mathbf{b}.$$

If $\mathbf{a} = x\mathbf{b}$ we say that the vectors $\mathbf{a}$ and $\mathbf{b}$ are *collinear*. This terminology arises from the fact that $\mathbf{a}$ and $\mathbf{b}$ can be represented by directed segments lying on the same line. It does not imply that *all* representatives of $\mathbf{a}$ and $\mathbf{b}$ lie on the same line.

EXAMPLE 10.2

Prove that the diagonals of a parallelogram bisect each other.

Proof

Consider parallelogram $ABCD$ (Figure 10.7). Let E be the mid-point of AC. Then it is sufficient to prove that BE and BD are collinear, that is, $BD = kBE$ for some $k \in R$. But $BE = BA + AE = BA + (\frac{1}{2})AC$ and

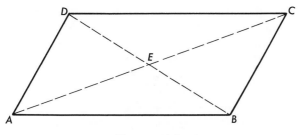

FIGURE 10.7

$BD = BA + AD = BA + AC + CD = BA + AC + BA = 2BA + AC = 2BE.$ •

10.6 The decomposition of a vector

Consider three vectors **v**, **a**, **b**. We have pointed out that we can choose as representatives of these vectors three line segments, each having initial point P. Suppose that all these representatives lie in the same plane. When this is true we refer to the three vectors as *coplanar*. We shall also assume that P, A, and B are not collinear. We denote the representative of **a** by PA, the representative of **b** by PB, and the representative of **v** by PC.

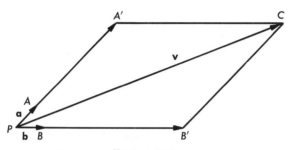

FIGURE 10.8

From Figure 10.8 we see that $PC = PA' + PB'$. But $PA' = xPA$ and $PB' = yPB$. Therefore we have $PC = xPA + yPB$, or $\mathbf{v} = x\mathbf{a} + y\mathbf{b}$. We call the vectors $x\mathbf{a}$ and $y\mathbf{b}$ the *components* of **v** along **a** and **b**, respectively.

In decomposing **v** into components, we have used the fact that **a**, **b**, **v** can be represented by directed segments lying in the same plane and also **a** and **b** are not collinear.

Now consider vectors **a**, **b**, **c** for which there is no set of representatives lying in the same plane. We want to prove that any vector **v** can be represented as

$$\mathbf{v} = x\mathbf{a} + y\mathbf{b} + z\mathbf{c}.$$

To visualize this decomposition we refer to Figure 10.9.

We choose representatives OA, OB, OC, and OM for **a**, **b**, **c**, and **v**, respectively, with a common initial point. Through M we draw a line parallel to OC. Let M' be the point on this line and also on the same plane as OA and OB. The point M' exists, since otherwise OC would be in the plane of OA and OB. Then $OM = OM' + OC'$, where $OC' = zOC$ for some $z \in R$. Since OM' is in the same plane as OA and OB, we have by the previous case $OM' = xOA + yOB$. Therefore $OM = xOA + yOB + zOC$, that is, $\mathbf{v} = x\mathbf{a} + y\mathbf{b} + z\mathbf{c}$.

We call $x\mathbf{a}$, $y\mathbf{b}$, $z\mathbf{c}$ the *components* of **v** along **a**, **b**, **c**, respectively, and x, y, z the *projections* or *coordinates* of **v** on **a**, **b**, **c**, respectively.

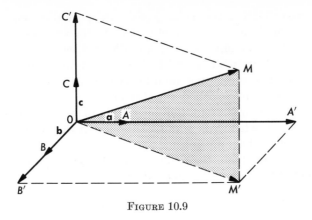

Figure 10.9

10.7 The scalar product

By using such geometric concepts as the congruence of segments and the congruence of angles, we can define other operations on the set of vectors. The first of these is the scalar product of two vectors. One motivation for the definition of this product is the expression of work in mechanics.

The scalar product is a function $f: V \times V \to R$. To define $f(\mathbf{a}, \mathbf{b})$ we must first define the angle between two vectors. The angle between $\mathbf{a}$ and $\mathbf{b}$, written $(\mathbf{a}, \mathbf{b})$, is defined as the angle between the segments AB and AC, written (AB, AC), where $AB = \mathbf{a}$ and $AC = \mathbf{b}$. As in the case of all definitions in terms of representatives, we must show that the angle $(\mathbf{a}, \mathbf{b})$ is independent of the choice of representatives, that is, is independent of the choice of the initial point A. This is clear when we consider Figure 10.10, with $t(A) = A'$, $t(B) = B'$, $t(C) = C'$ for some translation t.

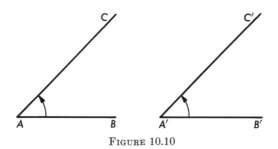

Figure 10.10

In Figure 10.10 we have indicated a direction of rotation for the angle. In terms of our ordered-pair notation we say that (AB, AC) is the angle through which AB must be rotated to become collinear with AC. This allows us to consider with any angle $(\mathbf{a}, \mathbf{b})$ its negative or opposite angle $(\mathbf{b}, \mathbf{a})$.

Before we can define the scalar product we must also consider the *magnitude, absolute value,* or *norm* of a vector. To this end we choose some segment in space and call it the unit segment. Any directed segment AB that is congruent to this unit segment is said to have length one and is called a *unit directed segment.* Any vector, one (and hence all) of whose representatives is a unit directed segment, is called a *unit vector.*

We write $|\mathbf{a}|$ to represent the magnitude of the vector $\mathbf{a}$ and define $|\mathbf{a}| = |a|$ if $\mathbf{a} = a\mathbf{v}$, where $\mathbf{v}$ is a unit vector. From this definition it follows that all unit vectors have magnitude 1.

We can now complete the definition of the scalar product. The value $f(\mathbf{a,b})$ is denoted by $\mathbf{a} \cdot \mathbf{b}$ and is defined as

$$\mathbf{a} \cdot \mathbf{b} = |\mathbf{a}|\,|\mathbf{b}| \cos (\mathbf{a,b}).$$

The following laws are useful in performing calculations:

1. $\mathbf{a} \cdot \mathbf{b} = \mathbf{b} \cdot \mathbf{a}$ (commutative law).
2. $x(\mathbf{a} \cdot \mathbf{b}) = (x\mathbf{a}) \cdot \mathbf{b} = \mathbf{a} \cdot (x\mathbf{b})$.
3. $\mathbf{c} \cdot (\mathbf{b} + \mathbf{a}) = \mathbf{c} \cdot \mathbf{b} + \mathbf{c} \cdot \mathbf{a}$ (distributive law).

Proof of 1

$$\begin{aligned}
\mathbf{a} \cdot \mathbf{b} &= |\mathbf{a}|\,|\mathbf{b}| \cos (\mathbf{a,b}) \\
&= |\mathbf{b}|\,|\mathbf{a}| \cos (\mathbf{b,a}) \\
&= \mathbf{b} \cdot \mathbf{a}.
\end{aligned}$$

Proof of 2

$$\begin{aligned}
x(\mathbf{a} \cdot \mathbf{b}) &= x|\mathbf{a}|\,|\mathbf{b}| \cos (\mathbf{a,b}) \\
&= |x\mathbf{a}|\,|\mathbf{b}| \cos (x\mathbf{a,b}) \\
&= (x\mathbf{a}) \cdot \mathbf{b},
\end{aligned}$$

and similarly, $x(\mathbf{a} \cdot \mathbf{b}) = \mathbf{a} \cdot (x\mathbf{b})$.

Before we prove the distributive law we state a general property concerning the scalar product of a unit vector. If $\mathbf{v}$ is a unit vector, then for any vector $\mathbf{a}$, $\mathbf{v} \cdot \mathbf{a} = |\mathbf{a}| \cos (\mathbf{v,a})$.

Proof of 3

Let l be any line on which a representative of the unit vector $\mathbf{v}$ lies. Pick a point O on l (see Figure 10.11). Let $AB = \mathbf{a}$. Let A', B' be the orthogonal projections of A, B on the line l. Then $OA' = x\mathbf{v}$, $OB' = y\mathbf{v}$, and $\mathbf{v} \cdot \mathbf{a} = y - x$.

Similarly in Figure 10.11 we see that $OC' = z\mathbf{v}$. Also $\mathbf{v} \cdot \mathbf{b} = z - y$ and $\mathbf{v} \cdot (\mathbf{a} + \mathbf{b}) = z - x$. Therefore $\mathbf{v} \cdot (\mathbf{a} + \mathbf{b}) = \mathbf{v} \cdot \mathbf{a} + \mathbf{v} \cdot \mathbf{b}$. This proves the distributive law for a unit vector.

In the general case we can write $\mathbf{c} \cdot (\mathbf{a} + \mathbf{b})$ as $|\mathbf{c}|(\mathbf{c}/|\mathbf{c}|) \cdot (\mathbf{a} + \mathbf{b})$. Since $\mathbf{c}/|\mathbf{c}|$ is a unit vector, we have $(\mathbf{c}/|\mathbf{c}|) \cdot (\mathbf{a} + \mathbf{b}) = (\mathbf{c}/|\mathbf{c}|) \cdot \mathbf{a} + (\mathbf{c}/|\mathbf{c}|) \cdot \mathbf{b}$ and $\mathbf{c} \cdot (\mathbf{a} + \mathbf{b}) = |\mathbf{c}|(\mathbf{c}/|\mathbf{c}|) \cdot \mathbf{a} + |\mathbf{c}|(\mathbf{c}/|\mathbf{c}|) \cdot \mathbf{b} = \mathbf{c} \cdot \mathbf{a} + \mathbf{c} \cdot \mathbf{b}$.

We can easily show that $\mathbf{a} \cdot \mathbf{a} = |\mathbf{a}|^2$, since $\cos (\mathbf{a,a}) = 1$. Also if $\mathbf{a} \neq \mathbf{0}$, $\mathbf{b} \neq \mathbf{0}$, then $\mathbf{a} \cdot \mathbf{b} = 0$ if and only if $(\mathbf{a,b}) = \pi/2 + k\pi$, $k \in Z$.

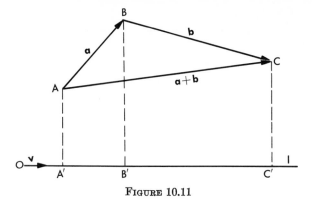

FIGURE 10.11

The scalar product is often called the dot product as suggested by the notation.

EXAMPLE   10.3

Prove that the angle subtended at the circumference by a diameter of a circle is a right angle.

Proof

Let B be the center of the circle, A, C the ends of a diameter, and D any point on the circumference other than A or C (see Figure 10.12). Then

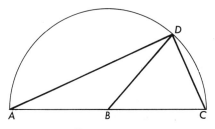

FIGURE 10.12

$DA = DB + BA$, $DC = DB + BC$, and therefore $DA \cdot DC = DB \cdot DB + DB \cdot BC + BA \cdot DB + BA \cdot BC = DB \cdot DB + DB \cdot (BC + BA) + BA \cdot BC = |DB||DB| - |BA||BC|$, since $BC + BA = 0$ and the angle between BA and BC is two right angles. Also $|DB| = |BA| = |BC|$, since they are all radii. Therefore $DA \cdot DC = 0$ and $DA \perp DC$. •

10.8   Rectangular coordinates

For some purposes, especially where products (either scalar products or vector or triple products, which we shall meet later) are involved, it is convenient to make use of a rectangular coordinate system. In fact any geometric problem involving angles or distances is best handled in terms of a coordinate system. We shall now construct such a system.

We select some point in space, denote it by O and call it the origin. Consider the directed segments of length 1, OA, OB, and OC where $(OA,OB) = (OB,OC) = (OC,OA) = \pi/2$. We describe this condition by saying that the segments are *mutually orthogonal*. There are many such sets of directed segments. Even if OA and OB are determined, we could still have this property by replacing OC by a directed segment OD, which is collinear with OC but oppositely directed (see Figure 10.13).

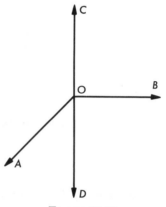

FIGURE 10.13

For the addition of vectors, multiplication of a vector by a scalar, or scalar multiplication of two vectors, it does not matter whether we use OC or OD. The choice is important, however, for the vector product to be introduced in the next section. We must therefore consider a means of distinguishing between these two cases.

Consider three noncoplanar-directed segments OE, OF, OG. There are six permutations of these segments, that is, six ways in which we can designate a first, second, and third segment, or six linear orders on the set. Consider the segments in one of these orders and observe them from such a position that the third segment points toward the eye. Then consider rotating the first segment until it is collinear with the second. This rotation must appear either clockwise or counterclockwise. If the rotation is counterclockwise, we say that the three segments *in this order* form a *right-handed triple*. If the rotation is clockwise we have a *left-handed triple*. If $\mathbf{a} = OE$, $\mathbf{b} = OF$, $\mathbf{c} = OG$, we say that the ordered triple $(\mathbf{a},\mathbf{b},\mathbf{c})$ is a right-handed triple of vectors if OE, OF, OG in this order form a right-handed triple of segments.

We now return to our construction of coordinates and require that OA, OB, OC in this order form a right-handed triple.

Denote by $\mathbf{i}$, $\mathbf{j}$, $\mathbf{k}$ the vectors represented by OA, OB, OC, respectively.

It is clear that these are all unit vectors. We say that $(\mathbf{i},\mathbf{j},\mathbf{k})$ is a *right-handed triple of mutually orthogonal unit vectors* (see Figure 10.14).

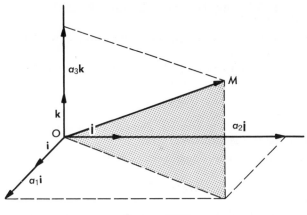

FIGURE 10.14

It is now clear from previous work that any vector $\mathbf{a}$ can be decomposed into the sum

$$\mathbf{a} = a_1\mathbf{i} + a_2\mathbf{j} + a_3\mathbf{k}.$$

If $\mathbf{a} = OM$, then (a_1,a_2,a_3) are called the rectangular coordinates of M.

It is easily verified that

$$\mathbf{i}\cdot\mathbf{j} = \mathbf{j}\cdot\mathbf{k} = \mathbf{k}\cdot\mathbf{i} = 0$$

and

$$\mathbf{i}^2 = \mathbf{j}^2 = \mathbf{k}^2 = 1,$$

where $\mathbf{i}^2$ means $\mathbf{i}\cdot\mathbf{i}$.

Furthermore we see that $\mathbf{a}\cdot\mathbf{i} = |\mathbf{a}|\cos(\mathbf{a},\mathbf{i}) = a_1, \mathbf{a}\cdot\mathbf{j} = a_2, \mathbf{a}\cdot\mathbf{k} = a_3$. Using these facts together with the distributive law for the scalar product, we have

$$\begin{aligned}
\mathbf{a}\cdot\mathbf{b} &= (a_1\mathbf{i} + a_2\mathbf{j} + a_3\mathbf{k})\cdot(b_1\mathbf{i} + b_2\mathbf{j} + b_3\mathbf{k}) \\
&= a_1\mathbf{i}\cdot(b_1\mathbf{i} + b_2\mathbf{j} + b_3\mathbf{k}) + a_2\mathbf{j}\cdot(b_1\mathbf{i} + b_2\mathbf{j} + b_3\mathbf{k}) \\
&\qquad\qquad\qquad\qquad\qquad\quad + a_3\mathbf{k}\cdot(b_1\mathbf{i} + b_2\mathbf{j} + b_3\mathbf{k}) \\
&= a_1b_1 + a_2b_2 + a_3b_3.
\end{aligned}$$

As a special case of this we have $|\mathbf{a}| = \sqrt{\mathbf{a}\cdot\mathbf{a}} = \sqrt{a_1^2 + a_2^2 + a_3^2}$. These results are of great importance in calculations with vectors.

EXERCISES

10.1. Assuming that the set of translations forms a group under the composition of functions, prove that the equipolence relation of Section 10.3 is an equivalence relation.

10.2. Let $\mathbf{a}$ be a fixed vector. We define a relation on the set of vectors as follows. We say $\mathbf{b} \rho \mathbf{c}$ if $\mathbf{b} = \mathbf{c}$ or if $\mathbf{b} \neq \mathbf{a}$, $\mathbf{c} \neq \mathbf{a}$, and $\mathbf{c}$ is parallel to the plane determined by $\mathbf{a}$ and $\mathbf{b}$. Is this an equivalence relation?

10.3. Let O, A, B be any three points in space. Write the vector AB in terms of the vectors OA and OB.

10.4. Prove that, in any quadrilateral, the mid-points of the sides are the vertices of a parallelogram.

10.5. Let O, A, B be three points in space. Find a vector from O to the mid-point of AB and write it in terms of OA and OB.

10.6. (a) Let ABC be any triangle with medians AD, BE, CF. Prove that $AD + BE + CF = \mathbf{0}$.

(b) Let ABC be any triangle. Show that there is a triangle with sides parallel to and equal to the medians of ABC.

10.7. If $\mathbf{a}$, $\mathbf{b}$, $\mathbf{c}$ are noncoplanar vectors and $x\mathbf{a} + y\mathbf{b} + z\mathbf{c} = \mathbf{0}$, prove that $x = y = z = 0$.

10.8. (a) Let $\mathbf{u}$, $\mathbf{v}$ be any vectors. Prove that $(\mathbf{u} + \mathbf{v}) \cdot (\mathbf{u} + \mathbf{v}) = \mathbf{u} \cdot \mathbf{u} + 2\mathbf{u} \cdot \mathbf{v} + \mathbf{v} \cdot \mathbf{v}$.

(b) Use the result from part (a) to prove the law of cosines for triangle ABC:

$$a^2 = b^2 + c^2 - 2bc \cos A.$$

10.9. If $\mathbf{a} = 2\mathbf{i} + 3\mathbf{j}$, $\mathbf{b} = \mathbf{i} + \mathbf{k}$, $\mathbf{c} = \mathbf{j} + 2\mathbf{k}$, and $\mathbf{v} = \mathbf{i} + \mathbf{j} + \mathbf{k}$, find x, y, z so that $\mathbf{v} = x\mathbf{a} + y\mathbf{b} + z\mathbf{c}$.

10.10. Prove that the diagonals of a rhombus are perpendicular to each other.

10.11. Find the following sums and differences:

(a) $(\mathbf{i} + 2\mathbf{j} - 3\mathbf{k}) + (2\mathbf{i} - \mathbf{j} + 5\mathbf{k})$.
(b) $(-\mathbf{i} - 5\mathbf{j} + 6\mathbf{k}) + (2\mathbf{i} + \mathbf{j} - \mathbf{k}) + (\mathbf{i} - 2\mathbf{j} + 6\mathbf{k})$.
(c) $(2\mathbf{i} + \mathbf{j} - 3\mathbf{k}) - (6\mathbf{i} + 2\mathbf{j} + \mathbf{k})$.
(d) $(\mathbf{i} + 2\mathbf{j} - 4\mathbf{k}) - (2\mathbf{i} + 5\mathbf{j} + 6\mathbf{k}) + (3\mathbf{i} - 5\mathbf{j} + 7\mathbf{k})$.

10.12. If $\mathbf{a} = \mathbf{i} + 2\mathbf{j} - 3\mathbf{k}$ and $\mathbf{b} = 2\mathbf{i} + \mathbf{j} - 2\mathbf{k}$, find unit vectors parallel to

(a) $\mathbf{a} + \mathbf{b}$.   (b) $\mathbf{a} - \mathbf{b}$.   (c) $2\mathbf{a} - 3\mathbf{b}$.

10.13. Find the magnitude of each of the following vectors:

(a) $\mathbf{a} = \mathbf{i} - 2\mathbf{j} + 4\mathbf{k}$.
(b) $\mathbf{b} = 2\mathbf{i} - \mathbf{j} + 3\mathbf{k}$.
(c) $\mathbf{c} = -3\mathbf{i} + 4\mathbf{j} - 5\mathbf{k}$.

10.14. Prove that the points $A(1,2,2)$, $B(3,3,4)$, $C(4,5,3)$, and $D(2,4,1)$ are the vertices of a parallelogram.

10.15. Given the points $A(2,1,4)$ and $B(3,6,1)$ express the vector AB in terms of $\mathbf{i}$, $\mathbf{j}$, $\mathbf{k}$. What is the magnitude of this vector?

10.16. Calculate the following scalar products

(a) $(\mathbf{i} - 2\mathbf{j} + 3\mathbf{k}) \cdot (2\mathbf{i} + \mathbf{j} - 4\mathbf{k})$.
(b) $(3\mathbf{i} - 2\mathbf{j} - 4\mathbf{k}) \cdot (-\mathbf{i} + 2\mathbf{j} + 6\mathbf{k})$.
(c) $(-2\mathbf{i} + 3\mathbf{j} + \mathbf{k}) \cdot (3\mathbf{i} - 2\mathbf{j} - \mathbf{k})$.

10.17. Find the unit vector that bisects the angle between $2\mathbf{i} + 3\mathbf{j} + \mathbf{k}$ and $\mathbf{i} + 2\mathbf{j} - 3\mathbf{k}$.

10.18. Find the value of x for which $x\mathbf{i} + 2\mathbf{j} + 3\mathbf{k}$ and $2\mathbf{i} - \mathbf{j} + 2\mathbf{k}$ are perpendicular.

10.19. Prove that there are no real values of x for which $x\mathbf{i} + 3\mathbf{j} + 4\mathbf{k}$ and $x\mathbf{i} - 2\mathbf{j} + 3\mathbf{k}$ are perpendicular.

10.20. Find the angles between the following pairs of vectors

(a) $\mathbf{i} + \mathbf{j}$, $\mathbf{j} + \mathbf{k}$.

(b) $\mathbf{i} + \mathbf{j} + \sqrt{2}\,\mathbf{k}$, $-2\mathbf{i} - 2\mathbf{j}$.

(c) $2\mathbf{i} + 2\mathbf{j}$, $2\mathbf{i} + \mathbf{j} - 2\mathbf{k}$.

10.21. Find all the angles of the triangle whose vertices are (1,2,3), (2,2,3), and (2,3,3).

10.22. Are the following sets of vectors coplanar?

(a) $\mathbf{i} + \mathbf{j} - \mathbf{k}$, $2\mathbf{i} + \mathbf{j} - 2\mathbf{k}$, $\mathbf{i} + 2\mathbf{j} + \mathbf{k}$.

(b) $\mathbf{i} + 2\mathbf{j} + \mathbf{k}$, $2\mathbf{i} + \mathbf{j} + 3\mathbf{k}$, $4\mathbf{i} + 5\mathbf{j} + 5\mathbf{k}$.

10.23. Are the following sets of points coplanar?

(a) (1,2,1), (3,1,2), (2,1,0), (2,3,2).

(b) (2,0,1), (3,1,0), (0,2,1), (1,3,0).

10.24. Let $\mathbf{a}$ be any vector. Let α, β, γ be the angles that $\mathbf{a}$ makes with $\mathbf{i}$, $\mathbf{j}$, $\mathbf{k}$, respectively. Prove that $\cos^2 \alpha + \cos^2 \beta + \cos^2 \gamma = 1$.

10.9   The vector product

We shall now define a new operation on the set of vectors, a function

$$f : V \times V \to V.$$

Since this operation associates a vector with each ordered pair of vectors, it is called the *vector product*. We write $f(\mathbf{a},\mathbf{b}) = \mathbf{a} \times \mathbf{b}$. In keeping with this notation we often refer to the operation as the *cross product*. The vector $\mathbf{a} \times \mathbf{b}$ is defined as follows:

1. $|\mathbf{a} \times \mathbf{b}| = |\mathbf{a}||\mathbf{b}||\sin(\mathbf{a},\mathbf{b})|$.

2. $\mathbf{a} \times \mathbf{b}$ is orthogonal to any plane determined by $\mathbf{a}$ and $\mathbf{b}$, that is, by their representatives.

3. $(\mathbf{a},\mathbf{b},\mathbf{a} \times \mathbf{b})$ is a right-handed triple.

From this definition it is obvious that

$$\mathbf{a} \times \mathbf{a} = 0, \qquad \mathbf{a} \times \mathbf{b} = -(\mathbf{b} \times \mathbf{a}),$$

and that, if $(\mathbf{i},\mathbf{j},\mathbf{k})$ is a right-handed triple of mutually orthogonal unit vectors, then

$$\mathbf{i} \times \mathbf{j} = \mathbf{k}, \qquad \mathbf{j} \times \mathbf{k} = \mathbf{i}, \qquad \mathbf{k} \times \mathbf{i} = \mathbf{j},$$

and

$$\mathbf{i} \times \mathbf{i} = \mathbf{j} \times \mathbf{j} = \mathbf{k} \times \mathbf{k} = 0.$$

An examination of the vector product and Figure 10.15, shows that $|\mathbf{a} \times \mathbf{b}|$ is the area of a parallelogram whose edges are representatives of $\mathbf{a}$ and $\mathbf{b}$.

It is also easily shown that $x(\mathbf{a} \times \mathbf{b}) = (x\mathbf{a}) \times \mathbf{b} = \mathbf{a} \times (x\mathbf{b})$.

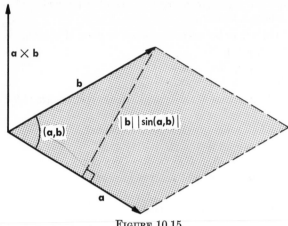

FIGURE 10.15

10.10　The triple scalar product

We can now combine the scalar product and vector product to define a new operation called the *triple scalar product*. This is a function

$$f : V \times V \times V \to R,$$

which associates a real number with each triple of vectors (a,b,c). We denote the value $f(a,b,c)$ by $[a,b,c]$ and define it as $[a,b,c] = (a \times b) \cdot c$.

For a geometric interpretation of the triple scalar product we refer to Figure 10.16. We know that the volume of the parallelepiped is the product of the height $C''C$ with the area of the base. We saw in the last section that the area of the base is $|a \times b|$. It is clear from the figure that $C''C = OC'$ and also that the height is equal to $|c||\cos (c, a \times b)|$. Therefore the volume is $|a \times b||c||\cos (c, a \times b)|$. But

$$|[a,b,c]| = |(a \times b) \cdot c| = |a \times b||c||\cos (a \times b,c)|.$$

Therefore the absolute value of the triple scalar product is equal to the volume of the parallelepiped determined by the three vectors.

A further examination of Figure 10.16 shows that, if (a,b,c) is a right-handed triple, then the angle between $a \times b$ and c is an acute angle and hence $[a,b,c] = (a \times b) \cdot c \geq 0$. Similarly, if (a,b,c) is a left-handed triple, then $[a,b,c] \leq 0$.

If a, b, c are coplanar, that is, if they have a set of representatives lying in the same plane, then $[a,b,c] = 0$. This is easily seen because, in this case, the parallelepiped has degenerated to a region of the plane and hence has zero volume. The converse is also true; if a, b, c are nonzero vectors and $[a,b,c] = 0$, then a, b, c are coplanar.

We now want to show that $(a \times b) \cdot c = a \cdot (b \times c)$. As a first step we

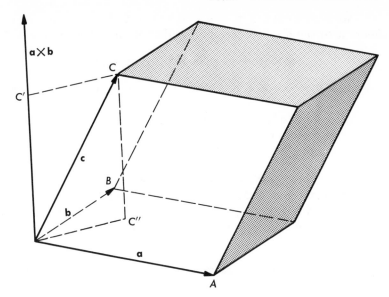

FIGURE 10.16

observe that $a \cdot (b \times c) = (b \times c) \cdot a$, since the dot product is commutative. The triples (a,b,c) and (b,c,a) determine the same parallelepiped and therefore $|[a,b,c]| = |[b,c,a]|$. Also the triples (a,b,c) and (b,c,a) are either both right-handed or both left-handed. Therefore $[a,b,c] = [b,c,a] = a \cdot (b \times c)$.

From this we see that

$$a \cdot (b \times c) = (a \times b) \cdot c = (b \times c) \cdot a = b \cdot (c \times a)$$
$$= (c \times a) \cdot b = c \cdot (a \times b) = -c \cdot (b \times a)$$
$$= -(b \times a) \cdot c = -b \cdot (a \times c) = -(a \times c) \cdot b = -a \cdot (c \times b)$$
$$= -(c \times b) \cdot a.$$

10.11 Vector product in rectangular coordinates

We can now make use of the triple scalar product to prove that the vector product is distributive, that is, $a \times (b + c) = (a \times b) + (a \times c)$. Consider the vector $v = a \times (b + c) - (a \times b) - (a \times c)$. Let u be any vector. Then

$$u \cdot v = u \cdot \{a \times (b + c)\} - u \cdot (a \times b) - u \cdot (a \times c).$$

By the properties of scalar triple products this becomes

$$u \cdot v = (u \times a) \cdot (b + c) - (u \times a) \cdot b - (u \times a) \cdot c$$
$$= (u \times a) \cdot (b + c) - (u \times a) \cdot (b + c)$$
$$= 0.$$

From this we must have $\mathbf{u} \perp \mathbf{v}$, or $\mathbf{u} = \mathbf{0}$, or $\mathbf{v} = \mathbf{0}$. Since $\mathbf{u}$ is any vector, we can choose it so the first two possibilities do not hold. Therefore $\mathbf{v} = \mathbf{0}$ and

$$\mathbf{a} \times (\mathbf{b} + \mathbf{c}) = (\mathbf{a} \times \mathbf{b}) + (\mathbf{a} \times \mathbf{c}).$$

Since $\mathbf{a} \times \mathbf{b} = -\mathbf{b} \times \mathbf{a}$, it is clear that the right distributive law holds also.

These distributive laws give us a convenient way to calculate the vector product of two vectors that are known in terms of the vectors $\mathbf{i}$, $\mathbf{j}$, $\mathbf{k}$ of the rectangular coordinate system. We have

$$\begin{aligned} \mathbf{a} \times \mathbf{b} &= (a_1\mathbf{i} + a_2\mathbf{j} + a_3\mathbf{k}) \times (b_1\mathbf{i} + b_2\mathbf{j} + b_3\mathbf{k}) \\ &= a_1b_1\mathbf{i} \times \mathbf{i} + a_1b_2\mathbf{i} \times \mathbf{j} + a_1b_3\mathbf{i} \times \mathbf{k} + a_2b_1\mathbf{j} \times \mathbf{i} \\ &\quad + a_2b_2\mathbf{j} \times \mathbf{j} + a_2b_3\mathbf{j} \times \mathbf{k} + a_3b_1\mathbf{k} \times \mathbf{i} + a_3b_2\mathbf{k} \times \mathbf{j} + a_3b_3\mathbf{k} \times \mathbf{k} \\ &= (a_1b_2 - a_2b_1)\mathbf{k} - (a_1b_3 - a_3b_1)\mathbf{j} + (a_2b_3 - a_3b_2)\mathbf{i}, \end{aligned}$$

since $\mathbf{i} \times \mathbf{i} = \mathbf{0}$, $\mathbf{i} \times \mathbf{j} = \mathbf{k}$, etc.

A simple form in which to carry out these calculations and also the calculations involved in the scalar triple product will be given in the next sections.

10.12   Determinants

We can combine the results of the last two sections to obtain a formula for the triple scalar product, that is, for the volume of a parallelepiped. This formula can be written in the form of a *determinant*. In fact, we shall use the scalar triple product to define the determinant function and to develop its properties, which are useful in performing calculations. Determinants are of considerable importance in many other contexts. We shall use them again when we study the intersection of planes and in the solution of linear equations. The reader will encounter other applications as he continues his study of mathematics.

Consider the vectors

$$\begin{aligned} \mathbf{a} &= a_1\mathbf{i} + a_2\mathbf{j} + a_3\mathbf{k}, \\ \mathbf{b} &= b_1\mathbf{i} + b_2\mathbf{j} + b_3\mathbf{k}, \\ \mathbf{c} &= c_1\mathbf{i} + c_2\mathbf{j} + c_3\mathbf{k}. \end{aligned}$$

We have seen that the volume of the parallelepiped with these vectors as adjacent edges is $|[\mathbf{a},\mathbf{b},\mathbf{c}]| = |\mathbf{a} \cdot (\mathbf{b} \times \mathbf{c})|$.
Also

$$\mathbf{b} \times \mathbf{c} = (b_2c_3 - b_3c_2)\mathbf{i} - (b_1c_3 - b_3c_1)\mathbf{j} + (b_1c_2 - b_2c_1)\mathbf{k},$$

and hence

$$[\mathbf{a},\mathbf{b},\mathbf{c}] = a_1(b_2c_3 - b_3c_2) - a_2(b_1c_3 - b_3c_1) + a_3(b_1c_2 - b_2c_1).$$

As a first step in simplifying this formula, we agree to write

$$\begin{vmatrix} b_2 & b_3 \\ c_2 & c_3 \end{vmatrix} \quad \text{or} \quad \det \begin{bmatrix} b_2 & b_3 \\ c_2 & c_3 \end{bmatrix}$$

to represent $b_2 c_3 - c_2 b_3$. We call this a *second-order determinant*.

The reader is warned against confusing this second-order determinant with the 2×2 matrix

$$\begin{bmatrix} b_2 & b_3 \\ c_2 & c_3 \end{bmatrix}.$$

The determinant is a single real number associated with the matrix. That is, the determinant is a function $\det: M \to R$ where M is the set of square matrices over the real numbers. The second notation suggested above for the determinant emphasizes this functional character. Our definition of M indicates that the determinant function can be defined for any square matrix. We shall use it only for 2×2 and 3×3 matrices.

We define a *third-order determinant* as

$$\begin{vmatrix} a_1 & a_2 & a_3 \\ b_1 & b_2 & b_3 \\ c_1 & c_2 & c_3 \end{vmatrix} = a_1 \begin{vmatrix} b_2 & b_3 \\ c_2 & c_3 \end{vmatrix} - a_2 \begin{vmatrix} b_1 & b_3 \\ c_1 & c_3 \end{vmatrix} + a_3 \begin{vmatrix} b_1 & b_2 \\ c_1 & c_2 \end{vmatrix}.$$

We also denote this determinant by

$$\det \begin{bmatrix} a_1 & a_2 & a_3 \\ b_1 & b_2 & b_3 \\ c_1 & c_2 & c_3 \end{bmatrix}.$$

We call the reader's attention to the minus sign before the second term, since it is a frequent source of error in calculations with determinants.

The scalar triple product can now be written in the convenient form

$$[\mathbf{a},\mathbf{b},\mathbf{c}] = \begin{vmatrix} a_1 & a_2 & a_3 \\ b_1 & b_2 & b_3 \\ c_1 & c_2 & c_3 \end{vmatrix}.$$

EXAMPLE 10.4

If $\mathbf{a} = 2\mathbf{i} - \mathbf{j} + 3\mathbf{k}$, $\mathbf{b} = \mathbf{i} + 2\mathbf{j} - 2\mathbf{k}$, and $\mathbf{c} = 3\mathbf{i} - 2\mathbf{j} + \mathbf{k}$, calculate $[\mathbf{a},\mathbf{b},\mathbf{c}]$.

We have

$$[\mathbf{a},\mathbf{b},\mathbf{c}] = \det \begin{bmatrix} 2 & -1 & 3 \\ 1 & 2 & -2 \\ 3 & -2 & 1 \end{bmatrix}$$

$$= 2 \begin{vmatrix} 2 & -2 \\ -2 & 1 \end{vmatrix} - (-1) \begin{vmatrix} 1 & -2 \\ 3 & 1 \end{vmatrix} + 3 \begin{vmatrix} 1 & 2 \\ 3 & -2 \end{vmatrix}$$

$$= 2(2 - 4) + 1(1 + 6) + 3(-2 - 6)$$

$$= -21.$$

In this example we have used the definition of second- and third-order determinants as our means of calculation. This can always be done, but it is not always the easiest way to evaluate a third-order determinant. We shall now develop a number of properties of determinants that can be used to simplify the calculations. We shall prove the properties only in the case of third-order determinants. Several proofs depend on the properties of the scalar triple product. The reader can easily verify that these properties are also true for second-order determinants.

Property 1

If two rows of a determinant are interchanged, the sign of the determinant is changed.

Proof

This follows from the fact that, if two vectors in [a,b,c] are interchanged, the sign of the triple product is changed. •

Property 2

A third-order determinant can be evaluated in terms of its second or third row:

$$
\begin{vmatrix} a_1 & a_2 & a_3 \\ b_1 & b_2 & b_3 \\ c_1 & c_2 & c_3 \end{vmatrix} = -b_1 \begin{vmatrix} a_2 & a_3 \\ c_2 & c_3 \end{vmatrix} + b_2 \begin{vmatrix} a_1 & a_3 \\ c_1 & c_3 \end{vmatrix} - b_3 \begin{vmatrix} a_1 & a_2 \\ c_1 & c_2 \end{vmatrix}
$$
$$
= c_1 \begin{vmatrix} a_2 & a_3 \\ b_2 & b_3 \end{vmatrix} - c_2 \begin{vmatrix} a_1 & a_3 \\ b_1 & b_3 \end{vmatrix} + c_3 \begin{vmatrix} a_1 & a_2 \\ b_1 & b_2 \end{vmatrix}.
$$

Proof

From Property 1 we obtain

$$
\begin{vmatrix} a_1 & a_2 & a_3 \\ b_1 & b_2 & b_3 \\ c_1 & c_2 & c_3 \end{vmatrix} = - \begin{vmatrix} b_1 & b_2 & b_3 \\ a_1 & a_2 & a_3 \\ c_1 & c_2 & c_3 \end{vmatrix}
$$
$$
= -b_1 \begin{vmatrix} a_2 & a_3 \\ c_2 & c_3 \end{vmatrix} + b_2 \begin{vmatrix} a_1 & a_3 \\ c_1 & c_3 \end{vmatrix} - b_3 \begin{vmatrix} a_1 & a_2 \\ c_1 & c_2 \end{vmatrix}.
$$

Also

$$
\begin{vmatrix} a_1 & a_2 & a_3 \\ b_1 & b_2 & b_3 \\ c_1 & c_2 & c_3 \end{vmatrix} = - \begin{vmatrix} c_1 & c_2 & c_3 \\ b_1 & b_2 & b_3 \\ a_1 & a_2 & a_3 \end{vmatrix} = \begin{vmatrix} c_1 & c_2 & c_3 \\ a_1 & a_2 & a_3 \\ b_1 & b_2 & b_3 \end{vmatrix}
$$
$$
= c_1 \begin{vmatrix} a_2 & a_3 \\ b_2 & b_3 \end{vmatrix} - c_2 \begin{vmatrix} a_1 & a_3 \\ b_1 & b_3 \end{vmatrix} + c_3 \begin{vmatrix} a_1 & a_2 \\ b_1 & b_2 \end{vmatrix}. •
$$

In view of this property we can evaluate or, as we say, *expand* a determinant in terms of any of its rows. We observe that in any expansion each term is the product of three factors: ± 1, the element from the row, and a second-order determinant. If we are performing the expansion in terms of the ith row and are working with the element from the jth column, the first factor is $(-1)^{i+j}$. The third factor in this case is the second-order determinant obtained by deleting the ith row and the jth column from the original third-order determinant.

EXAMPLE 10.5

$$\begin{vmatrix} 1 & 2 & 1 \\ 3 & 1 & 0 \\ 2 & 1 & 1 \end{vmatrix} = -3 \begin{vmatrix} 2 & 1 \\ 1 & 1 \end{vmatrix} + 1 \begin{vmatrix} 1 & 1 \\ 2 & 1 \end{vmatrix} - 0 \begin{vmatrix} 1 & 2 \\ 2 & 1 \end{vmatrix}$$
$$= -3(2 - 1) + 1(1 - 2) - 0(1 - 4) = -4.$$

Property 3

If all the elements of one row of a determinant are zero, the determinant is zero.

Proof

In this case one of the vectors in [a,b,c] is the zero vector and hence the volume must be zero. •

Property 4

If the elements of one row of a determinant can be obtained by multiplying by a constant the corresponding elements of another row, then the determinant is zero.

Proof

This condition states that two of the vectors in [a,b,c] are collinear, and hence the volume is zero. •

EXAMPLE 10.6

$$\begin{vmatrix} 4 & 8 & 4 \\ 3 & 6 & 3 \\ 1 & 5 & 2 \end{vmatrix} = \begin{vmatrix} 4 & 8 & 4 \\ \tfrac{3}{4}(4) & \tfrac{3}{4}(8) & \tfrac{3}{4}(4) \\ 1 & 5 & 2 \end{vmatrix} = 0.$$

Property 5

If all the elements of one row of a determinant are multiplied by a constant, the determinant is multiplied by the same constant.

Proof

Consider the determinants corresponding to [a,b,c] and to [ka,b,c]. Then $[ka,b,c] = (ka) \cdot (b \times c) = k\{a \cdot (b \times c)\} = k[a,b,c]$. A similar proof holds if the second or third row is multiplied by k. •

EXAMPLE 10.7

$$\begin{vmatrix} 8 & 4 & 8 \\ 1 & 3 & 1 \\ 2 & 0 & 3 \end{vmatrix} = 4 \begin{vmatrix} 2 & 1 & 2 \\ 1 & 3 & 1 \\ 2 & 0 & 3 \end{vmatrix}$$

$$= 4 \left\{ 2 \begin{vmatrix} 1 & 2 \\ 3 & 1 \end{vmatrix} - 0 \begin{vmatrix} 2 & 2 \\ 1 & 1 \end{vmatrix} + 3 \begin{vmatrix} 2 & 1 \\ 1 & 3 \end{vmatrix} \right\}$$

$$= 4\{2(1-6) - 0 \cdot 0 + 3(6-1)\}$$

$$= 4(-10+15) = 20.$$

Property 6

If to each element of the ith row of a determinant there is added a constant multiple of the corresponding element in the jth row, the determinant is unchanged. In particular

$$\begin{vmatrix} a_1 & a_2 & a_3 \\ b_1 & b_2 & b_3 \\ c_1 & c_2 & c_3 \end{vmatrix} = \begin{vmatrix} a_1 & a_2 & a_3 \\ b_1 & b_2 & b_3 \\ c_1 + ka_1 & c_2 + ka_2 & c_3 + ka_3 \end{vmatrix}.$$

Proof

For this particular case it is sufficient to prove that

$$[a,b,c] = [a,b,c + ka].$$

By making use of the definition of the triple scalar product we obtain

$$\begin{aligned} [a,b,c + ka] &= (a \times b) \cdot (c + ka) \\ &= (a \times b) \cdot c + k(a \times b) \cdot a \\ &= [a,b,c] + k[a,b,a] \\ &= [a,b,c] \end{aligned}$$

since $[a,b,a] = 0$.

The proofs for the other cases are similar. •

This property can be used to obtain a row containing a zero, and hence a simplified expansion.

EXAMPLE 10.8

Expand

$$\begin{vmatrix} 2 & 1 & 4 \\ 3 & 2 & 2 \\ 4 & 2 & 3 \end{vmatrix}.$$

We add -2 times the first row to the second to get

$$\begin{vmatrix} 2 & 1 & 4 \\ -1 & 0 & -6 \\ 4 & 2 & 3 \end{vmatrix} = (-1)^{2+1}(-1)\begin{vmatrix} 1 & 4 \\ 2 & 3 \end{vmatrix} + (-1)^{2+3}(-6)\begin{vmatrix} 2 & 1 \\ 4 & 2 \end{vmatrix}$$

$$= 1(3 - 8) + 6(0) = -5.$$

Property 7

If corresponding rows and columns of a determinant are interchanged, the determinant is unchanged, that is,

$$\begin{vmatrix} a_1 & a_2 & a_3 \\ b_1 & b_2 & b_3 \\ c_1 & c_2 & c_3 \end{vmatrix} = \begin{vmatrix} a_1 & b_1 & c_1 \\ a_2 & b_2 & c_2 \\ a_3 & b_3 & c_3 \end{vmatrix}.$$

Proof

We expand the determinant and rearrange the terms as follows:

$$\begin{vmatrix} a_1 & a_2 & a_3 \\ b_1 & b_2 & b_3 \\ c_1 & c_2 & c_3 \end{vmatrix} = a_1\begin{vmatrix} b_2 & b_3 \\ c_2 & c_3 \end{vmatrix} - a_2\begin{vmatrix} b_1 & b_3 \\ c_1 & c_3 \end{vmatrix} + a_3\begin{vmatrix} b_1 & b_2 \\ c_1 & c_2 \end{vmatrix}$$

$$= a_1(b_2c_3 - b_3c_2) - a_2(b_1c_3 - b_3c_1) + a_3(b_1c_2 - b_2c_1)$$

$$= a_1\begin{vmatrix} b_2 & c_2 \\ b_3 & c_3 \end{vmatrix} - b_1(a_2c_3 - a_3c_2) + c_1(a_2b_3 - a_3b_2)$$

$$= a_1\begin{vmatrix} b_2 & c_2 \\ b_3 & c_3 \end{vmatrix} - b_1\begin{vmatrix} a_2 & c_2 \\ a_3 & c_3 \end{vmatrix} + c_1\begin{vmatrix} a_2 & b_2 \\ a_3 & b_3 \end{vmatrix}$$

$$= \begin{vmatrix} a_1 & b_1 & c_1 \\ a_2 & b_2 & c_2 \\ a_3 & b_3 & c_3 \end{vmatrix}. \quad \bullet$$

By means of Property 7 we obtain immediately a new set of properties by replacing "row" by "column" in each property we have proved.

We shall show by examples the use of these properties in expanding a determinant. We have seen that the presence of zeros simplifies our task. We can apply Property 6 and the corresponding property for columns in order to obtain zeros.

EXAMPLE   10.9

Expand

$$\begin{vmatrix} 1 & 2 & 1 \\ 3 & 1 & 0 \\ 2 & 1 & 1 \end{vmatrix}.$$

We shall make use of the zero that is present and obtain another in the same column by adding to the first row -1 times the third row. This gives

$$\begin{vmatrix} -1 & 1 & 0 \\ 3 & 1 & 0 \\ 2 & 1 & 1 \end{vmatrix} = (-1)^{3+3}(1) \begin{vmatrix} -1 & 1 \\ 3 & 1 \end{vmatrix} = 1(-1-3) = -4.$$

The factor $(-1)^{3+3}$ is obtained from the fact that we are working with the element in the third row and the third column.

EXAMPLE   10.10

Expand

$$\begin{vmatrix} 3 & 4 & 5 \\ 4 & 6 & 7 \\ 3 & 2 & 3 \end{vmatrix}.$$

To obtain zeros it is convenient to start with an element that is a factor of all the elements in its row or of all the elements in its column. In our case the element in the third row and second column is a factor of all the elements in the second column. First we add -2 times the third row to the first row:

$$\begin{vmatrix} -3 & 0 & -1 \\ 4 & 6 & 7 \\ 3 & 2 & 3 \end{vmatrix}.$$

Then we add -3 times the third row to the second row:

$$\begin{vmatrix} -3 & 0 & -1 \\ -5 & 0 & -2 \\ 3 & 2 & 3 \end{vmatrix}.$$

If we now expand the determinant in terms of the second column, we have only one nonzero term, corresponding to the element in the third row and second column. Thus the determinant is

$$(-1)^{3+2}(2) \begin{vmatrix} -3 & -1 \\ -5 & -2 \end{vmatrix} = -2(6-5) = -2.$$

10.13   The vector product as a determinant

In Section 10.11 we saw that, for $\mathbf{a} = a_1\mathbf{i} + a_2\mathbf{j} + a_3\mathbf{k}$ and $\mathbf{b} = b_1\mathbf{i} + b_2\mathbf{j} + b_3\mathbf{k}$, we have $\mathbf{a} \times \mathbf{b} = (a_2b_3 - a_3b_2)\mathbf{i} - (a_1b_3 - a_3b_1)\mathbf{j} + (a_1b_2 - a_2b_1)\mathbf{k}$. If we ignore for the moment the distinction between real numbers and vectors we observe that this has the form

$$\mathbf{a} \times \mathbf{b} = \begin{vmatrix} \mathbf{i} & \mathbf{j} & \mathbf{k} \\ a_1 & a_2 & a_3 \\ b_1 & b_2 & b_3 \end{vmatrix}.$$

In our study of determinants so far the elements have all been real numbers. Here we have one row of vectors. The properties of determinants we have developed are not all valid in this case; for instance, it is meaningless to add the second row to the first. Despite these limitations it is convenient to remember and calculate the cross product as a symbolic determinant. The reader is advised to expand this determinant in terms of its first row without attempting to make any use of any of the properties of determinants we have developed.

EXAMPLE   10.11

$$(2\mathbf{i} + \mathbf{j} - 3\mathbf{k}) \times (\mathbf{i} - 2\mathbf{j} + \mathbf{k}) = \begin{vmatrix} \mathbf{i} & \mathbf{j} & \mathbf{k} \\ 2 & 1 & -3 \\ 1 & -2 & 1 \end{vmatrix}$$
$$= \mathbf{i}(1 - 6) - \mathbf{j}(2 + 3) + \mathbf{k}(-4 - 1)$$
$$= -5\mathbf{i} - 5\mathbf{j} - 5\mathbf{k}.$$

EXERCISES

10.25. Prove that $x(\mathbf{a} \times \mathbf{b}) = (x\mathbf{a}) \times \mathbf{b} = \mathbf{a} \times (x\mathbf{b})$ for all $x \in R$, $\mathbf{a} \in V$, $\mathbf{b} \in V$.

10.26. Prove that $\mathbf{a} \times \mathbf{b} = -\mathbf{b} \times \mathbf{a}$ for all $\mathbf{a} \in V$, $\mathbf{b} \in V$.

10.27. Prove that, if $\mathbf{a} \cdot \mathbf{b} = 0$ and $\mathbf{a} \times \mathbf{b} = \mathbf{0}$, then either $\mathbf{a} = \mathbf{0}$ or $\mathbf{b} = \mathbf{0}$.

10.28. Prove that

$$(\mathbf{a} \times \mathbf{b}) \cdot (\mathbf{a} \times \mathbf{b}) = \begin{vmatrix} \mathbf{a} \cdot \mathbf{a} & \mathbf{a} \cdot \mathbf{b} \\ \mathbf{a} \cdot \mathbf{b} & \mathbf{b} \cdot \mathbf{b} \end{vmatrix}$$

for all $\mathbf{a} \in V$, $\mathbf{b} \in V$.

10.29. Show that Properties 1 to 7 in Section 10.12 are valid for all second-order determinants.

10.30. State the properties in terms of columns that are analogous to Properties 1 to 6 for rows in Section 10.12.

10.31. Evaluate the following without expanding any determinants.

$$\begin{vmatrix} 2 & 1 & 0 \\ 3 & 3 & 1 \\ 2 & 0 & 1 \end{vmatrix} + \begin{vmatrix} 2 & 1 & 0 \\ 3 & 3 & 1 \\ 1 & 2 & 0 \end{vmatrix} + \begin{vmatrix} 1 & 2 & 1 \\ 3 & 3 & 1 \\ 3 & 2 & 1 \end{vmatrix}.$$

10.32. Evaluate the following determinants:

(a) $\begin{vmatrix} 1 & 3 & 2 \\ 2 & 1 & 4 \\ 3 & 1 & 0 \end{vmatrix}.$

(b) $\begin{vmatrix} 1 & 1 & 0 \\ 2 & 4 & 1 \\ 3 & 6 & 1 \end{vmatrix}.$

(c) $\begin{vmatrix} 2 & 4 & 8 \\ 6 & 3 & 2 \\ 4 & 1 & 3 \end{vmatrix}.$

(d) $\begin{vmatrix} 2 & 3 & 1 \\ 4 & 0 & 2 \\ 6 & 1 & 3 \end{vmatrix}.$

10.33. Without expanding any of the determinants, state which of the following are equal to each other.

(a) $\det \begin{bmatrix} a_1 & a_2 & a_3 \\ b_1 & b_2 & b_3 \\ c_1 & c_2 & c_3 \end{bmatrix}.$

(b) $\det \begin{bmatrix} -a_1 & a_2 & -a_3 \\ b_1 & -b_2 & b_3 \\ c_1 & -c_2 & c_3 \end{bmatrix}.$

(c) $\det \begin{bmatrix} 3a_1 & 3a_2 & 3a_3 \\ b_1 & b_2 & b_3 \\ c_1 & c_2 & c_3 \end{bmatrix}.$

(d) $\det \begin{bmatrix} a_1 + b_1 & a_2 + b_2 & a_3 + b_3 \\ b_1 & b_2 & b_3 \\ c_1 & c_2 & c_3 \end{bmatrix}.$

10.34. Find the volume of the parallelepiped with one vertex at $(1,2,1)$ and three adjacent vertices at $(1,3,2)$, $(4,1,3)$, and $(2,1,6)$.

10.35. Calculate $[\mathbf{a},\mathbf{b},\mathbf{c}]$, where

(a) $\mathbf{a} = \mathbf{i} + 2\mathbf{j} - 3\mathbf{k}$, $\mathbf{b} = 2\mathbf{i} + \mathbf{j} - \mathbf{k}$, $\mathbf{c} = -\mathbf{i} + \mathbf{j} + 3\mathbf{k}$.
(b) $\mathbf{a} = 2\mathbf{i} - \mathbf{j} + \mathbf{k}$, $\mathbf{b} = 3\mathbf{i} - \mathbf{j} + \mathbf{k}$, $\mathbf{c} = \mathbf{i} + 2\mathbf{j} - 3\mathbf{k}$.

10.36. Calculate the following vector products:

(a) $(\mathbf{i} + 2\mathbf{j} + 3\mathbf{k}) \times (2\mathbf{i} - \mathbf{j} + \mathbf{k})$.
(b) $(-\mathbf{i} + 3\mathbf{j} + 4\mathbf{k}) \times (3\mathbf{i} - 2\mathbf{j} + 2\mathbf{k})$.
(c) $(3\mathbf{i} - 2\mathbf{j} - \mathbf{k}) \times (-\mathbf{i} + 6\mathbf{j} - 3\mathbf{k})$.

10.37. Repeat Exercise 10.22 but use a different method.

10.38. Repeat Exercise 10.23 but use a different method.

10.39. Find the area of the parallelogram with vertices $A(1,2,2)$, $B(3,3,4)$, $C(4,5,3)$, $D(2,4,1)$.

10.40. Find the area of the triangle with vertices $A(1,3,1)$, $B(2,0,3)$, $C(4,1,2)$.

10.41. Find a unit vector perpendicular to the vectors $\mathbf{a} = \mathbf{i} - 3\mathbf{j} + 2\mathbf{k}$ and $\mathbf{b} = 2\mathbf{i} - \mathbf{j} + 3\mathbf{k}$.

10.42. Compute $\mathbf{a} \cdot \mathbf{b}$, $\mathbf{b} \cdot \mathbf{c}$, $\mathbf{a} \times \mathbf{b}$, $\mathbf{a} \times \mathbf{c}$, $[\mathbf{a},\mathbf{b},\mathbf{c}]$, $(\mathbf{a} \times \mathbf{b}) \times (\mathbf{a} \times \mathbf{c})$, and $(\mathbf{a} \times \mathbf{b}) \cdot (\mathbf{a} \times \mathbf{c})$, where $\mathbf{a} = \mathbf{i} + \mathbf{j} - 2\mathbf{k}$, $\mathbf{b} = 2\mathbf{i} - \mathbf{j} + 3\mathbf{k}$, and $\mathbf{c} = \mathbf{i} + 2\mathbf{j} + \mathbf{k}$.

10.43. If $\mathbf{a} = \mathbf{i} - 2\mathbf{j} + 3\mathbf{k}$, $\mathbf{b} = 2\mathbf{i} + 3\mathbf{j} - \mathbf{k}$, and $\mathbf{c} = -\mathbf{i} + 2\mathbf{j} - 2\mathbf{k}$, calculate $|\mathbf{c}|$, $\mathbf{a} \cdot \mathbf{b}$, $\mathbf{b} \times \mathbf{c}$, $[\mathbf{a},\mathbf{b},\mathbf{c}]$, and the angle between $\mathbf{a}$ and $\mathbf{b}$.

10.44. Prove that the vectors $\mathbf{a} = (\frac{1}{3})\mathbf{i} - (\frac{2}{3})\mathbf{j} + (\frac{2}{3})\mathbf{k}$, $\mathbf{b} = (\frac{2}{3})\mathbf{i} + (\frac{2}{3})\mathbf{j} + (\frac{1}{3})\mathbf{k}$, and $\mathbf{c} = (-\frac{2}{3})\mathbf{i} + (\frac{1}{3})\mathbf{j} + (\frac{2}{3})\mathbf{k}$ form a right-handed triple of mutually orthogonal unit vectors.

10.45. Is the vector (cross) product associative? Give reasons for your answer.

10.46. Which of the following operations are meaningless?

(a) $\mathbf{a} \cdot (\mathbf{b} \times \mathbf{c})$.

(b) $(\mathbf{a} \cdot \mathbf{b}) \times \mathbf{c}$.

(c) $\mathbf{a} \times \mathbf{b} \times \mathbf{c}$.

(d) $(\mathbf{a} \times \mathbf{b}) \cdot (\mathbf{b} \times \mathbf{c})$.

(e) $\dfrac{\mathbf{a} \times \mathbf{b}}{\mathbf{a} \cdot \mathbf{b}}$.

(f) $\dfrac{\mathbf{a} \cdot \mathbf{b}}{\mathbf{a} \times \mathbf{b}}$.

10.47. (a) Show that the function $f: V \to V$, where $f(a_1\mathbf{i} + a_2\mathbf{j} + a_3\mathbf{k}) = a_2\mathbf{i} + a_1\mathbf{j} + a_3\mathbf{k}$, is a group isomorphism of $(V, +)$ onto itself.

(b) Does f preserve the cross product? Give reasons for your answer.

10.48. The following question appeared on an examination. "Select the one correct statement (a), (b), or (c) to complete the statement: '$\mathbf{a}$ $\mathbf{b}$ if and only if $\cdot$ $\cdot$ $\cdot$'

(a) $\mathbf{a} \cdot \mathbf{b} = 0$,

(b) $\mathbf{a} \times \mathbf{b} = \mathbf{0}$,

(c) $\mathbf{a} = k\mathbf{b}$."

It is clear that a symbol was omitted between $\mathbf{a}$ and $\mathbf{b}$. What was the symbol meant to be?

11

Lines and Planes

11.1 Rectangular coordinate system

We can now apply the vector algebra we have developed to the solution of certain geometric problems. As a first step we recall what we did in setting up the system of rectangular coordinates. We chose a point, which we call the origin and denote by O, and three mutually orthogonal unit segments that form a right-handed system. The segments are representatives of vectors denoted $\mathbf{i}$, $\mathbf{j}$, $\mathbf{k}$. These vectors have the following important properties

1. $\mathbf{i}^2 = \mathbf{j}^2 = \mathbf{k}^2 = 1$ (unit vectors).
2. $\mathbf{i} \cdot \mathbf{j} = \mathbf{j} \cdot \mathbf{k} = \mathbf{k} \cdot \mathbf{i} = 0$ (mutually orthogonal).
3. $\mathbf{i} \times \mathbf{j} = \mathbf{k}$, $\mathbf{j} \times \mathbf{k} = \mathbf{i}$, $\mathbf{k} \times \mathbf{i} = \mathbf{j}$ (right handed).

We denote by OX, OY, OZ, respectively, the lines from O in which the representatives of $\mathbf{i}$, $\mathbf{j}$, $\mathbf{k}$ lie. These lines are called, respectively, the *x axis*, *y axis*, and *z axis*. We call the plane containing the x axis and the y axis the *xy plane*. Similarly the *yz plane* contains the y axis and z axis, and the *xz plane* contains the x axis and z axis.

We can now study any point A in space in terms of this coordinate system. We know that A determines a unique directed segment OA, which represents a vector $\mathbf{a}$. We also know that $\mathbf{a}$ can be represented in terms of $\mathbf{i}$, $\mathbf{j}$, $\mathbf{k}$ as $\mathbf{a} = x\mathbf{i} + y\mathbf{j} + z\mathbf{k}$. We call the ordered triple (x,y,z) the *coordinates* of A in the system O, $\mathbf{i}$, $\mathbf{j}$, $\mathbf{k}$.

Conversely, if an ordered triple of real numbers (x,y,z) is given, there is a unique point A such that $OA = x\mathbf{i} + y\mathbf{j} + z\mathbf{k}$. This method of representing points by ordered triples of real numbers is at the heart of analytic geometry.

The reader is familiar with the fact that any two distinct points determine a line. We stated among the axioms in Section 10.2 that three noncollinear points determine a plane. We shall depend chiefly on geometric intuition to see that there are other ways of determining planes and lines. We want the necessary and sufficient conditions for a point to lie on a given line or a given plane. Since every point A is determined by a vector $\mathbf{a}$ represented by OA, we can develop these conditions in terms of $\mathbf{a}$ or OA and then translate them into a relation among the coordinates (x,y,z) of A.

11.2 Distance between two points

If P_1 and P_2 are two points, then the distance between them, which we denote by dist (P_1,P_2) is the length of the directed segment P_1P_2, that is, $|\mathbf{a}|$, where $\mathbf{a} = P_1P_2$. But $|\mathbf{a}|^2 = \mathbf{a} \cdot \mathbf{a}$ and therefore dist $(P_1,P_2) = \sqrt{\mathbf{a} \cdot \mathbf{a}}$. We know that $P_1P_2 = OP_2 - OP_1$ and hence $\mathbf{a} = (x_2 - x_1)\mathbf{i} + (y_2 - y_1)\mathbf{j} + (z_2 - z_1)\mathbf{k}$. Therefore $\mathbf{a}^2 = (x_2 - x_1)^2 + (y_2 - y_1)^2 + (z_2 - z_1)^2$ and

$$\text{dist } (P_1,P_2) = \sqrt{(x_2 - x_1)^2 + (y_2 - y_1)^2 + (z_2 - z_1)^2}.$$

11.3 Equation of a plane determined by three points

According to our axioms a plane is determined by three noncollinear points lying on it. Let $P_1(x_1,y_1,z_1)$, $P_2(x_2,y_2,z_2)$, and $P_3(x_3,y_3,z_3)$ be three noncollinear points. We wish to find the conditions under which $P(x,y,z)$ will lie on the plane determined by P_1, P_2, P_3.

Since the points P_1, P_2, P_3 are noncollinear, the segments P_1P_2 and P_1P_3 are noncollinear. Therefore, for any P on the plane the segment P_1P can be decomposed in terms of P_1P_2 and P_1P_3, that is, $P_1P = qP_1P_2 + rP_1P_3$ where q and r are real numbers determined by the point P. But $P_1P = OP - OP_1$ and therefore

$$OP = OP_1 + qP_1P_2 + rP_1P_3.$$

This might be called the vector equation of the plane (see Figure 11.1).

In terms of $\mathbf{i}$, $\mathbf{j}$, and $\mathbf{k}$ this equation becomes

$$\begin{aligned}
x\mathbf{i} + y\mathbf{j} + z\mathbf{k} = {} & [x_1 + q(x_2 - x_1) + r(x_3 - x_1)]\mathbf{i} \\
& + [y_1 + q(y_2 - y_1) + r(y_3 - y_1)]\mathbf{j} \\
& + [z_1 + q(z_2 - z_1) + r(z_3 - z_1)]\mathbf{k}.
\end{aligned}$$

From this we obtain the *parametric equations of the plane:*

$$\begin{aligned}
x &= x_1 + q(x_2 - x_1) + r(x_3 - x_1), \\
y &= y_1 + q(y_2 - y_1) + r(y_3 - y_1), \\
z &= z_1 + q(z_2 - z_1) + r(z_3 - z_1).
\end{aligned}$$

These equations show that, for each ordered pair of real numbers (q,r) called *parameters*, there is a point in the plane, that is, they determine

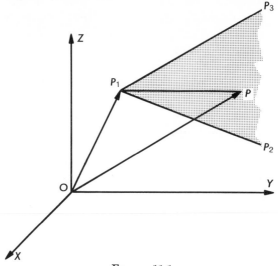

FIGURE 11.1

an injective function of $R \times R$ into the three-dimensional space whose range is the plane through P_1, P_2, P_3. For example, to $(0,0)$ corresponds P_1, to $(1,0)$ corresponds P_2, and to $(0,1)$ corresponds P_3.

EXAMPLE   11.1

The plane through $P_1(1,0,2)$, $P_2(2,2,1)$, and $P_3(3,3,3)$ has the parametric equations:

$$x = 1 + q(2 - 1) + r(3 - 1) = 1 + q + 2r,$$
$$y = 0 + q(2 - 0) + r(3 - 0) = 2q + 3r,$$
$$z = 2 + q(1 - 2) + r(3 - 2) = 2 - q + r.$$

We can use the properties of the scalar triple product to find another expression for the condition that P be on the plane. We know that P, P_1, P_2, P_3 are coplanar if and only if the vectors represented by P_1P, P_1P_2, and P_1P_3 are coplanar. But this means that

$$[P_1P, \ P_1P_2, \ P_1P_3] = 0.$$

If we write these three vectors in terms of their components, we have $P_1P = (x - x_1)\mathbf{i} + (y - y_1)\mathbf{j} + (z - z_1)\mathbf{k}$, $P_1P_2 = (x_2 - x_1)\mathbf{i} + (y_2 - y_1)\mathbf{j} + (z_2 - z_1)\mathbf{k}$, and $P_1P_3 = (x_3 - x_1)\mathbf{i} + (y_3 - y_1)\mathbf{j} + (z_3 - z_1)\mathbf{k}$. The condition that P be on the plane can now be written

$$\det \begin{bmatrix} x - x_1 & y - y_1 & z - z_1 \\ x_2 - x_1 & y_2 - y_1 & z_2 - z_1 \\ x_3 - x_1 & y_3 - y_1 & z_3 - z_1 \end{bmatrix} = 0.$$

This can be expressed as

$$a_1x + a_2y + a_3z = d,$$

where

$$a_1 = (y_2 - y_1)(z_3 - z_1) - (y_3 - y_1)(z_2 - z_1),$$
$$a_2 = -(x_2 - x_1)(z_3 - z_1) + (x_3 - x_1)(z_2 - z_1),$$
$$a_3 = (x_2 - x_1)(y_3 - y_1) - (x_3 - x_1)(y_2 - y_1),$$

and

$$d = a_1x_1 + a_2y_1 + a_3z_1.$$

We call this the *Cartesian equation of the plane*.

The equation $a_1x + a_2y + a_3z = d$ is called a *linear equation* because it involves only first-degree or linear terms in x, y, and z. The reader knows from previous studies that in two-dimensional geometry a linear equation represents a line. We emphasize the fact that *in three-dimensional geometry a single linear equation represents a plane, not a line*.

EXAMPLE   11.2

If we write the equation of the plane containing the points $(1,0,2)$, $(2,2,1)$, and $(3,3,3)$ in the form of a determinant, we have

$$\det \begin{bmatrix} x - 1 & y - 0 & z - 2 \\ 2 - 1 & 2 - 0 & 1 - 2 \\ 3 - 1 & 3 - 0 & 3 - 2 \end{bmatrix} = 0.$$

This gives us

$$\det \begin{bmatrix} x - 1 & y & z - 2 \\ 1 & 2 & -1 \\ 2 & 3 & 1 \end{bmatrix} = 0.$$

and hence the equation is $5x - 3y - z - 3 = 0$.

11.4   Equation of a plane determined by a point and a normal

A plane can also be determined by giving a point on it and a nonzero vector perpendicular to it. We call this vector a *normal* vector to the plane. Consider the plane that passes through $P_0(x_0,y_0,z_0)$ and that has, as a normal, the nonzero vector $\mathbf{a} = a_1\mathbf{i} + a_2\mathbf{j} + a_3\mathbf{k}$ (see Figure 11.2). Let $P(x,y,z)$ be any point on the plane. Then the directed segment P_0P lies in the plane and hence is perpendicular to $\mathbf{a}$. We can express this as $\mathbf{a} \cdot P_0P = 0$.

Conversely, if $\mathbf{a} \cdot P_0P = 0$, we know that either $P_0P = \mathbf{0}$ or $\mathbf{a}$ and P_0P are perpendicular, since $\mathbf{a} \neq \mathbf{0}$. In either case we see that P is on the plane.

This gives us the necessary and sufficient condition

$$\mathbf{a} \cdot P_0P = 0,$$

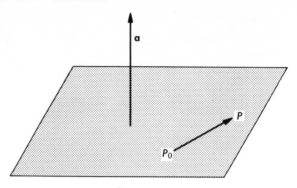

FIGURE 11.2

which we call the vector equation of the plane. But $\mathbf{a} = a_1\mathbf{i} + a_2\mathbf{j} + a_3\mathbf{k}$ and $P_0P = (x - x_0)\mathbf{i} + (y - y_0)\mathbf{j} + (z - z_0)\mathbf{k}$. This gives us the Cartesian equation $a_1(x - x_0) + a_2(y - y_0) + a_3(z - z_0) = 0$ or

$$a_1x + a_2y + a_3z = d,$$

where $d = a_1x_0 + a_2y_0 + a_3z_0$.

EXAMPLE 11.3

The Cartesian equation of the plane containing $P_0(2,-1,3)$ and perpendicular to $\mathbf{a} = \mathbf{i} - 2\mathbf{j} + 4\mathbf{k}$ is $1(x - 2) - 2(y + 1) + 4(z - 3) = 0$, that is, $x - 2y + 4z = 16$.

11.5 Plane through a point and parallel to two vectors

A third way to determine a plane is to give a point $P_0(x_0,y_0,z_0)$ on it and two vectors $\mathbf{a} = a_1\mathbf{i} + a_2\mathbf{j} + a_3\mathbf{k}$ and $\mathbf{b} = b_1\mathbf{i} + b_2\mathbf{j} + b_3\mathbf{k}$, which are parallel to it. If the point M is to be on this plane, we have the vector equation $P_0M = p\mathbf{a} + q\mathbf{b}$ (see Figure 11.3). That is,

$$OM = OP_0 + p\mathbf{a} + q\mathbf{b}.$$

In terms of $\mathbf{i}$, $\mathbf{j}$, $\mathbf{k}$ this equation becomes $x\mathbf{i} + y\mathbf{j} + z\mathbf{k} = \{x_0 + pa_1 + qb_1\}\mathbf{i} + \{y_0 + pa_2 + qb_2\}\mathbf{j} + \{z_0 + pa_3 + qb_3\}\mathbf{k}$. From this we obtain the parametric equations

$$x = x_0 + pa_1 + qb_1,$$
$$y = y_0 + pa_2 + qb_2,$$
$$z = z_0 + pa_3 + qb_3.$$

To each ordered pair of real numbers (p,q) there corresponds a point on the plane. In particular, to $(0,0)$ corresponds P_0, to $(0,1)$ corresponds B, and to $(1,0)$ corresponds A (see Figure 11.3).

We could now eliminate p and q to obtain the Cartesian equation, but there is a more convenient way to develop it.

The vector $\mathbf{a} \times \mathbf{b}$ is perpendicular to $\mathbf{a}$ and to $\mathbf{b}$ and hence is perpendicular to any plane parallel to both $\mathbf{a}$ and $\mathbf{b}$. From this we see that in order for

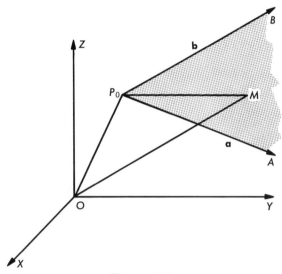

FIGURE 11.3

M to lie on the plane through P_0 and parallel to $\mathbf{a}$ and $\mathbf{b}$ we must have P_0M perpendicular to $\mathbf{a} \times \mathbf{b}$. This condition can be written as $(\mathbf{a} \times \mathbf{b}) \cdot P_0M = 0$. But this is equivalent to

$$\begin{vmatrix} a_1 & a_2 & a_3 \\ b_1 & b_2 & b_3 \\ x - x_0 & y - y_0 & z - z_0 \end{vmatrix} = 0.$$

From this we obtain the equation

$$c_1(x - x_0) + c_2(y - y_0) + c_3(z - z_0) = 0,$$

where $c_1 = a_2b_3 - a_3b_2$, $c_2 = -(a_1b_3 - a_3b_1)$, $c_3 = a_1b_2 - a_2b_1$.

EXAMPLE 11.4

Find the equation of the plane through the point $P_0(2,1,-3)$ and parallel to the vectors $\mathbf{a} = \mathbf{i} - 2\mathbf{j} + \mathbf{k}$ and $\mathbf{b} = 2\mathbf{i} + \mathbf{j} - 3\mathbf{k}$.

There are two ways to approach this problem. We can observe that $[\mathbf{a},\mathbf{b},P_0P] = 0$, since P_0P is parallel to the plane determined by $\mathbf{a}$ and $\mathbf{b}$.

But

$$[\mathbf{a,b},P_0P] = \begin{vmatrix} 1 & -2 & 1 \\ 2 & 1 & -3 \\ x-2 & y-1 & z+3 \end{vmatrix}$$
$$= 5(x-2) + 5(y-1) + 5(z+3) = 5(x+y+z).$$

Therefore the equation is $x + y + z = 0$.

On the other hand we can observe that the plane is perpendicular to $\mathbf{a} \times \mathbf{b}$ and passes through $(2,1,-3)$. Also

$$\mathbf{a} \times \mathbf{b} = \begin{vmatrix} \mathbf{i} & \mathbf{j} & \mathbf{k} \\ 1 & -2 & 1 \\ 2 & 1 & -3 \end{vmatrix} = 5\mathbf{i} + 5\mathbf{j} + 5\mathbf{k}.$$

Therefore the equation of the plane is $5(x - 2) + 5(y - 1) + 5(z + 3) = 0$, or $x + y + z = 0$.

11.6   Intercept equation of a plane

We have seen that the equation of a plane is linear (that is, of first degree in x, y, and z) and of the form

$$ax + by + cz = d.$$

If the plane passes through the origin, then $(0,0,0)$ must satisfy this equation and hence $d = 0$. Conversely, if $d = 0$, then $(0,0,0)$ satisfies the equation. Therefore the plane passes through the origin if and only if $d = 0$.

If $d \neq 0$ we can enquire where the plane meets the x axis, that is, for what value of x will $(x,0,0)$ be on the plane? We can easily see that the answer is $x = d/a$ provided $a \neq 0$. Similarly, the plane intersects the y axis at $(0,d/b,0)$, provided $b \neq 0$, and the z axis at $(0,0,d/c)$, provided $c \neq 0$.

If $a = 0$ there is no intersection with the x axis, that is, the plane is parallel to the x axis. A similar interpretation holds for $b = 0$ or $c = 0$.

We call the points $(d/a,0,0)$, $(0,d/b,0)$, and $(0,0,d/c)$ the x *intercept*, y *intercept*, and z *intercept*, respectively. If all three intercepts exist, that is, if $abc \neq 0$ we can write the equation of the plane as

$$\frac{x}{d/a} + \frac{y}{d/b} + \frac{z}{d/c} = 1.$$

This is called the intercept form of the equation of the plane (see Figure 11.4).

Conversely, if we know that the intercepts of a plane are $(e,0,0)$, $(0,f,0)$, and $(0,0,g)$, then its equation is $x/e + y/f + z/g = 1$.

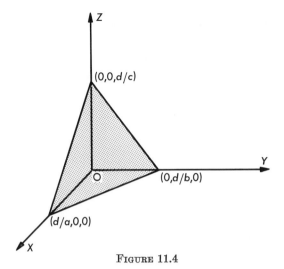

FIGURE 11.4

EXAMPLE 11.5

Find the x intercept of the plane $3x + 4y + 5z = 60$.

We substitute $y = 0$ and $z = 0$ in the equation and solve for x. This gives us the point $(20,0,0)$ as the x intercept.

Similarly, the y and z intercepts can be found to be $(0,15,0)$ and $(0,0,12)$, respectively.

EXAMPLE 11.6

Find the equation of the plane passing through $A(2,0,0)$, $B(0,3,0)$, and $C(0,0,1)$.

Since these points are the intercepts, we immediately obtain $x/2 + y/3 + z/1 = 1$.

11.7 Angle between two planes

Consider two planes p and p' whose equations are

$$ax + by + cz = d,$$
$$a'x + b'y + c'z = d'.$$

We want to find the angle between them. In solid geometry the angle between two planes is defined as the angle between two lines (AB and AB' in Figure 11.5), one lying in each plane and both perpendicular to the line of intersection of the planes. If, through B and B', we draw lines perpendicular to the planes p and p', respectively, we see that they meet in a point C, and that angle (AB,AB') and angle (CB,CB') are supplementary and hence have the same cosine, except for sign.

But CB is parallel to $\mathbf{v} = a\mathbf{i} + b\mathbf{j} + c\mathbf{k}$, since it is perpendicular (or normal) to p. Similarly, CB' is parallel to $\mathbf{v}' = a'\mathbf{i} + b'\mathbf{j} + c'\mathbf{k}$.

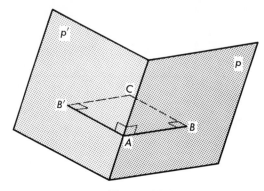

FIGURE 11.5

We can now apply our knowledge about the angle between two lines to determine the angle between the planes. Thus we have

$$
\begin{aligned}
|\cos (p,p')| &= |\cos (AB,AB')| \\
&= |\cos (CB,CB')| \\
&= |\cos (\mathbf{v},\mathbf{v}')| \\
&= \frac{|aa' + bb' + cc'|}{\sqrt{a^2 + b^2 + c^2}\ \sqrt{a'^2 + b'^2 + c'^2}}.
\end{aligned}
$$

EXAMPLE   11.7

Find the angle between the planes p_1 with equation $2x + 4y + 6z = 3$ and p_2 with equation $x + 7z = 2$.

We know that the normals to the two planes are $\mathbf{v}_1 = 2\mathbf{i} + 4\mathbf{j} + 6\mathbf{k}$ and $\mathbf{v}_2 = \mathbf{i} + 7\mathbf{k}$. Then $|\cos (p_1,p_2)| = |\cos (\mathbf{v}_1,\mathbf{v}_2)| = |\mathbf{v}_1 \cdot \mathbf{v}_2|/(|\mathbf{v}_1|\,|\mathbf{v}_2|) = (2 + 42)/\sqrt{56}\,\sqrt{50} = 11/5\,\sqrt{7}$. Thus we see that the angle between the planes is arccos $(11/5\,\sqrt{7})$.

EXAMPLE   11.8

Find the equation of a plane that passes through $A(1,1,1)$ and is perpendicular to the plane p_1 with equation $x + y + z = 1$.

To do this we refer to Figure 11.6. Our geometric intuition tells us that there is an infinite number of such planes. Each must contain the line determined by A and A' where $A'A$ is perpendicular to p.

Let $ax + by + cz = d$ be the equation of such a plane, p. Then the normal to p is $\mathbf{v} = a\mathbf{i} + b\mathbf{j} + c\mathbf{k}$ and the normal to p_1 is $\mathbf{u} = \mathbf{i} + \mathbf{j} + \mathbf{k}$. Since p and p_1 are perpendicular, so are $\mathbf{v}$ and $\mathbf{u}$, that is, $\mathbf{v} \cdot \mathbf{u} = 0$, or $a + b + c = 0$. From this we get $c = -(a + b)$ and hence any plane through

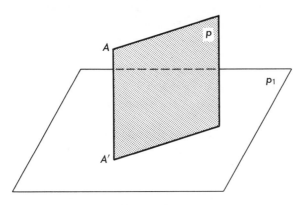

FIGURE 11.6

$A(1,1,1)$ and perpendicular to p_1 has the form $a(x - 1) + b(y - 1) - (a + b)(z - 1) = 0$, which reduces to $ax + by - (a + b)z = 0$.

EXERCISES

11.1. Find the distance between the points $P_1(2,4,1)$ and $P_2(3,1,0)$.

11.2. Find the equation of the plane through $A(2,0,1)$, $B(3,2,1)$, and $C(0,1,2)$.

11.3. Find the equation of the plane through $P_1(1,2,1)$, $P_2(2,3,1)$, and $P_3(0,-2,4)$.

11.4. Find the equation of the plane through $P(6,1,5)$ perpendicular to $\mathbf{i} - 3\mathbf{j} + 2\mathbf{k}$.

11.5. Find the equation of the plane through $(1,2,1)$ perpendicular to $\mathbf{a} = \mathbf{i} - 2\mathbf{j} + 3\mathbf{k}$.

11.6. Find the equation of the plane through $P_1(2,1,6)$ and perpendicular to P_1P_2, where P_2 has the coordinates $(1,-1,3)$.

11.7. Given two points $A(2,1,6)$ and $B(-4,3,3)$ find the equation of the plane through A and perpendicular to the line joining A and B.

11.8. Find the equation of the plane through $P(4,1,6)$ parallel to $\mathbf{i} - 3\mathbf{j} + \mathbf{k}$ and $2\mathbf{i} - \mathbf{j} + \mathbf{k}$.

11.9. Find the equation of the plane through $(3,0,1)$ parallel to the plane $2x + y - 3z = 8$.

11.10. If $\mathbf{u} = \mathbf{i} + 2\mathbf{j} + 2\mathbf{k}$, $\mathbf{v} = 2\mathbf{i} - 3\mathbf{j} - 4\mathbf{k}$, and $\mathbf{w} = \mathbf{i} - \mathbf{j}$, find the projection of $\mathbf{u}$ on a line perpendicular to a plane parallel to $\mathbf{v}$ and $\mathbf{w}$.

11.11. Find the equation of the plane passing through the points $(4,0,0)$, $(0,2,0)$, and $(0,0,1)$.

11.12. Find a unit vector perpendicular to the plane passing through $(2,0,0)$, $(0,3,0)$, $(0,0,2)$.

11.13. Find the equation of the plane through $(2,1,0)$ that is perpendicular to the planes $x + 2y - 3z = 2$ and $2x - y + 4z = 1$.

11.14. Given the plane $y = z$ and the points $P_1(1,0,0)$ and $P_2(1,0,1)$, find the equation of the plane through P_1 and P_2 that is perpendicular to the given plane.

11.15. Find the angle between the planes $2x + 2y - 5 = 0$ and $y + z + 10 = 0$.

11.16. Find the angle between the plane through $(1,1,1)$, $(1,0,1)$, $(1,1,0)$ and the plane through $(0,0,1)$ and $(0,0,0)$ parallel to $\mathbf{i} + \mathbf{j}$.

11.17. Find the angle between the plane through $(3,1,2)$ perpendicular to $\mathbf{i} - 2\mathbf{j} + 3\mathbf{k}$ and the plane $2x + 3y - z = 8$.

11.18. Find the angle between the planes $2x + 9y + 6z + 14 = 0$ and $3x - 4y + 5z - 37 = 0$.

11.19. Find the cosine of the angle between the planes $3x + 4y + 5z = 10$ and $x + 4y - z = 15$.

11.20. A regular tetrahedron (solid whose faces are four congruent equilateral triangles) has one face in the xy plane and vertices at $(1,0,0)$ and $(0,0,0)$.

(a) Find the equations of the planes in which the other three faces lie.
(b) Find the angle between two of these planes.

11.21. Find the equation of the plane that bisects the angle between the planes $x + y - z = 0$ and $2x - y + z = 1$.

11.8   A line as the intersection of planes

Let p and p' be two planes whose equations are, respectively,

$$ax + by + cz = d,$$
$$a'x + b'y + c'z = d'.$$

Then $D = p \cap p'$ consists of all points $M(x,y,z)$ such that x, y, z satisfy both these equations.

If p and p' are parallel, then $D = \varnothing$. If $p = p'$, then $D = p \cap p' = p = p'$. In all other cases D is a line, that is, D is a line if and only if p and p' are neither equal nor parallel.

It thus becomes important to be able to tell when two planes are parallel or equal. This is done in terms of their normal vectors. We know that $\mathbf{v} = a\mathbf{i} + b\mathbf{j} + c\mathbf{k}$ is normal to p, and $\mathbf{v}' = a'\mathbf{i} + b'\mathbf{j} + c'\mathbf{k}$ is normal to p'. The planes are equal or parallel if and only if $\mathbf{v}$ and $\mathbf{v}'$ are parallel. But the condition for this is $\mathbf{v} = m\mathbf{v}'$, that is, $a = ma'$, $b = mb'$, $c = mc'$, or $a/a' = b/b' = c/c' = m$. D is a straight line if this does not hold, that is, if at least one of the numbers $bc' - b'c$, $ca' - c'a$, $ab' - a'b$ is nonzero. But these numbers are the components of $\mathbf{v} \times \mathbf{v}'$ and thus the condition for D to be a line is $\mathbf{v} \times \mathbf{v}' \neq \mathbf{0}$.

Since D lies in both p and p', it must be perpendicular to both $\mathbf{v}$ and $\mathbf{v}'$, that is, D is parallel to $\mathbf{v} \times \mathbf{v}'$ (see Figure 11.7).

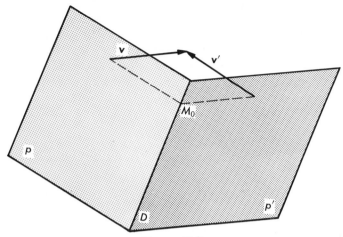

FIGURE 11.7

Since two distinct nonparallel planes determine a line we speak of the equations of the two planes as forming the equations of the line. We emphasize the fact that one linear equation represents a plane; two linear equations, under suitable conditions, represent a straight line. We shall see various ways of writing the equations of a line, but we shall find that in three dimensions a line is never represented by a single equation.

11.9   Coordinates of a point dividing a segment

Let P_1 and P_2 be two given points with coordinates (x_1, y_1, z_1) and (x_2, y_2, z_2), respectively (see Figure 11.8). We want to find a point P with coordinates (x, y, z) that lies on the line through P_1 and P_2 and that divides the segment P_1P_2 in a given ratio.

Since P is on the line, we have $P_1P = rP_1P_2$ for some real number r. Also $P_1P = OP - OP_1$ and $P_1P_2 = OP_2 - OP_1$. Therefore $OP - OP_1 = r(OP_2 - OP_1)$, that is,

$$OP = (1 - r)OP_1 + rOP_2.$$

The segments OP, OP_1, and OP_2 represent vectors that can be expressed in terms of $\mathbf{i}$, $\mathbf{j}$, $\mathbf{k}$. This gives

$$x\mathbf{i} + y\mathbf{j} + z\mathbf{k} = \{(1 - r)x_1 + rx_2\}\mathbf{i} + \{(1 - r)y_1 + ry_2\}\mathbf{j} \\ + \{(1 - r)z_1 + rz_2\}\mathbf{k},$$

and hence the coordinates of P are

$$x = (1 - r)x_1 + rx_2,$$
$$y = (1 - r)y_1 + ry_2,$$
$$z = (1 - r)z_1 + rz_2.$$

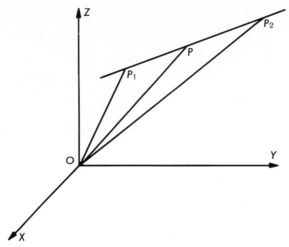

FIGURE 11.8

If $0 < r < 1$, then P is between P_1 and P_2, since $P_1P = rP_1P_2$ (see Figure 11.9a).

If $r = 1$, then P coincides with P_2; if $r = 0$, P coincides with P_1.

If $r = \frac{1}{2}$, then $P_1P = (\frac{1}{2})P_1P_2$ and P is the mid-point of P_1P_2. Thus the coordinates of the mid-point of P_1P_2 are $((x_1 + x_2)/2,\ (y_1 + y_2)/2,\ (z_1 + z_2)/2)$.

If $r < 0$, then P_1 lies between P and P_2 (see Figure 11.9b). If $r = -\infty$, then P is at infinity on the same side of P_2 as P_1. If $r > 1$, then P_2 is between P and P_1 (see Figure 11.9c). If $r = +\infty$, then P is at infinity on the same side of P_1 as P_2.

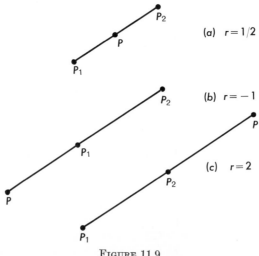

(a) $r = 1/2$

(b) $r = -1$

(c) $r = 2$

FIGURE 11.9

11.10   Equations of a straight line

We saw in Section 11.9 that the necessary and sufficient conditions for a point with coordinates (x,y,z) to lie on the line through $P_1(x_1,y_1,z_1)$ and $P_2(x_2,y_2,z_2)$ are

$$x = x_1 + r(x_2 - x_1),$$
$$y = y_1 + r(y_2 - y_1),$$
$$z = z_1 + r(z_2 - z_1).$$

We refer to these equations as the *parametric equations of the line*.

If $x_2 - x_1$, $y_2 - y_1$, $z_2 - z_1$ are all nonzero, we obtain

$$\frac{x - x_1}{x_2 - x_1} = \frac{y - y_1}{y_2 - y_1} = \frac{z - z_1}{z_2 - z_1}.$$

These are called the *symmetric equations of the line* through (x_1,y_1,z_1) and (x_2,y_2,z_2). We observe that, if these are written

$$\frac{x - x_1}{x_2 - x_1} = \frac{y - y_1}{y_2 - y_1}, \qquad \frac{y - y_1}{y_2 - y_1} = \frac{z - z_1}{z_2 - z_1},$$

we have the line represented as the intersection of two planes.

If any of the denominators in the symmetric form is zero, the parametric equations show that the corresponding coordinate is a constant.

EXAMPLE   11.9

Find the equations of the line through the points $P_1(1,0,2)$ and $P_2(2,1,3)$. In symmetric form we have

$$\frac{x - 1}{2 - 1} = \frac{y - 0}{1 - 0} = \frac{z - 2}{3 - 2},$$

that is, $x - 1 = y = z - 2$.

EXAMPLE   11.10

Find the equations of the line through the points $(2,0,2)$ and $(1,3,2)$. In the parametric form we have

$$x = 2 + r(1 - 2) = 2 - r,$$
$$y = 0 + r(3 - 0) = 3r,$$
$$z = 2 + r(2 - 2) = 2.$$

In this case $z_2 - z_1 = 0$, and hence we cannot use the symmetric form for all the coordinates. We can however combine the two forms by using the symmetric form for an equation in x and y and the parametric form for z.

This gives us

$$\frac{x-2}{-1} = \frac{y-0}{3}, \qquad z = 2,$$

that is, $3(x-2) + y = 0, z = 2$.

A line is also determined by a point on it and a vector parallel to it. Consider the line passing through $P_1(x_1,y_1,z_1)$ and parallel to the vector $\mathbf{a} = a_1\mathbf{i} + a_2\mathbf{j} + a_3\mathbf{k}$. Let $P(x,y,z)$ be any point on the line. Then P_1P and $\mathbf{a}$ are parallel and hence $P_1P = t\mathbf{a}$. But $P_1P = OP - OP_1 = (x-x_1)\mathbf{i} + (y-y_1)\mathbf{j} + (z-z_1)\mathbf{k}$. Therefore,

$$
\begin{aligned}
x &= x_1 + ta_1, \\
y &= y_1 + ta_2, \\
z &= z_1 + ta_3,
\end{aligned}
$$

the parametric equations of the line.

If a_1, a_2, a_3 are all nonzero and we solve these equations for t, we obtain the symmetric equations of the line

$$\frac{x-x_1}{a_1} = \frac{y-y_1}{a_2} = \frac{z-z_1}{a_3}.$$

If $a_1 = 0$, the equations of the line take the form

$$
\begin{aligned}
x - x_1 &= 0, \\
\frac{y-y_1}{a_2} &= \frac{z-z_1}{a_3}.
\end{aligned}
$$

If $a_1 = a_2 = 0$, the equations are $x = x_1$, $y = y_1$, and z is arbitrary.

If P_1 and P_2 are on the line we can take $\mathbf{a} = P_1P_2 = (x_2-x_1)\mathbf{i} + (y_2-y_1)\mathbf{j} + (z_2-z_1)\mathbf{k}$ and get the equation in terms of two points.

EXAMPLE 11.11

Find the equation of the line through $P_1(1,0,2)$ and parallel to $\mathbf{a} = \mathbf{i} - 2\mathbf{j} + 3\mathbf{k}$.

Since none of the components of the vector is zero, we have, in symmetric form,

$$\frac{x-1}{1} = \frac{y-0}{-2} = \frac{z-2}{3},$$

that is, $x - 1 = -y/2 = (z-2)/3$.

EXAMPLE 11.12

Find the equation of the line through $P_2(2,1,3)$ and parallel to the vector $\mathbf{b} = 2\mathbf{j} - \mathbf{k}$.

Since the first component of the vector is zero, we must use a modified symmetric form. This gives the equations

$$x - 2 = 0, \qquad \frac{y-1}{2} = \frac{z-3}{-1}.$$

As a third form of definition for a line consider the line through $P_0(x_0,y_0,z_0)$ and perpendicular to the plane whose equation is $ax + by + cz = d$. The vector $a\mathbf{i} + b\mathbf{j} + c\mathbf{k}$ is normal to the plane and hence parallel to the line. Thus this case reduces to the previous one, and the symmetric equations are

$$\frac{x - x_0}{a} = \frac{y - y_0}{b} = \frac{z - z_0}{c}.$$

EXAMPLE 11.13

Find the equation of the line through $A(2,3,1)$ and perpendicular to the plane $x + 2y + 3z = 1$.

If $P(x,y,z)$ is on the line, then AP is parallel to the normal to the plane, that is, parallel to the vector $\mathbf{a} = \mathbf{i} + 2\mathbf{j} + 3\mathbf{k}$. Then $AP = t\mathbf{a}$ and, since $AP = (x - 2)\mathbf{i} + (y - 3)\mathbf{j} + (z - 1)\mathbf{k}$, we have the parametric equations

$$x = 2 + t,$$
$$y = 3 + 2t,$$
$$z = 1 + 3t,$$

and the symmetric equations

$$\frac{x - 2}{1} = \frac{y - 3}{2} = \frac{z - 1}{3}.$$

From the symmetric equations of a line, that is, from

$$\frac{x - x_0}{a} = \frac{y - y_0}{b} = \frac{z - z_0}{c},$$

we see that the line is the intersection of the three planes

$$\text{(I)} \qquad \frac{x - x_0}{a} = \frac{y - y_0}{b},$$

$$\text{(II)} \qquad \frac{y - y_0}{b} = \frac{z - z_0}{c},$$

$$\text{(III)} \qquad \frac{z - z_0}{c} = \frac{x - x_0}{a}.$$

In the equation of plane I the z term is missing and the normal vector $\mathbf{a}_1 = (1/a)\mathbf{i} - (1/b)\mathbf{j}$ is parallel to the xy plane. Plane I cuts the xy plane in a line (D_1 in Figure 11.10) and is parallel to the z axis. Also the angle between I and the xy plane is a right angle.

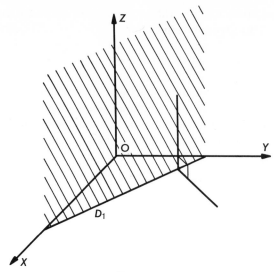

FIGURE 11.10

Similarly, plane II is parallel to the x axis and makes a right angle with the yz plane; plane III is parallel to the y axis and makes a right angle with the xz plane.

Planes I, II, and III are called the projection planes of the line. Any two of them determine the line.

EXAMPLE 11.14

Find the projection planes of the line whose equations are

$$x + 2y + 3z = 4,$$
$$x - 2y + 3z = -4.$$

For the projection plane parallel to the z axis, we eliminate z from the two equations. This gives $x + 2y - 4 = -3z = x - 2y + 4$ and hence $x + 2y - 4 = x - 2y + 4$. This reduces to $4y = 8$ or $y = 2$.

This plane is parallel to the xz plane and hence is also the projection plane parallel to the x axis.

The projection plane parallel to the y axis is found by eliminating y. It is $x + 3z = 0$.

11.11 Angle between two lines

Unlike the geometry of the plane, there are three possibilities for the position relative to each other of two distinct lines l_1 and l_2 in space.

1. The lines l_1 and l_2 intersect in a point and determine a plane.

2. The lines l_1 and l_2 are parallel, that is, they lie in the same plane and do not intersect (they are parallel in the sense of plane geometry).

3. The lines l_1 and l_2 are neither parallel nor intersecting.

In case 1, the angle (l_1, l_2) is the same as in plane geometry. In case 2, the angle (l_1, l_2) is considered zero. In case 3, we define the angle (l_1, l_2) as follows (see Figure 11.11). Select any point $A \in l_1$. Draw through A a line

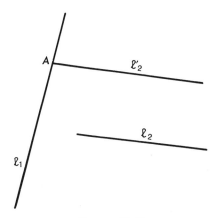

FIGURE 11.11

l_2' parallel to l_2. The angle (l_1, l_2) is now defined to be the angle (l_1, l_2'). The reader can verify that this definition is independent of the choice of $A \in l_1$.

If l_1 is the intersection of two planes whose equations are

$$a_1 x + b_1 y + c_1 z = d_1,$$
$$e_1 x + f_1 y + g_1 z = h_1,$$

and l_2 is the intersection of the planes

$$a_2 x + b_2 y + c_2 z = d_2,$$
$$e_2 x + f_2 y + g_2 z = h_2,$$

then the vectors

$$\mathbf{v}_1 = (b_1 g_1 - c_1 f_1)\mathbf{i} - (a_1 g_1 - c_1 e_1)\mathbf{j} + (a_1 f_1 - b_1 e_1)\mathbf{k},$$
$$\mathbf{v}_2 = (b_2 g_2 - c_2 f_2)\mathbf{i} - (a_2 g_2 - c_2 e_2)\mathbf{j} + (a_2 f_2 - b_2 e_2)\mathbf{k},$$

are parallel to l_1 and l_2, respectively, and

$$\cos (l_1, l_2) = \cos (\mathbf{v}_1, \mathbf{v}_2)$$
$$= \frac{\mathbf{v}_1 \cdot \mathbf{v}_2}{|\mathbf{v}_1|\, |\mathbf{v}_2|}.$$

We shall not write this expression out in terms of the components, but in a particular example this can easily be done.

EXAMPLE   11.15

Find the angle between the lines l_1 with equations

$$x + y + z = 1,$$
$$x - y - z = 1,$$

and l_2 with equations

$$\frac{x - 1}{2} = \frac{y - 2}{3} = \frac{z - 3}{4}.$$

For l_2 we have the parallel vector $\mathbf{a}_2 = 2\mathbf{i} + 3\mathbf{j} + 4\mathbf{k}$. For l_1 we find a vector normal to each plane, that is, $\mathbf{b}_1 = \mathbf{i} + \mathbf{j} + \mathbf{k}$ and $\mathbf{b}_2 = \mathbf{i} - \mathbf{j} - \mathbf{k}$. Then $\mathbf{a}_1 = \mathbf{b}_1 \times \mathbf{b}_2$ is parallel to l_1. But $\mathbf{b}_1 \times \mathbf{b}_2 = 2\mathbf{j} - 2\mathbf{k}$. Then

$$\cos (l_1, l_2) = \cos (\mathbf{a}_1, \mathbf{a}_2) = \frac{\mathbf{a}_1 \cdot \mathbf{a}_2}{|\mathbf{a}_1|\,|\mathbf{a}_2|}$$
$$= \frac{6 - 8}{\sqrt{8}\,\sqrt{29}} = \frac{-1}{\sqrt{58}}.$$

11.12   Distance from a point to a plane

By the distance from a point to a plane we mean the shortest distance, that is, the distance measured along the line perpendicular to the plane. We

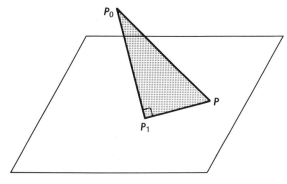

FIGURE 11.12

shall find the distance from the point $P_0(x_0, y_0, z_0)$ to the plane whose equation is $ax + by + cz = d$. If P_1 is the point on the plane such that P_1P_0 is perpendicular to the plane, we want dist (P_0, P_1) (see Figure 11.12). We know that the vector $\mathbf{v} = a\mathbf{i} + b\mathbf{j} + c\mathbf{k}$ is perpendicular to the plane. Therefore $P_0P_1 = s\mathbf{v}$. Let P be any point on the plane. Then P_0P_1 is perpendicular to P_1P and

$$\text{dist } (P_0,P_1) = |P_0P| \, |\cos (P_0P_1, P_0P)|$$
$$= \frac{|P_0P_1 \cdot P_0P|}{|P_0P_1|}.$$

But $P_0P_1 = s\mathbf{v}$, and $P_0P = (x - x_0)\mathbf{i} + (y - y_0)\mathbf{j} + (z - z_0)\mathbf{k}$, where (x,y,z) are the coordinates of P. Therefore $P_0P_1 \cdot P_0P = s(a(x - x_0) + b(y - y_0) + c(z - z_0)) = s(d - ax_0 - by_0 - cz_0)$, since $ax + by + cz = d$. Also $|s\mathbf{v}| = s\sqrt{a^2 + b^2 + c^2}$. If we substitute these into the above expression for dist (P_0,P_1), we have

$$\text{dist } (P_0,P_1) = \frac{|ax_0 + by_0 + cz_0 - d|}{\sqrt{a^2 + b^2 + c^2}}.$$

EXAMPLE 11.16

Find the distance between the point $(3,2,1)$ and the plane $3x - 4y + 5z = 15$.

If we substitute into the above formula we obtain

$$\text{distance} = \frac{|9 - 8 + 5 - 15|}{\sqrt{9 + 16 + 25}} = \frac{9}{5\sqrt{2}}.$$

11.13   Distance from a point to a line

By the distance from a point to a line we mean the shortest distance from the given point to a point on the line, that is the distance measured along a

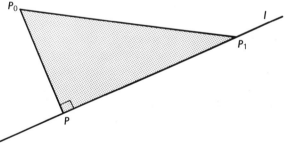

FIGURE 11.13

line perpendicular to the given line. Suppose we are given the point $P_0(x_0,y_0,z_0)$ and the line l, which passes through the point $P_1(x_1,y_1,z_1)$ and is parallel to the vector $\mathbf{v} = a\mathbf{i} + b\mathbf{j} + c\mathbf{k}$. Let P be the point on the line so that PP_0 is perpendicular to l (see Figure 11.13). We want to calculate

$|PP_0|$. It is clear that $|PP_0|^2 = |P_0P_1|^2 - |PP_1|^2$. But $|PP_1| = |\mathbf{v} \cdot P_0P_1|/|\mathbf{v}|$. Therefore we have

$$|PP_0|^2 = (x_1 - x_0)^2 + (y_1 - y_0)^2 + (z_1 - z_0)^2$$
$$- \frac{[a(x_1 - x_0) + b(y_1 - y_0) + c(z_1 - z_0)]^2}{a^2 + b^2 + c^2}.$$

It is not intended that this result be memorized, rather the reader should learn to apply the method in each particular case.

EXAMPLE   11.17

Find the distance between the point (2,1,0) and the line whose symmetric equations are

$$\frac{x - 2}{2} = \frac{y}{1} = \frac{z + 1}{3}.$$

In this case P_0 is (2,1,0), P_1 is (2,0,-1), and $\mathbf{v} = 2\mathbf{i} + \mathbf{j} + 3\mathbf{k}$. Then $|P_0P_1|^2 = 0^2 + (-1)^2 + (-1)^2 = 2$ and

$$\frac{P_0P_1 \cdot \mathbf{v}}{|\mathbf{v}|} = \frac{-4}{\sqrt{14}}.$$

Therefore $|PP_0|^2 = 2 - 4/\sqrt{14}$.

11.14   Distance between two lines

When we speak of the distance between two lines, we mean the distance measured along a line perpendicular to the two given lines. For such a definition of distance to be acceptable, we must show that there is a line intersecting the two given lines and perpendicular to both of them. We shall not only prove the existence of such a line but shall also develop a means of obtaining its equation. We shall assume that the two lines are not parallel; if they are, the problem can be solved by the methods of plane geometry.

Suppose we are given the line l_1 passing through the point P_1 and parallel to the vector $\mathbf{v}_1$, and the line l_2 passing through the point P_2 and parallel to the vector $\mathbf{v}_2$ (see Figure 11.14). The vector $\mathbf{v}_1 \times \mathbf{v}_2$ is perpendicular to both l_1 and l_2. We want to find a line parallel to $\mathbf{v}_1 \times \mathbf{v}_2$ that intersects both l_1 and l_2. We first find the equation of the plane that is parallel to $\mathbf{v}_1 \times \mathbf{v}_2$ and to $\mathbf{v}_2$ and passes through the point P_2. We shall call this plane p_2. It is clear by the construction of p_2 that l_2 lies in it. We want to show that p_2 contains a line perpendicular to both l_1 and l_2 and intersecting both of them. We must first show that l_1 intersects p_2. The only other possibility is that l_1 is parallel to p_2. If this is so, there is a line l_1' in p_2 parallel to l_1. Since l_1 and l_2 are not parallel, l_1' and l_2 must intersect, say at A. Now the lines l_2 and l_1' both pass through A and are both perpendicular to $\mathbf{v}_1 \times \mathbf{v}_2$. But

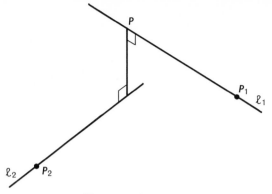

FIGURE 11.14

this is impossible, therefore l_1 is not parallel to p_2, that is, l_1 intersects p_2 at some point, which we denote by P. Through P we construct a line parallel to $\mathbf{v}_1 \times \mathbf{v}_2$. This line lies in p_2 and is not parallel to l_2. Therefore it intersects l_2. This line is the required common perpendicular.

EXAMPLE 11.18

Find the equation of the common perpendicular to the line l_1 whose equations are $x = -8 + t$, $y = -3 - 2t$, $z = 8 + 3t$, and the line l_2 whose equations are

$$\frac{x - 1}{2} = \frac{y + 1}{1} = \frac{z}{3}.$$

In the above notation we have $P_1(-8, -3, 8)$, $P_2(1, -1, 0)$, $\mathbf{v}_1 = \mathbf{i} - 2\mathbf{j} + 3\mathbf{k}$, and $\mathbf{v}_2 = 2\mathbf{i} + \mathbf{j} + 3\mathbf{k}$. Then $\mathbf{v}_1 \times \mathbf{v}_2 = -9\mathbf{i} + 3\mathbf{j} + 5\mathbf{k}$. The plane p_2 containing P_2 and parallel to $\mathbf{v}_1 \times \mathbf{v}_2$ and $\mathbf{v}_2$ has the equation

$$\begin{vmatrix} x - 1 & y + 1 & z \\ -9 & 3 & 5 \\ 2 & 1 & 3 \end{vmatrix} = 0,$$

from which we obtain $4x + 37y - 15z + 33 = 0$. To find the intersection of p_2 with the line l_1, we substitute the parametric equations of l_1 into this equation. This gives us $t = -2$ and hence the intersection is $P(-10, 1, 2)$. Finally, the line through P parallel to $\mathbf{v}_1 \times \mathbf{v}_2$ is the common perpendicular. It has the symmetric equations

$$\frac{x + 10}{-9} = \frac{y - 1}{3} = \frac{z - 2}{5}.$$

If we require only the distance between the lines, it is not necessary to find the equation of the common perpendicular.

Consider the line l_1 passing through P_1 parallel to $\mathbf{v}_1$ and line l_2 passing through P_2 parallel to $\mathbf{v}_2$. We assume that l_1 and l_2 are not parallel, otherwise we have a problem in plane geometry. Let P and Q be the intersection of the common perpendicular with l_1 and l_2, respectively, as in Figure 11.15. We want to find the distance between the lines, that is, $|PQ|$.

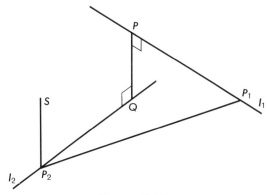

FIGURE 11.15

Let p be the plane containing the line l_1 and parallel to l_2. At P_2 draw a line parallel to QP meeting the plane p at S. Then $|PQ| = |P_2S|$. But $|P_2S|$ is the projection of $|P_2P_1|$ on a line parallel to QP, that is, parallel to $\mathbf{v}_1 \times \mathbf{v}_2$. From this we see that

$$|PQ| = \frac{|P_2P_1 \cdot (\mathbf{v}_1 \times \mathbf{v}_2)|}{|\mathbf{v}_1 \times \mathbf{v}_2|}.$$

EXAMPLE   11.19

Find the distance between the line l_1 with equations $x = -8 + t$, $y = -3 - 2t$, $z = 8 + 3t$, and the line l_2 with equations

$$\frac{x-1}{2} = \frac{y+1}{1} = \frac{z}{3}.$$

These are the same lines as in the previous example. Again we have $P_1(-8,-3,8)$, $P_2(1,-1,0)$, $\mathbf{v}_1 = \mathbf{i} - 2\mathbf{j} + 3\mathbf{k}$, $\mathbf{v}_2 = 2\mathbf{i} + \mathbf{j} + 3\mathbf{k}$,   and $\mathbf{v}_1 \times \mathbf{v}_2 = -9\mathbf{i} + 3\mathbf{j} + 5\mathbf{k}$. Also $P_2P_1 = -9\mathbf{i} - 2\mathbf{j} + 8\mathbf{k}$. Therefore the distance is

$$|PQ| = \frac{|P_2P_1 \cdot (\mathbf{v}_1 \times \mathbf{v}_2)|}{|\mathbf{v}_1 \times \mathbf{v}_2|}$$

$$= \frac{|81 - 6 + 40|}{\sqrt{81 + 9 + 25}} = \frac{115}{\sqrt{115}} = \sqrt{115}.$$

11.15   Intersection of three planes

We saw in Section 11.8 that two planes may coincide, may be parallel, or may intersect in a line. What is the situation if we consider three planes? If two of the planes intersect in a line, the line may lie in the third plane, may be parallel to the third plane, or may have a single point in common with the third plane.

Let us consider the three planes whose equations are

$$a_1x + b_1y + c_1z = d_1,$$
$$a_2x + b_2y + c_2z = d_2,$$
$$a_3x + b_3y + c_3z = d_3.$$

We denote the normals to these by $\mathbf{v}_1 = a_1\mathbf{i} + b_1\mathbf{j} + c_1\mathbf{k}$, $\mathbf{v}_2 = a_2\mathbf{i} + b_2\mathbf{j} + c_2\mathbf{k}$, $\mathbf{v}_3 = a_3\mathbf{i} + b_3\mathbf{j} + c_3\mathbf{k}$, respectively.

The first two planes intersect in a line if $\mathbf{v}_1 \times \mathbf{v}_2 \neq \mathbf{0}$. In this case the line of intersection is parallel to $\mathbf{v}_1 \times \mathbf{v}_2$. The condition under which these three planes will determine a point is that $\mathbf{v}_1 \times \mathbf{v}_2$ should not be parallel to nor lie in the third plane, that is, $(\mathbf{v}_1 \times \mathbf{v}_2) \cdot \mathbf{v}_3 \neq 0$.

We can state this result as follows: The three planes determine a point if and only if $[\mathbf{v}_1,\mathbf{v}_2,\mathbf{v}_3] \neq 0$. This in turn can be written

$$\begin{vmatrix} a_1 & b_1 & c_1 \\ a_2 & b_2 & c_2 \\ a_3 & b_3 & c_3 \end{vmatrix} \neq 0.$$

If $[\mathbf{v}_1,\mathbf{v}_2,\mathbf{v}_3] = 0$, there are three possibilities.

1. There is no point on all three planes (for example, the three planes may be parallel).

2. There may be one line common to the three planes.

3. The three planes may coincide.

We now have a convenient way to answer the question of whether three planes determine a point. Is there a way to use determinants to find the point of intersection? Before we answer this question we point out that we are in fact concerned with finding the solution of a system of three linear equations.

To solve the equations for x, we want to eliminate y and z. We multiply the first equation by $b_2c_3 - b_3c_2$, the second by $-(b_1c_3 - b_3c_1)$, and the third by $b_1c_2 - b_2c_1$. This gives

$$a_1(b_2c_3 - b_3c_2)x + b_1(b_2c_3 - b_3c_2)y + c_1(b_2c_3 - b_3c_2)z = d_1(b_2c_3 - b_3c_2),$$
$$-a_2(b_1c_3 - b_3c_1)x - b_2(b_1c_3 - b_3c_1)y - c_2(b_1c_3 - b_3c_1)z = -d_2(b_1c_3 - b_3c_1),$$
$$a_3(b_1c_2 - b_2c_1)x + b_3(b_1c_2 - b_2c_1)y + c_3(b_1c_2 - b_2c_1)z = d_3(b_1c_2 - b_2c_1).$$

We now add these three equations and obtain

$$[a_1(b_2c_3 - b_3c_2) - a_2(b_1c_3 - b_3c_1) + a_3(b_1c_2 - b_2c_1)]x$$
$$= d_1(b_2c_3 - b_3c_2) - d_2(b_1c_3 - b_3c_1) + d_3(b_1c_2 - b_2c_1).$$

We observe that the coefficient of x and the right-hand side are expansions of determinants. Thus we have

$$\begin{vmatrix} a_1 & b_1 & c_1 \\ a_2 & b_2 & c_2 \\ a_3 & b_3 & c_3 \end{vmatrix} x = \begin{vmatrix} d_1 & b_1 & c_1 \\ d_2 & b_2 & c_2 \\ d_3 & b_3 & c_3 \end{vmatrix}.$$

We can handle y and z similarly to get the solution

$$x = \frac{\begin{vmatrix} d_1 & b_1 & c_1 \\ d_2 & b_2 & c_2 \\ d_3 & b_3 & c_3 \end{vmatrix}}{\begin{vmatrix} a_1 & b_1 & c_1 \\ a_2 & b_2 & c_2 \\ a_3 & b_3 & c_3 \end{vmatrix}}, \quad y = \frac{\begin{vmatrix} a_1 & d_1 & c_1 \\ a_2 & d_2 & c_2 \\ a_3 & d_3 & c_3 \end{vmatrix}}{\begin{vmatrix} a_1 & b_1 & c_1 \\ a_2 & b_2 & c_2 \\ a_3 & b_3 & c_3 \end{vmatrix}}, \quad z = \frac{\begin{vmatrix} a_1 & b_1 & d_1 \\ a_2 & b_2 & d_2 \\ a_3 & b_3 & d_3 \end{vmatrix}}{\begin{vmatrix} a_1 & b_1 & c_1 \\ a_2 & b_2 & c_2 \\ a_3 & b_3 & c_3 \end{vmatrix}}.$$

We remember these as follows: The denominator in each case is the determinant formed from the coefficients. The numerator for x is the determinant obtained from the determinant of coefficients by replacing the coefficients of x by the constant terms from the right-hand side. Similar rules apply for y and z.

EXAMPLE   11.20

Do the following planes determine a point of intersection? If so, what is it?

$$2x + y - 3z = 2,$$
$$x - 2y + z = 1,$$
$$x + y + 4z = 7.$$

We have

$$\begin{vmatrix} 2 & 1 & -3 \\ 1 & -2 & 1 \\ 1 & 1 & 4 \end{vmatrix} = -30,$$

and therefore there is a unique point of intersection. The coordinates of this point are

$$x = \frac{\begin{vmatrix} 2 & 1 & -3 \\ 1 & -2 & 1 \\ 7 & 1 & 4 \end{vmatrix}}{-30} = 2, \quad y = \frac{\begin{vmatrix} 2 & 2 & -3 \\ 1 & 1 & 1 \\ 1 & 7 & 4 \end{vmatrix}}{-30} = 1, \quad z = \frac{\begin{vmatrix} 2 & 1 & 2 \\ 1 & -2 & 1 \\ 1 & 1 & 7 \end{vmatrix}}{-30} = 1.$$

Can anything interesting be said about the case where the determinant of coefficients is zero? We have seen that either there is no solution or there is an infinite number of solutions, in fact all the points on either a line or a plane. If we know that there is a common point and the determinant is zero, we can say that there must be an infinite number of common points, that is, the system of equations has an infinite number of solutions.

For the case in which $d_1 = d_2 = d_3 = 0$, it is obvious that the origin is on all three planes. These equations are referred to as *homogeneous*. A solution other than (0,0,0) is called a *nontrivial solution*. We can now state that a homogeneous system has a nontrivial solution if and only if the determinant of coefficients is zero.

EXAMPLE   11.21

Does the following system of equations have a nontrivial solution?

$$x - 3y + 2z = 0,$$
$$2x - y + z = 0,$$
$$4x + 3y - z = 0.$$

We have

$$\begin{vmatrix} 1 & -3 & 2 \\ 2 & -1 & 1 \\ 4 & 3 & -1 \end{vmatrix} = 0,$$

and hence there is a nontrivial solution and, in fact, an infinite number of solutions.

EXERCISES

11.22. Do the following pairs of planes intersect in a line?
   (a) $x + 2y - 3z = 4$ and $2x - 4y + 2z = 1$.
   (b) $2x - 3y + 4z = 3$ and $4x - 6y + 8z = 0$.

11.23. Which of the following pairs of equations represent a line?
   (a) $2x - y + z = 2$, $2x - y - z = 5$.
   (b) $3x + y - 2z = 0$, $6x + 2y + 4z = 0$.
   (c) $2x - 4y + 6z = 7$, $3x - 6y + 9z = 10$.

11.24. If P_1 has coordinates (1,3,4) and P_2 has coordinates (3,4,2), find the coordinates of the point P that lies on the line through P_1 and P_2 and divides the segment P_1P_2 in the ratio 2:3.

11.25. Find the equations, in both parametric and symmetric form, of the line through $P_1(0,2,5)$ and $P_2(1,5,2)$.

11.26. Find the equations of the line through $A(1,3,2)$ and $B(2,3,4)$.

11.27. Find the equations of the line through $P(1,2,3)$ and parallel to $\mathbf{i} - \mathbf{j} + \mathbf{k}$.

11.28. Find the equations of the line through $P(4,2,1)$ and parallel to $2\mathbf{i} - 3\mathbf{k}$.

11.29. Given the points $P_1(2,1,4)$ and $P_2(5,-1,2)$:

(a) Find the parametric equations of the line through P_1 and P_2.

(b) Find the intersections (if any) of the line with the xy plane, the xz plane, and the yz plane.

(c) Find the equation of a plane containing the line and perpendicular to the xy plane. Do the same for the xz plane and the yz plane.

11.30. A line is given as the intersection of the planes $2x + 4y + z = 1$ and $x + 2y - z = 5$. Find two planes, one perpendicular to the xy plane and one perpendicular to the xz plane, that intersect in this line.

11.31. Find the equation of the line through $(3,1,2)$ that is parallel to the planes $2x + 3y + 2z = 5$ and $3x - y + 2z = 4$.

11.32. Find the equation of the plane through $(7,-5,2)$ perpendicular to the line $x = 2y = 3z$.

11.33. A plane has intercepts $(4,0,0)$, $(0,6,0)$, and $(0,0,10)$. Find the equations of the line through $(7,-2,3)$ that is perpendicular to this plane.

11.34. Find the equations of the line through $(6,-2,4)$ perpendicular to a plane containing representatives of the vectors $3\mathbf{i} + 7\mathbf{j} - 5\mathbf{k}$ and $4\mathbf{i} - 6\mathbf{j} + \mathbf{k}$.

11.35. Find the equation of the plane containing the line $x/4 = y/3 = z$ that is perpendicular to the plane $6x + 5y + 2z = 10$.

11.36. The planes $3x - y + z + 1 = 0$ and $5x + y - 3z = 0$ intersect in the line l. Find the equation of the line that intersects l at right angles and contains $(1,2,1)$.

11.37. Prove that the angle between two lines as defined in Section 11.11 is independent of the choice of $A \in l_1$.

11.38. Find the angle between the line whose equations are $x - 1 = y - 1 = \sqrt{2}\,z$ and the line whose equations are $x - y + z = 0$ and $2x - 2y + 3z = 0$.

11.39. The planes $2x + y + 3z = 2$ and $x + 2y + z = 5$ determine a line l. Find the equation of the plane p_1 containing l and perpendicular to the xy plane. Find the equations of the line l_1 of intersection of p_1 with the xy plane. Find the equation of the plane p_2 containing l perpendicular to the xz plane. Find the equations of the line l_2 of intersection of p_2 with the xz plane. Find the cosine of the angle between l_1 and l_2.

11.40. At what angle does the intersection of the planes $x + y + 2z - 3 = 0$ and $2x + y + 3z - 5 = 0$ intersect the plane $4x + 2y - 4z + 1 = 0$? What are the coordinates of the point of intersection?

11.41. Find the distance from $(0,2,3)$ to the plane $2x + 3y - z = 5$.

11.42. Find the distance from the origin to the plane passing through $(9,7,3)$, which is perpendicular to the line joining $(8,2,7)$ and $(11,6,19)$.

11.43. Find the distance from the point $(2,3,0)$ to the line through $(3,1,0)$ and $(2,0,1)$.

11.44. Let l_1 be the line through $(2,-2,1)$ and $(-1,1,1)$ and let l_2 be the line through $(3,2,4)$ and $(0,0,4)$. Find the common perpendicular to these two lines and the coordinates of its intersection with each. Find the distance between l_1 and l_2 by two different methods.

11.45. Find the distance between the lines whose equations are

$$\frac{x-1}{2} = \frac{y+1}{1} = \frac{z}{2}$$

and

$$\frac{x+2}{1} = \frac{y-1}{2} = \frac{z-2}{3}.$$

11.46. Find the distance between the lines whose equations are

$$\frac{x-1}{2} = \frac{y+1}{2} = \frac{z}{4}$$

and

$$\frac{x+2}{3} = \frac{y-3}{3} = \frac{z+4}{6}.$$

11.47. Find the distance between the line of intersection of the planes $x + y + z = 1$ and $2z = 1$ and the line joining $(1,1,1)$ and $(2,1,0)$.

11.48. Find the distance from $(3,6,-1)$ to the line through $(-1,2,-3)$ and $(1,3,-1)$.

11.49. The points $A(1,2,3)$, $B(2,3,1)$, $C(3,1,2)$ and $D(1,2,1)$ are given.

(a) Find the equations of the planes ABC and ABD.
(b) Find the cosine of the angle between the planes ABC and ABD.
(c) What is the cosine of the angle between the lines AC and AB?
(d) Find the distance between the lines AB and CD.
(e) Find the equations of the line in the plane ABC passing through A and perpendicular to the intersection of the plane ABC and the xy plane.

11.50. Do the following sets of planes determine a point? If so, what is the point?

(a) $3x + 2y - z = 8$, $2x - 5y + 2z = -3$, $x - y + z = 1$.
(b) $4x - y + 2z = 4$, $3x - y + z = 10$, $11x - 3y + 5z = 0$.
(c) $2x - y + z = 3$, $3x - 2y - z = -1$, $2x - y + 3z = 7$.

11.51. Which of the following sets of homogeneous equations have nontrivial solutions?

(a) $2x + 5y - 3z = 0$,
$3x - y + z = 0$,
$2x - 2y + z = 0$.
(c) $5x - y + 2z = 0$,
$x + y - 5z = 0$,
$2x + 2y + 3z = 0$.

(b) $3x - 2y + z = 0$,
$x + 3z = 0$,
$2x - 2y - 5z = 0$.

11.52. Do the three planes $2x + y - z = 8$, $x - 2y + 3z = 7$, and $x - 3y + z = 0$ intersect in a plane, a line, or a point?

11.53. Find all the real numbers λ such that the following system of equations has a nontrivial solution.

$$\lambda x + y + \sqrt{2}\, z = 0,$$
$$x + \lambda y + \sqrt{2}\, z = 0,$$
$$\sqrt{2}\, x + \sqrt{2}\, y + (\lambda - 2)z = 0.$$

11.54. Let l_1 be the line through $(2,1,1)$ and $(1,2,2)$; let l_2 be the line through $(2,2,1)$ parallel to $\mathbf{i} + \mathbf{j} - \mathbf{k}$. Find the equations of l_1 and of l_2. Find the coordinates of intersection of l_1 and l_2.

Part Four

THE CALCULUS

12

Sequences and Series

12.1 The calculus

In this part we deal with topics that are found in texts on the calculus. It is not our purpose to duplicate the material of these books but to show how the techniques of set theory, number systems, and algebra can be used to make the concepts of the calculus precise. This will bear out our claim that the language of set theory is fundamental to all mathematics. In keeping with this purpose, we shall emphasize the conceptual aspects of the calculus rather than computation. We shall use the computational aspect to illustrate the concepts we discuss.

The next few chapters are not a substitute for a course in calculus. They are rather an introduction or a supplement to such a course.

12.2 Sequences

In Section 3.3 we defined a sequence as a function whose domain is N, the set of natural numbers. We also warned the reader against the confusion, found in some older texts, between a sequence and a set. The codomain is often indicated by the terminology we use for a sequence. If the codomain is Z, the set of integers, we shall refer to a sequence of integers; if the codomain is R, the set of real numbers, we speak of a real sequence or a sequence of real numbers; if the codomain is C, the set of complex numbers, we have a complex sequence or a sequence of complex numbers.

In this chapter we shall primarily consider real sequences, but we shall also observe that the results can easily be applied to complex sequences, which we shall see can be considered pairs of real sequences.

Since we are going to study real sequences, it is important that we recall the algebraic and order structures of the real numbers. We can sum up the algebraic structure by saying that the real numbers form a field. The most important features of the order structure are the facts that the real numbers are densely ordered and that every nonempty bounded set of real numbers has a least upper bound (lub or sup) and a greatest lower bound (glb or inf). The details of these facts are given in Chapter 6.

The complex numbers also form a field, but we did not discuss an order relation for them. In fact, there is no useful way to order the complex numbers. In Chapter 7 the complex numbers are introduced as the Cartesian product $R \times R$. This fact enables us to apply results for real sequences to complex sequences.

The most important concept we shall introduce is the limit of a real sequence. This concept of limit is the cornerstone of mathematical analysis and the key to understanding the calculus.

12.3   Definition of sequences

In our discussion of the sequence $u : N \to A$ we shall write the value of the sequence for $n \in N$ as $u(n)$ or u_n. It is sometimes convenient to denote the sequence by $(u_n)_{n \in N}$.

Since the domain of a sequence is the set N of natural numbers, we can make use of definition by induction in defining a sequence (see Section 5.7). This method can be combined with the composition of functions (see Section 3.8) to define many sequences.

If $f : N \to A$ is a sequence and $g : A \to A$ is any function, then the composite $g \cdot f : N \to A$ is also a sequence with values in the set A.

EXAMPLE   12.1

Let $f : N \to R$, where $f(n) = a^n$ for some $a \in R$, $a > 0$, and $g : R \to R$, where $g(x) = \sin x$. Then we have $g \cdot f : N \to R$, where $g \cdot f(n) = \sin (a^n)$.

EXAMPLE   12.2

Let $f_1 : N \to R$ and $f_2 : N \to R$ be two sequences. Let $\varphi : N \to R \times R$, where $\varphi(n) = (f_1(n), f_2(n))$. Since $R \times R$ can be considered the set of complex numbers C, we can write $\varphi : N \to C$. From this we can see that *defining a complex sequence is equivalent to defining an ordered pair of real sequences.*

In a similar way we can define a real sequence in terms of two given real sequences. Let $f_1 : N \to R$ and $f_2 : N \to R$ be the given sequences. Let $\varphi : N \to R \times R$, where $\varphi(n) = (f_1(n), f_2(n))$, and let $g : R \times R \to R$. Then $g \cdot \varphi : N \to R$ is a real sequence.

EXAMPLE 12.3

If $g:R \times R \to R$, where $g(x,y) = x + y$, then the sequence $g \cdot \varphi:N \to R$ is such that $g \cdot \varphi(n) = f_1(n) + f_2(n)$. The sequence $g \cdot \varphi$ is called the *sum of the sequences* f_1 and f_2. We can similarly define the *product of two sequences* $h \cdot \varphi$, where $h(x,y) = xy$ and $h \cdot \varphi(n) = f_1(n) \cdot f_2(n)$. This product is sometimes denoted by $f_1 \cdot f_2$. The reader must use the context to distinguish between the product of sequences and the composition of functions when they are denoted in the same way.

EXAMPLE 12.4

A subsequence[1] can also be defined by means of the composition of functions. If $f:N \to A$ is any sequence and $g:N \to N$ a function, then the composite $f \cdot g:N \to A$ is also a sequence, called a *subsequence*.

For many purposes it is more convenient to use the subscript notation for a subsequence. If the sequence $f:N \to A$ is denoted $f(n) = a_n$ and if we denote the value $g(n)$ by $i_n \in N$, then the value of the subsequence $f \cdot g$ at n is denoted by $f \cdot g(n) = a_{i_n}$.

With each infinite subset $B \subset N$ we can associate a subsequence of $f:N \to A$. For each such B there is a function $g:N \to N$, which is increasing [that is, if $n < m$, then $g(n) < g(m)$] and such that $g(N) = B$. To prove the existence of this function we would require a more complete study of infinite sets than we undertook in Part I. We can, however, prove that, if such a function exists, it is unique. Suppose there are two such functions $g:N \to N$ and $h:N \to N$. If $g \neq h$, there is a smallest $n \in N$ such that $g(n) \neq h(n)$. Suppose that $g(n) < h(n)$. Since $h(N) = B$, there is an $m \in N$ such that $h(m) = g(n)$. Then $h(m) < h(n)$ and hence $m < n$, since h is an increasing function. Also $g(m) \neq h(m)$, since g is increasing and hence injective. But this contradicts our choice of n. Therefore $g = h$ and the function is unique.

12.4 Monotone sequences

In this section we shall consider only real sequences $f:N \to R$. Both N and R are ordered by the usual order relation $\leq$. If the function f is monotone, that is, is either nondecreasing or nonincreasing (see Section 4.8), we call it a monotone sequence. We shall discuss in detail only nondecreasing sequences. The reader can supply the parallel development for nonincreasing sequences. If the sequence $u:N \to R$ is denoted by the subscript notation, then u is non-

[1] A subsequence is sometimes described as a restriction of a sequence. This definition would not allow us to consider that a subsequence is a sequence.

decreasing if and only if $u_1 \leq u_2 \leq u_3 \leq \cdots$ and is nonincreasing if and only if $u_1 \geq u_2 \geq u_3 \geq \cdots$.

If a sequence $f: N \to R$ is such that its range $f(N)$ has an upper bound, we say that the *sequence f is bounded above*. If the range $f(N)$ does not have an upper bound, we say that the sequence f is not bounded above, or simply that it is unbounded. If the range $f(N)$ has a lower bound, we say that the *sequence f is bounded below*. We say that the *sequence f is bounded* if it is bounded above and below.

EXAMPLE   12.5

The sequence $f: N \to R$, where $f(n) = n/(n + 1)$, is nondecreasing. Also $f(N)$ has 1 as an upper bound; therefore f is bounded above. The sequence $g: N \to R$, where $g(n) = n!$, is nondecreasing, but it is not bounded above.

According to Theorem 4.7, the composite function of two monotone functions is monotone. From this it follows that any subsequence of a monotone sequence is monotone.

We shall approach the concept of the limit of a sequence, a central concept of analysis, by considering the behavior of a nondecreasing sequence that is bounded above. Such a sequence can be represented

$$a_1 \leq a_2 \leq a_3 \leq \cdots \leq a_n \leq \cdots .$$

Since the sequence is bounded above, Theorem 6.10 shows that the set $\{a_n | n \in N\}$ has a least upper bound, $\sup\limits_{n \in N} a_n$. We denote this least upper bound by b. For any $c < b$ we know that c cannot be an upper bound, that is, there is an element a_n such that $c \leq a_n \leq b$. Since the sequence is nondecreasing, we have $a_n \leq a_m$ whenever $n < m$. Then we have $c \leq a_n \leq a_m \leq b$. This situation is illustrated in Figure 12.1.

FIGURE 12.1

The number c has been chosen arbitrarily, subject only to the condition that $c < b$. The results of the previous paragraph are valid no matter how close c is to b. We sometimes say that c is *arbitrarily close to b*, or *as close to b as we want*, or that the difference $b - c$ is *arbitrarily small*. It would be better to say "arbitrarily chosen" rather than "arbitrarily small," since the latter gives no precise meaning to "small." The phrase "arbitrarily small" is, however, well-established by tradition and provides a useful visualization.

We can now see that the elements $a_n, a_{n+1}, \cdots$ lie in the interval[2] $[c,b]$; in fact all the values of the sequence except perhaps $a_1, a_2, \cdots, a_n$ lie in this

[2] See Section 4.6 for this notation for intervals.

interval. The suitable value for n depends upon the value of c. We can state our results as follows.

If $(a_n)_{n \in N}$ is a nondecreasing sequence bounded above, if $b = \sup a_n$, and if $c < b$ is given, then there is a number $n \in N$, depending on c, which we denote by $n(c)$, such that for $m > n(c)$ we have $c \leq a_m \leq b$.

It is customary to specify the difference $b - c = \varepsilon$ rather than the value of c. Since c is an arbitrary number less than b, ε is an arbitrary positive number. With this change in terminology our results can be stated as the following theorem.

THEOREM   12.1

If $(a_n)_{n \in N}$ is a nondecreasing sequence bounded above and with $\sup a_n = b$, then for any real number $\varepsilon > 0$ there is a natural number $n(\varepsilon)$ such that $b - \varepsilon \leq a_m \leq b$ for all natural numbers $m \geq n(\varepsilon)$.

EXAMPLE   12.6

Consider the nondecreasing bounded sequence $a_n = (n - 1)/n$ for $n \in N$. Then $\sup a_n = 1$. For $\varepsilon = 1$ we have $[b - \varepsilon, b] = [0,1]$. Thus all a_n except a_1 lie in the interval and $n(1) = 1$. For $\varepsilon = \frac{1}{2}$ we have $[b - \varepsilon, b] = [\frac{1}{2}, 1]$ and $n(\frac{1}{2}) = 2$. For $\varepsilon = \frac{1}{10}$ we have $[\frac{9}{10}, 1]$ and $n(\frac{1}{10}) = 10$. This indicates that, the smaller we choose $\varepsilon > 0$, the larger $n(\varepsilon)$ must be, but the theorem assures us that such a *finite* $n(\varepsilon)$ always exists.

12.5 Convergent sequences

The behavior we have just observed for bounded monotone sequences motivates the definition of limit of a sequence. We shall slightly alter the form to allow for nonmonotone sequences.

Consider the sequence $f: N \to R$. If there is a number $l \in R$ such that for each $\varepsilon > 0$ there is only a finite number of values of $f(n)$ outside the interval $[l - \varepsilon, l + \varepsilon]$, then we call l *the limit of the sequence*. We denote this limit by $\lim_{n \to \infty} f(n) = l$, $\lim_{n \to \infty} a_n = l$, $\lim_{n \to \infty} f = l$. (The first two are the more usual notations.)

We have used the interval $[l - \varepsilon, l + \varepsilon]$ rather than $[l - \varepsilon, l]$, since we are not restricting ourselves to nondecreasing sequences. The reader can easily see that, for a nondecreasing sequence that is bounded above, the least upper bound is a limit.

The concept of limit is important enough to justify restating the definition in a slightly different but equivalent form.

The number $l \in R$ is called a limit of the sequence $(a_n)_{n \in N}$ if, for any real number $\varepsilon > 0$, there is a natural number $n(\varepsilon)$ such that

$$l - \varepsilon \leq a_n \leq l + \varepsilon$$

for all natural numbers $n > n(\varepsilon)$. The condition for a_n can also be written $|l - a_n| \leq \varepsilon$. The number $n(\varepsilon)$ is greater than or equal to the number of values $a_1, a_2, \cdots$ that lie outside the interval $[l - \varepsilon, l + \varepsilon]$. This means that, if there is a limit, only a finite number of values lie outside this interval.

EXAMPLE 12.7

Consider the sequence $(a_n)_{n \in N}$, where $a_n = 1 + (-1)^n/n$. Then $a_1 = 0$, $a_2 = \frac{3}{2}$, $a_3 = \frac{2}{3}$, $a_4 = \frac{5}{4}$. It is clear that this sequence is not monotone. If we represent the values as in Figure 12.2 we see that they are getting closer

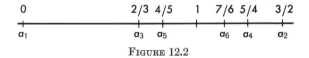

FIGURE 12.2

and closer to 1. This suggests that 1 is a limit of the sequence. If we choose $\varepsilon = \frac{1}{2}$, we see that all values except a_1 are in the interval $[1 - \frac{1}{2}, 1 + \frac{1}{2}]$; therefore we may take $n(\frac{1}{2}) = 2$. For $\varepsilon = \frac{1}{10}$ we see that all values from a_{10} on are in $[1 - \frac{1}{10}, 1 + \frac{1}{10}]$; therefore we may take $n(\frac{1}{10}) = 10$. For any ε we have $a_n \in [1 - \varepsilon, 1 + \varepsilon]$ provided $1/n \leq \varepsilon$, that is, $n(\varepsilon)$ can be taken as the smallest integer greater than $1/\varepsilon$.

EXAMPLE 12.8

We have seen that a monotone sequence that is bounded always has a limit. It is possible, however, for a sequence that is not monotone to be bounded but to have no limit. For example, consider the sequence $(b_n)_{n \in N}$, where $b_n = (-1)^n$. It is clear that $|b_n| \leq 1$ for all $n \in N$, and hence the sequence is bounded above by 1 and below by -1. But the sequence has no limit since

$$b_n = 1 \qquad \text{for } n \text{ even}$$
$$= -1 \qquad \text{for } n \text{ odd}.$$

Hence for any $l > 0$ and any $\varepsilon < 1$ we have $b_{2n-1} \notin [l - \varepsilon, l + \varepsilon]$ for all $n \in N$. Similarly, for $l < 0$ we have $b_{2n} \notin [l - \varepsilon, l + \varepsilon]$ for all $n \in N$.

THEOREM 12.2

If a sequence has a limit, then the limit is unique.

Proof

Suppose there are two limits l and l', with $l < l'$. If $\varepsilon = (l' - l)/3$, then $[l - \varepsilon, l + \varepsilon] \cap [l' - \varepsilon, l' + \varepsilon] = \varnothing$. Since l is a limit, there is a number $n_1 \in N$ such that $a_n \in [l - \varepsilon, l + \varepsilon]$ for $n > n_1$. Since l' is a limit there is a number $n_2 \in N$ such that $a_n \in [l' - \varepsilon, l' + \varepsilon]$ for $n > n_2$. If $m > n_1$ and $m > n_2$, then $a_m \in [l - \varepsilon, l + \varepsilon] \cap [l' - \varepsilon, l' + \varepsilon]$, but this is a contradiction. Therefore there cannot be two limits. •

DEFINITION

A sequence $(a_n)_{n \in N}$ that has a limit is called a *convergent sequence;* we also say that *the sequence converges.*

A sequence that is not convergent is called *divergent.* We also say that *the sequence diverges.*

12.6 Convergent sequences of complex numbers

In Section 12.3 we showed that defining a complex sequence was the same as defining an ordered pair of real sequences. If $f: N \to C$ is the complex sequence and $f_1: N \to R$ and $f_2: N \to R$ are the two real sequences, we have $f(n) = (f_1(n), f_2(n))$ or $f(n) = f_1(n) + if_2(n)$, depending on the notation we choose for complex numbers. We also write $f = (f_1, f_2)$ or $f = f_1 + if_2$. We call the real sequence f_1 the real part of the sequence f and the real sequence f_2 the imaginary part of f.

We have not defined an order for the complex numbers and so cannot ask for a monotone complex series. We can, however, define a bounded complex sequence.

DEFINITION

A complex sequence $f: N \to C$ is called *bounded*[3] if the nonnegative real sequence $|f|: N \to R$, where $|f|(n) = |f(n)|$, is bounded above. (See Section 7.5 for the meaning of the modulus $|f(n)|$.)

In geometric terms this means that, if the values $f(n)$ are plotted on the Argand diagram and they all lie in some circle with center at the origin, as in Figure 12.3, then the sequence is bounded. If there is no circle containing the range of f as in Figure 12.4, then the sequence is not bounded; we say it is *unbounded.*

---

[3] Since we have not established an order on the complex numbers, we cannot discuss bounded above or bounded below.

EXAMPLE   12.9

If $a: N \to C$, where $a_n = \cos n + i \sin n$, then all a_n lie on the unit circle and $(a_n)_{n \in N}$ is bounded (see Figure 12.3).

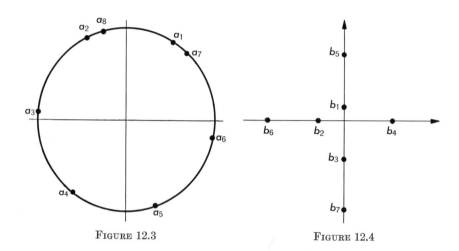

FIGURE 12.3   FIGURE 12.4

EXAMPLE   12.10

If $b: N \to C$, where $b_n = ni^n$, then b_n lies on the axis of reals if n is even and on the axis of imaginaries if n is odd, as in Figure 12.4. There is no circle containing all the b_n, since $|b_n| = n$. Hence b is unbounded.

THEOREM   12.3

If $f = (f_1, f_2)$ is a complex sequence, then f is bounded if and only if the two real sequences f_1 and f_2 are bounded above and below.

Proof

1. Suppose that f_1 and f_2 are bounded above and below. Then for all $n \in N$, $|f_1(n)| < m_1$, $|f_2(n)| < m_2$. But $|f(n)| = \sqrt{(f_1(n))^2 + (f_2(n))^2}$. Therefore $|f(n)| < \sqrt{m_1{}^2 + m_2{}^2}$ and f is bounded.

2. Suppose f is bounded, that is, $|f(n)| < m$ for all $n \in N$. Then $(f_1(n))^2 + (f_2(n))^2 < m^2$. Therefore $-m < f_1(n) < m$ and $-m < f_2(n) < m$ for all $n \in N$, i.e., f_1 and f_2 are bounded above and below. •

We can also define the notion of convergence for complex sequences.

DEFINITION

The complex sequence $f = (f_1, f_2)$ is called *convergent* if the two real sequences f_1 and f_2 are convergent.

With a convergent complex sequence $f = (f_1, f_2)$, we can associate the complex number $l = \lim f_1 + i \lim f_2$. Theorem 12.4 shows that l plays a role for the complex sequence similar to the role of the limit for a real sequence. We shall call l the *limit of the complex sequence f*.

THEOREM 12.4

If the complex sequence $f = (f_1, f_2)$ is convergent then for each real $\varepsilon > 0$ there is a natural number $n(\varepsilon)$ such that

$$|l - f(m)| < \varepsilon$$

for all $m > n(\varepsilon)$, $m \in N$, where $l = \lim f_1 + i \lim f_2$.

Proof

Since f converges, the real sequences f_1 and f_2 converge. Therefore we can find natural numbers $n_1(\varepsilon)$ and $n_2(\varepsilon)$ such that

$$|f_1(m) - \lim f_1| < \varepsilon/2 \qquad \text{for } m > n_1(\varepsilon),$$

and

$$|f_2(m) - \lim f_2| < \varepsilon/2 \qquad \text{for } m > n_2(\varepsilon).$$

We now choose $n(\varepsilon) = \max(n_1(\varepsilon), n_2(\varepsilon))$, that is, the larger of $n_1(\varepsilon)$ and $n_2(\varepsilon)$. We can then use the properties of the modulus of complex numbers from Section 7.5 as follows:

$$
\begin{aligned}
|l - f(m)| &= |l - f_1(m) - if_2(m)| \\
&= |\lim f_1 - f_1(m) + i \lim f_2 - if_2(m)| \\
&\leq |\lim f_1 - f_1(m)| + |i||\lim f_2 - f_2(m)| \\
&= |\lim f_1 - f_1(m)| + |\lim f_2 - f_2(m)| \\
&\leq \varepsilon/2 + \varepsilon/2 = \varepsilon,
\end{aligned}
$$

for $m > n(\varepsilon)$. •

In the case of real sequences we defined a sequence as convergent if it had a limit. We could have used a similar definition in the complex case. Theorem 12.5 shows that such a definition is equivalent to the one we have used.

THEOREM 12.5

The complex sequence $f = (f_1, f_2)$ is convergent if and only if there is a complex number $l = l_1 + il_2$ such that, for each real $\varepsilon > 0$, there is a natural number $n(\varepsilon)$ such that

$$|l - f(m)| < \varepsilon$$

for $m > n(\varepsilon)$.

Proof

We have already proved in Theorem 12.4 that, if f is convergent, there is a complex number l with these properties.

Suppose there is a complex number l with the required properties. We want to prove that f is a convergent sequence. From the definition of the modulus in Section 7.5 it is clear that $|x| \leq |x + iy|$ and $|y| \leq |x + iy|$. Then

$$|l_1 - f_1(m)| \leq |l_1 + il_2 - f_1(m) - if_2(m)| < \varepsilon$$

for $m > n(\varepsilon)$, and

$$|l_2 - f_2(m)| \leq |l_1 + il_2 - f_1(m) - if_2(m)| < \varepsilon$$

for $m > n(\varepsilon)$. Therefore f_1 and f_2 have limits l_1 and l_2, respectively, and hence are convergent. •

EXAMPLE   12.11

The values $a_n = i^n/n$ of the sequence $a : N \to C$ are plotted on the Argand diagram in Figure 12.5. If we draw a circle with center at the origin and

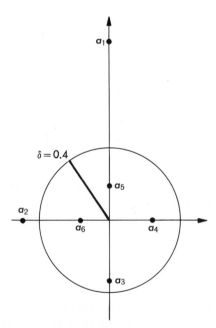

FIGURE 12.5

radius ε, then all a_n for $n > 1/\varepsilon$ lie inside this circle. The sequence is convergent and has zero as its limit.

12.7 Cauchy's theorem

We have defined the convergence of a real sequence in terms of the existence of a limit. The direct application of this definition depends on finding (or proving the nonexistence of) an element that is not used in the description of the sequence. We might say that it is an "external test." Is it possible to find an internal criterion for convergence, that is, a criterion stated entirely in terms of the values of the sequence? Such a criterion was discovered by A. L. Cauchy and published in his famous *Analyse algébrique* in 1821. It is referred to as Cauchy's theorem.

As a first step toward this criterion we define a "Cauchy sequence."

DEFINITION

A sequence $s:N \to R$ is called a *Cauchy sequence* if for any real $\varepsilon > 0$ there is a natural number $n(\varepsilon)$ such that

$$|s_m - s_{m'}| < \varepsilon$$

for $m \geq n(\varepsilon)$, $m' > n(\varepsilon)$.

This states that, by taking m, m' large enough, we can make the difference between the values of the sequence s_m and $s_{m'}$ smaller than a specified positive number. The definition does not depend on the difference between m and m'. To determine whether a sequence is a Cauchy sequence, we need only consider values of the sequence, not external objects such as the limit.

It is easily seen that the following characterization of a Cauchy sequence is equivalent to our definition. A sequence $s:N \to R$ is a Cauchy sequence if for any real $\varepsilon > 0$ there is a natural number $n(\varepsilon)$ such that

$$|s_m - s_{m+k}| < \varepsilon$$

for all $m > n(\varepsilon)$ and all $k \in N$.

EXAMPLE   12.12

Consider the sequence $s_n = 1 + 1/n$. Then $s_n - s_{n+k} = 1 + 1/n - 1 - 1/(n+k) = k/n(n+k) < 1/n < \varepsilon$ for $n > 1/\varepsilon$. Therefore s is a Cauchy sequence.

EXAMPLE   12.13

Consider the sequence $a_n = 1/n + (-1)^n$. Then $a_{2n} - a_{2n+1} = 1/(2n) + (-1)^{2n} - 1/(2n+1) - (-1)^{2n+1} = 2 + 1/(2n)(2n+1)$. If we choose $\varepsilon < 2$ and $k = 1$, the condition is not satisfied and hence a is not a Cauchy sequence.

LEMMA   12.1

A Cauchy sequence is bounded.

Proof

Choose $\varepsilon = 1$. Then for $m > n(1)$ we have $|s_m - s_{n(1)}| < 1$, i.e., $s_{n(1)} - 1 < s_m < s_{n(1)} + 1$. Then $(s_n)_{n \in N}$ is bounded above by the least upper bound of the set $\{s_1, s_2, \cdots, s_{n(1)-1}, s_{n(1)} + 1\}$ and is bounded below

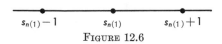

$$s_{n(1)} - 1 \qquad s_{n(1)} \qquad s_{n(1)} + 1$$

FIGURE 12.6

by the greatest lower bound of $\{s_1, s_2, \cdots, s_{n(1)-1}, s_{n(1)} - 1\}$. In other words, all s_m with $m > n(1)$ are in the interval $[s_{n(1)} - 1, s_{n(1)} + 1]$ as shown in Figure 12.6. •

We can now prove part of the main theorem.

THEOREM   12.6

Every convergent sequence is a Cauchy sequence.

Proof

Since the sequence $s: N \to R$ is convergent, it has a limit $l \in R$ such that $|l - s_m| < \varepsilon/2$ for $m > n(\varepsilon/2)$. Then, by using the properties of absolute values from Section 7.5, we obtain

$$|s_m - l + l - s_{m'}| \leq |s_m - l| + |l - s_{m'}| < \varepsilon/2 + \varepsilon/2 = \varepsilon$$

for $m > n(\varepsilon/2)$, $m' > n(\varepsilon/2)$. Therefore s is a Cauchy sequence. •

Before completing the proof of Cauchy's theorem we must show that, from any bounded real sequence, it is possible to select a subsequence that is convergent. In proving this we shall make use of the facts that a bounded set of real numbers has a least upper bound and a greatest lower bound, and that a monotone bounded sequence has a limit.

THEOREM   12.7

For any bounded real sequence $(a_n)_{n \in N}$ there is a subsequence $(s_n)_{n \in N}$ ($s_n = a_{i_n}$, where $i_n < i_m$ if $n < m$) such that $(s_n)_{n \in N}$ has a limit.

Proof

We define a new sequence of real numbers $(t_k)_{k \in N}$ as follows:

$$t_1 = \sup_{n \geq 1} \{a_n\},$$
$$t_2 = \sup_{n \geq 2} \{a_n\},$$
$$\cdots$$
$$t_k = \sup_{n \geq k} \{a_n\}.$$

It is clear that this is a nonincreasing sequence and that it is bounded below by $\inf_{n \in N} \{a_n\}$. Hence it has a greatest lower bound and we write $t = \inf_{k \in N} t_k$. We shall now show that $(a_n)_{n \in N}$ has a subsequence that converges to t.

Since t is the greatest lower bound of $(t_k)_{k \in N}$, there is some k_1 such that $|t - t_{k_1}| < \frac{1}{2}$. But $t_{k_1} = \sup_{n \geq k_1} \{a_n\}$. Therefore there is an a_{i_1} such that $|t_{k_1} - a_{i_1}| < \frac{1}{2}$ (see Figure 12.7), and hence $|t - a_{i_1}| < 1$. We can now take

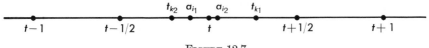

$$t-1 \qquad t-1/2 \qquad t \qquad t+1/2 \qquad t+1$$

FIGURE 12.7

t_{k_2}, with $k_2 > k_1$, such that $|t - t_{k_2}| < \frac{1}{4}$. Then there is an a_{i_2} with $i_2 > i_1$ such that $|t_{k_2} - a_{i_2}| < \frac{1}{4}$, and hence $|t - a_{i_2}| < \frac{1}{2}$. In this way we get a subsequence $(a_{i_n})_{n \in N}$ such that $|t - a_{i_n}| < \frac{1}{2}^{n-1}$. For a given ε we can choose for $n(\varepsilon)$ the smallest natural number such that $2^{n(\varepsilon)-1} > 1/\varepsilon$. Then

$$|t - a_{i_n}| < \varepsilon$$

for all $n \geq n(\varepsilon)$, and so the subsequence converges to t. ●

THEOREM 12.8 (CAUCHY'S THEOREM)

A real sequence is convergent if and only if it is a Cauchy sequence.

Proof

We have already proved in Theorem 12.6 that every convergent sequence is a Cauchy sequence. We must now prove that every Cauchy sequence is convergent.

Consider the Cauchy sequence $s : N \to R$. By Lemma 12.1, s is a bounded sequence, and by Theorem 12.7 there is a convergent subsequence $t : N \to R$, where $t_n = s_{i_n}$. If $\lim t = l$, we shall prove that $\lim s = l$. Suppose $\varepsilon > 0$ is given. Since s is a Cauchy sequence, there is $n(\varepsilon/2) \in N$ such that $|s_m - s_{m'}| < \varepsilon/2$ for $m > n(\varepsilon/2)$, $m' > n(\varepsilon/2)$. Since the sequence t converges, there is $n'(\varepsilon/2) \in N$ such that, for $n > n'(\varepsilon/2)$, $|l - t_n| = |l - s_{i_n}| < \varepsilon/2$. Choose m so that $m > n(\varepsilon/2)$, $m > n'(\varepsilon/2)$. Then $i_m > n(\varepsilon/2)$, $i_m > n'(\varepsilon/2)$, and $|l - s_m| = |l - s_{i_m} + s_{i_m} - s_m| \leq |l - s_{i_m}| + |s_{i_m} - s_m| < \varepsilon/2 + \varepsilon/2 = \varepsilon$. Therefore $\lim s = l$ and s is a convergent sequence. •

EXAMPLE   12.14

Consider the sequence

$$s_n = 1 + \frac{1}{2} + \frac{1}{3} + \cdots + \frac{1}{n}.$$

We want to determine whether this sequence converges by using Cauchy's theorem. Suppose $\varepsilon = \frac{1}{4}$. We have

$$s_{2n} - s_n = \frac{1}{n+1} + \frac{1}{n+2} + \cdots + \frac{1}{2n} > \frac{n}{2n} = \frac{1}{2}.$$

Therefore s is not a Cauchy sequence and is not convergent. It is clear that this is an increasing sequence. Therefore it is not bounded because, if it were bounded and increasing, it would be convergent.

12.8   Cauchy's theorem for complex sequences

We can also define the concept of Cauchy sequences for complex sequences and prove that a complex sequence is convergent if and only if it is a Cauchy sequence.

DEFINITION

A complex sequence $s : N \to C$ is called a *Cauchy sequence* if, for each $\varepsilon > 0$, there is a natural number $n(\varepsilon) > 0$ such that

$$|s_m - s_{m'}| < \varepsilon$$

for all $m > n(\varepsilon)$, $m' > n(\varepsilon)$.

LEMMA   12.2

A complex Cauchy sequence is bounded.

Proof

If we take $\varepsilon = 1$, there is $n(1) \in N$ such that

$$|s_m - s_{n(1)}| < 1$$

for all $m > n(1)$. Thus all s_m except, perhaps, $s_1, s_2, \cdots, s_{n(1)-1}$ are in a circle with center at $s_{n(1)}$ and radius 1. Let r' be the largest of $|s_n - s_{n(1)}|$ for $n = 1, 2, \cdots, n(1) - 1$, and let r be the larger of r' and 1. Then all s_n lie in a circle with center at $s_{n(1)}$ and radius r. Therefore the sequence is bounded.

Consider the complex sequence s as an ordered pair of real sequences $s = u + iv$. If s is a complex Cauchy sequence, then u and v are real Cauchy sequences, since

$$|u_m - u_{m'}| \leq |s_m - s_{m'}| < \varepsilon$$

and

$$|v_m - v_{m'}| \leq |s_m - s_{m'}| < \varepsilon$$

for $m > n(\varepsilon)$, $m' > n(\varepsilon)$.

It follows from Theorem 12.8 that u and v are convergent sequences and, from the definition of convergence for complex sequences, that s is convergent.

Consider on the other hand a convergent sequence $s : N \to C$. Then there is a limit l, that is, for each $\varepsilon > 0$ there is $n(\varepsilon/2) \in N$ such that

$$|l - s_m| < \frac{\varepsilon}{2}$$

for $m > n(\varepsilon/2)$. If $m > n(\varepsilon/2)$ and $m' > n(\varepsilon/2)$, then

$$|s_m - s_{m'}| \leq |s_m - l| + |l - s_{m'}| < \frac{\varepsilon}{2} + \frac{\varepsilon}{2} = \varepsilon.$$

Therefore s is a Cauchy sequence. •

This completes the proof of the following theorem.

THEOREM 12.9

A complex sequence is convergent if and only if it is a Cauchy sequence.

12.9 Properties of convergent sequences

The limit of a real sequence is a real number, that is, the limit associates with each convergent real sequence a real number. If we let $\mathfrak{C}_R$ represent the set of all convergent real sequences, we thus have a function

$$\lim : \mathfrak{C}_R \to R.$$

Also the concept of limit associates with a convergent complex sequence a complex number. If $\mathfrak{C}_C$ is the set of all convergent complex sequences, we have the function

$$\lim : \mathfrak{C}_C \to C.$$

We have used lim to denote the function in each case. In fact, the function for the real case is a restriction of the function for the complex case if we consider the real sequence s is the complex sequence $s + i0$. In our proofs we shall deal with the complex case. It is clear that the results also hold for the real case.

The results of this section will enable us to obtain new convergent sequences from given convergent sequences. We shall begin by defining the sum and product of two sequences, as we did in Section 9.3.

DEFINITION

If $s = (s_n)_{n \in N}$ and $t = (t_n)_{n \in N}$ are complex sequences, we call the sequence $s + t = (s_n + t_n)_{n \in N}$ the *sum* of s and t, and the sequence $st = (s_n t_n)_{n \in N}$ the *product* of s and t.

Theorems 12.10 and 12.11 show that the sum and product of convergent sequences are also convergent.

THEOREM   12.10

If s and t are convergent complex sequences, then the sum $s + t$ is also convergent and

$$\lim (s_n + t_n) = \lim s_n + \lim t_n.$$

Proof

For $\varepsilon > 0$ we have $n_1(\varepsilon) \in N$, $n_2(\varepsilon) \in N$, such that

$$|\lim s - s_n| < \frac{\varepsilon}{2} \qquad \text{for } n > n_1(\varepsilon)$$

and

$$|\lim t - t_n| < \frac{\varepsilon}{2} \qquad \text{for } n > n_2(\varepsilon).$$

Let $n(\varepsilon)$ be the larger of $n_1(\varepsilon)$ and $n_2(\varepsilon)$. Then

$$|\lim s + \lim t - (s_n + t_n)| \le |\lim s - s_n| + |\lim t - t_n| < \varepsilon$$

for $n > n(\varepsilon)$. •

EXAMPLE   12.15

If s and t are convergent complex sequences, then the difference $s - t = (s_n - t_n)_{n \in N}$ is also convergent and

$$\lim (s_n - t_n) = \lim s_n - \lim t_n.$$

THEOREM 12.11

If s and t are convergent complex sequences, then the product st is also convergent and

$$\lim (s_n t_n) = \lim s_n \lim t_n.$$

Proof

We observe that

$$s_n t_n - \lim s \lim t = s_n t_n - s_n \lim t + s_n \lim t - \lim s \lim t$$
$$= s_n(t_n - \lim t) + (s_n - \lim s) \lim t.$$

Since the sequences s and t are convergent, they are bounded (by Lemma 12.2). Let k be the larger of lub $|s_n|$ and lub $|t_n|$. Then

$$|s_n t_n - \lim s \lim t| \leq |s_n||t_n - \lim t| + |s_n - \lim s||\lim t|$$
$$\leq k(|t_n - \lim t| + |s_n - \lim s|).$$

Also, since s and t are convergent, there are, for each ε, $n_1(\varepsilon/2k) \in N$ and $n_2(\varepsilon/2k) \in N$ such that

$$|s_n - \lim s| < \frac{\varepsilon}{2k} \qquad \text{for } n > n_1\left(\frac{\varepsilon}{2k}\right)$$

and

$$|t_n - \lim t| < \frac{\varepsilon}{2k} \qquad \text{for } n > n_2\left(\frac{\varepsilon}{2k}\right).$$

Let $n(\varepsilon)$ be the larger of $n_1\left(\frac{\varepsilon}{2k}\right)$ and $n_2\left(\frac{\varepsilon}{2k}\right)$. Then

$$|s_n t_n - \lim s \lim t| \leq k\left(\frac{\varepsilon}{2k} + \frac{\varepsilon}{2k}\right) = \varepsilon$$

for $n > n(\varepsilon)$. •

The reader can easily see that the sum and product of sequences we have just defined are the same as those defined in Section 9.3. Then $\mathfrak{F}(N,C)$ and, similarly, $\mathfrak{F}(N,R)$ are rings. The subset $\mathfrak{R}$ of $\mathfrak{F}(N,C)$, which consists of sequences $s = (s_1,s_2)$ such that $s_2(n) = 0$ for all $n \in N$, is a subring of $\mathfrak{F}(N,C)$. Furthermore $\mathfrak{R}$ is isomorphic to $\mathfrak{F}(N,R)$. We often choose to identify the real sequence s_1 with the complex sequence s. When this is done we refer to $\mathfrak{F}(N,R)$ as a subring of $\mathfrak{F}(N,C)$ rather than use the more precise description of $\mathfrak{F}(N,R)$ as being isomorphic to a subring of $\mathfrak{F}(N,C)$.

Since $\mathfrak{F}(N,C)$ is a ring, we can prove two theorems, which together are equivalent to Theorems 12.10 and 12.11, although neither one alone is equivalent to either of these.

THEOREM   12.12

1. The set of convergent complex sequences $\mathcal{C}_C$ is a subring of $\mathcal{F}(N,C)$.
2. The set of convergent real sequences $\mathcal{C}_R$ is a subring of $\mathcal{F}(N,R)$.

Proof

We shall give the proof of 1 only; the proof of 2 is similar. If $s \in \mathcal{C}_C$ and $t \in \mathcal{C}_C$, then, by Example 12.15, $s - t \in \mathcal{C}_C$ and $\mathcal{C}_C$ is a subgroup. Theorem 12.11 shows that $st \in \mathcal{C}_C$. Therefore $\mathcal{C}_C$ is a subring of $\mathcal{F}(N,C)$. •

THEOREM   12.13

The map $\lim : \mathcal{C}_C \to C$ is a homomorphism of the ring $\mathcal{C}_C$ onto the ring C.

Proof

To be a ring homomorphism the function must preserve addition and multiplication. But this has already been proved in Theorems 12.10 and 12.11, that is,

$$\lim (s + t) = \lim s + \lim t$$

and

$$\lim (s \cdot t) = \lim s \cdot \lim t. \quad •$$

In the ring $\mathcal{C}_C$ the sequence $z : N \to C$, where $z(n) = 0$ for all $n \in N$, is the zero element, and the sequence $e : N \to C$, where $e(n) = 1$ for all $n \in N$, is the identity element.

For all $a \in C$ the constant sequence $s_n = a$ has the property that $\lim s = a$. Therefore the function $\lim$ is onto. But if $s_n = 0$ and $t_n = 1/n$, then $\lim s = 0$ and $\lim t = 0$. Therefore the function $\lim$ is not injective.

DEFINITION

A sequence $s \in \mathcal{C}_C$ is called a *null sequence* if $\lim s = 0$.

A similar definition can be given for a null sequence in the set of real sequences.

Example 12.16 shows one way in which a new null sequence can be constructed from a known null sequence.

EXAMPLE   12.16

If $(x_n)_{n \in N}$ is a null sequence, then the sequence $(x_n')_{n \in N}$, where $x_n' = (x_1 + \cdots + x_n)/n$, is a null sequence. To see this we observe that for each

$\varepsilon > 0$ there is a natural number $m(\varepsilon)$ such that $|x_n| < \varepsilon/2$ if $n > m(\varepsilon)$. Then

$$
\begin{aligned}
|x_n'| &\leq \frac{|x_1 + x_2 + \cdots + x_{m(\varepsilon)}|}{n} + \frac{|x_{m(\varepsilon)+1} + \cdots + x_n|}{n} \\
&\leq \frac{|x_1 + \cdots + x_{m(\varepsilon)}|}{n} + \frac{\varepsilon}{2} \cdot \frac{n - m(\varepsilon)}{n} \\
&< \frac{|x_1 + \cdots + x_{m(\varepsilon)}|}{n} + \frac{\varepsilon}{2}.
\end{aligned}
$$

We can now choose a natural number $p(\varepsilon)$ such that

$$
\frac{|x_1 + \cdots + x_{m(\varepsilon)}|}{n} < \frac{\varepsilon}{2}
$$

for all $n > p(\varepsilon)$. Now choose for $n(\varepsilon)$ the larger of $m(\varepsilon)$ and $p(\varepsilon)$. Then for $n > n(\varepsilon)$ we have $|x_n'| < \varepsilon/2 + \varepsilon/2 = \varepsilon$ and hence $(x_n')_{n \in N}$ is a null sequence.

We shall now prove a theorem concerning the algebraic structure of the set of null sequences.

THEOREM   12.14

The set of all null sequences is a subring of the ring $\mathcal{C}_C$.

Proof

It is clear from the definition of null sequences that the set of all null sequences is the kernel of the ring homomorphism $\lim : \mathcal{C}_C \to C$ (see Section 9.6). But Theorem 9.8 shows that the kernel is a subring. •

In the exercises on natural numbers in Chapter 5 the reader was asked to prove that $(1 + a)^n \geq 1 + an$ for all $a \in N$ and all $n \in N$. We leave the reader to prove that this result is also true for $a \in R_+$. This result is known as *Bernoulli's inequality*. We shall use it in Theorem 12.15 to obtain an important example of a null sequence.

THEOREM   12.15

For a complex number b such that $|b| < 1$, the sequence $(u_n)_{n \in N}$, where $u_n = b^n$, is a null sequence.

Proof

If $|b| = 0$, the result is obvious. If $0 < |b| < 1$ we can write $|b| = 1/(1 + a)$, where $a \in R_+$. We know that $|b^n| = |b|^n$. Then Bernoulli's inequality shows that

$$
|b^n| = |b|^n = \frac{1}{(1 + a)^n} \leq \frac{1}{1 + na} < \frac{1}{na}.
$$

Then $\lim b^n = 0$, that is, $(u_n)_{n \in N}$ is a null sequence. •
The following corollary is easily obtained.

Corollary 1

If b is a complex number such that $|b| < 1$, then the sequence $(v_n)_{n \in N}$, where $v_n = nb^n$, is a null sequence.

Proof

We have already seen that $|b^n| = 1/(1 + a)^n$ for some $a \in R_+$. But $(1 + a)^n = 1 + na + n(n - 1)a^2/2 + \cdots + a^n > n(n - 1)a^2/2$ and hence

$$|nb^n| < \frac{2}{(n - 1)a^2}.$$

Therefore $\lim nb^n = 0$ and $(v_n)_{n \in N}$ is a null sequence. •
The proof of the following theorem is left as an exercise.

THEOREM   12.16

Two convergent complex sequences have the same limit if and only if their difference is a null sequence.

We have studied the sum, difference, and product of two sequences. The quotient can also be defined, but it must be handled with greater care. Before we define it we shall prove Theorem 12.17.

THEOREM   12.17

If $s \in \mathcal{C}_C$, $s_n \neq 0$ for all n and $\lim s \neq 0$, then the sequence t, where $t(n) = 1/s_n$, is also a convergent sequence and

$$\lim t = \frac{1}{\lim s}.$$

Proof

We shall use Cauchy's theorem (Theorem 12.9) to prove convergence. To do this we consider the difference

$$\left| \frac{1}{s_i} - \frac{1}{s_j} \right| = \frac{|s_i - s_j|}{|s_i s_j|}.$$

Since $\lim s \neq 0$, there is a k such that $0 < k < |\lim s|$ and $n_1(k) \in N$ such that $|s_i| > k$, $|s_j| > k$ for $i > n_1(k)$, $j > n_1(k)$. Then

$$\left| \frac{1}{s_i} - \frac{1}{s_j} \right| \leq \frac{|s_i - s_j|}{k^2}$$

for $i > n_1(k)$, $j > n_1(k)$.

For each $\varepsilon > 0$ there is $n_2(k^2\varepsilon)$ such that $|s_i - s_j| < k^2\varepsilon$ for $i > n_2(k^2\varepsilon)$, $j > n_2(k^2\varepsilon)$. Let $n(k,\varepsilon)$ be the larger of $n_1(k)$, $n_2(k^2\varepsilon)$. Then

$$\left| \frac{1}{s_i} - \frac{1}{s_j} \right| \leq k^2 \frac{\varepsilon}{k^2} = \varepsilon$$

for $i > n(k,\varepsilon)$, $j > n(k,\varepsilon)$. Therefore $t \in \mathfrak{C}_C$.

The product sequence $s \cdot t$ is $e : N \to C$, where $e(n) = 1$ for all $n \in N$. By Theorem 12.11,

$$\lim s \cdot \lim t = \lim (s \cdot t) = \lim e = 1.$$

Since $\lim s \neq 0$, we have $\lim t = 1/\lim s$. •

In the exercises we shall see that, for a given sequence $s \in \mathfrak{C}_C$, it is possible to find more than one sequence t such that $\lim t = 1/\lim s$.

We can now define the quotient of sequences.

DEFINITION

The sequence $s/t = (s_n/t_n)_{n \in N}$, provided $t_n \neq 0$ for all $n \in N$, is called the *quotient* of the sequences $s = (s_n)_{n \in N}$ and $t = (t_n)_{n \in N}$.

Using this definition of the quotient sequence, we can obtain the following corollary to Theorem 12.17.

Corollary 1

If $s \in \mathfrak{C}_C$, $t \in \mathfrak{C}_C$, $t_n \neq 0$, and $\lim t_n \neq 0$, then the quotient sequence s/t is convergent and

$$\lim \left(\frac{s}{t} \right) = \frac{\lim s}{\lim t}.$$

Proof

By Theorem 12.16 we know that the sequence $a : N \to C$, where $a_n = 1/t_n$, is convergent and $\lim a = 1/\lim t$. Also the sequence $s \cdot a$ converges by Theorem 12.11 and $\lim (s \cdot a) = \lim s \cdot \lim a = (\lim s)/(\lim t)$. But $s \cdot a = s/t$ and $\lim (s/t) = (\lim s)/(\lim t)$. •

In the definition of the quotient sequence s/t we have required $t_n \neq 0$ but have placed no restriction on $\lim t$ or on s. It may be that $\lim s = 0$ and $\lim t = 0$ but $\lim (s/t)$ exists; or it may happen that sequences s and t are not convergent, but the sequence s/t is convergent.

If we know the limits of certain complex sequences, the theorems of this section enable us to calculate the limits of new sequences formed from these by addition, subtraction, multiplication, or division, or by combinations of these.

EXAMPLE 12.17

If $x_n = n/(n + 1)$, what is $\lim x_n$? We might try Corollary 1 to Theorem 12.16, but we would find that the two sequences of which this is the quotient are not convergent. We can, however, write

$$x_n = \frac{1}{1 + 1/n}.$$

Then we are concerned with the quotient of the sequences $s_n = 1$ and $t_n = 1 + 1/n$. But $\lim s = 1$ and $\lim t = 1$. Therefore $\lim x_n = \lim s/\lim t = 1$.

EXAMPLE 12.18

What is $\lim x_n$, where $x_n = (n + i)/(3 + n^2 i)$? We can write

$$x_n = \frac{1/n + i(1/n^2)}{3/n^2 + i}.$$

But $\lim (1/n + i(1/n^2)) = \lim (1/n) + \lim (i(1/n^2)) = 0$ and $\lim (3/n^2 + i) = i$. Therefore $\lim x_n = 0$.

EXERCISES

12.1. Consider the sequence $f:N \to R$, where $f(n) = n^3$, and the function $g:R \to R$, where $g(x) = 1/x$. Describe the sequence $g \cdot f$.

12.2. What are the sum and product of the sequences $f_1:N \to R$, where $f_1(n) = n/(1 + n)$, and $f_2:N \to R$, where $f_2(n) = (1 - n)/n$?

12.3. If $f:N \to R$ is a sequence such that $f(n) = \cos n\pi/3$ and $g:N \to N$ is a function such that $g(n) = 3n$, what is the value of the subsequence $f \cdot g$ for $n = 1,2,3,4,k$?

12.4. Show that there is a unique sequence $f_1:N \to N$ such that

$$f_1(1) = 1,$$
$$f_1(n + 1) = 2 + f_1(n).$$

This sequence is called the *arithmetic progression with common difference* 2.

12.5. Show that there is a unique sequence of sequences $(f_n)_{n \in N}$, where $f_n:N \to N$,

$$f_1(1) = 1,$$
$$f_1(m + 1) = f_1(m) + 2,$$

and for $k > 1$,

$$f_k(1) = 1,$$
$$f_k(m + 1) = f_k(m) + f_{k-1}(m).$$

The sequence f_n is called the *arithmetic progression of order n with common difference* 2.

12.6. With f_n defined as in Exercise 12.5, find n such that $f_n(1) = 1, f_n(2) = 2, f_n(3) = 4, f_n(4) = 8, f_n(5) = 17, f_n(6) = 36, f_n(7) = 72$.

12.7. With f_n defined as in Exercise 12.5 prove that f_1 is a polynomial of degree 1 and that f_k is a polynomial of degree k for all $k \in N$.

12.8. Let $g: N \to R_+$ be the function whose graph is defined by $g(x) = \sqrt{x}$. The sequence $f: N \to R$ is defined as follows:

$$f(1) = \sqrt{2},$$
$$f(n + 1) = g(f(n) + 2).$$

What are the first five terms of the sequence, that is, $f(1), f(2), \cdots, f(5)$?

12.9. Show that the relation defined by: s is a subsequence of t, is an order relation on the set of real sequences $\mathcal{F}(N, R)$.

12.10. For real sequences s and t we define: $s \prec t$ if and only if $s(n) \leq t(n)$ for all $n \in N$. Prove that this is an order relation on the set $\mathcal{F}(N, R)$.

12.11. Let f_1 be the arithmetic progression defined in Exercise 12.4 and let $f_1{}^n$ be the $(n - 1)$th iteration (see Section 3.9).

(a) Prove that $f_1{}^{n+1}$ is a subsequence of $f_1{}^n$.

(b) Prove that there is no sequence $g: N \to N$ that is a subsequence of $f_1{}^n$ for all $n \in N$.

12.12. State and prove the analogue of Theorem 12.1 dealing with a non-increasing sequence.

12.13. Prove that the sequence defined in Exercise 12.8 is monotone and bounded.

12.14. Consider the sequence $(x_n)_{n \in N}$, where

$$x_1 = 1,$$
$$x_2 = 1,$$
$$x_n = x_{n-1} + x_{n-2}, \qquad n \geq 3.$$

Is this sequence monotone? Is it bounded?

12.15. Is the sequence $(u_n)_{n \in N}$, where $u_1 = 0$, $u_2 = 1$, $u_n = (1/2)(u_{n-1} + u_{n-2})$ for $n \geq 3$, monotone? Is it bounded?

12.16. Is the sequence $f: N \to R$, where

$$f(n) = \frac{\sqrt[n]{n!}}{n},$$

bounded?

12.17. The limit of the sequence $(u_n)_{n \in N}$, where $u_n = 1/2^n$, is 0. For $\varepsilon = 1/100$ find $n(\varepsilon)$ such that $|1/2^n - 0| < \varepsilon$ for all $n > n(\varepsilon)$.

12.18. Consider the sequence $(u_n)_{n \in N}$, where

$$u_n = (1/n - 1)^n.$$

Let l be a given real number and let $\varepsilon = 1/10$. Show that there is an infinite subsequence of u_n each of whose values is outside $[l - \varepsilon, l + \varepsilon]$.

12.19. Prove that the sequence $(x_n)_{n \in N}$, where

$$x_n = n^n - n^{(-1)^n}$$

is not convergent. Is it bounded?

12.20. What are the least upper bound and the greatest lower bound for the sequence $(x_n)_{n\in N}$, where

$$x_n = (-1)^n \frac{n-1}{n}.$$

12.21. Show that the two characterizations of a Cauchy sequence given at the beginning of Section 12.7 are equivalent.

12.22. Prove Bernoulli's inequality, that is,

$$(1+a)^n \geq 1 + an$$

for all $a \in R_+$, all $n \in N$.

12.23. Prove that the sequence $(x_n)_{n\in N}$, where $x_n = (1 + 1/n)^n$ is an increasing sequence.

12.24. Prove that the sequence $(y_n)_{n\in N}$, where $y_n = (1 + 1/n)^{n+1}$, is a decreasing sequence. [*Hint:* We want to show that $(1 + 1/(n-1))^n > (1 + 1/n)^{n+1}$. Divide both sides of this by $(1 + 1/n)^n$ and apply Bernoulli's inequality (Exercise 12.22).]

12.25. Let $(x_n)_{n\in N}$ be the sequence in Exercise 12.23 and $(y_n)_{n\in N}$ the sequence in Exercise 12.24. Prove that $y_n > x_n$ for all $n \in N$. Do these sequences have limits?

12.26. With $\mathfrak{R}$ defined as in Section 12.9, prove that $\mathfrak{R}$ is a subring of $\mathfrak{F}(N,C)$.

12.27. Prove that the ring $\mathfrak{R}$ in Exercise 12.26 is isomorphic to $\mathfrak{F}(N,R)$.

12.28. Complete the proof of Theorem 12.12., that is prove that $\mathfrak{C}_R$ is a subring of $\mathfrak{F}(N,R)$.

12.29. Prove Theorems 12.10 and 12.11 from the results of Theorems 12.12 and 12.13.

12.30. Prove Theorem 12.15.

12.31. For fixed $k \in N$ show that the sequence $(u_n)_{n\in N}$, where $u_n = 1/n^k$, is a null sequence.

12.32. (a) What is the limit of the sequence $(x_n)_{n\in N}$, where

$$x_n = \frac{n^2+1}{n^2+n+1}?$$

(b) For $\varepsilon = \frac{1}{10}$ find $n(\varepsilon)$ for x_n as required in the definition of convergence.

12.33. Prove that the complex sequences $(x_n)_{n\in N}$ and $(y_n)_{n\in N}$, where $x_n = i/\sqrt{n}$ and $y_n = (-1)^n/n!$, are null sequences.

12.34. Consider the real sequences s, t, u, where $s_n = n^2$, $t_n = 1/n^2$, $u_n = 1/(n^2+1)$. Prove that the product sequences $s \cdot t$ and $s \cdot u$ are both $e:N \to R$, where $e(n) = 1$ for all $n \in N$. This shows that s does not have a unique inverse.

12.35. Consider the sequences s and t, where $s_n = 1/n$ and $t_n = 1/n^2$. Show that s and t are null sequences, but that s/t is not a null sequence.

12.36. Show that the sequences s and t, where $s_n = n^2 + 1$ and $t_n = (n+1)^2$ are divergent, but s/t is convergent.

12.37. Prove that, if the quotient sequence s/t converges, then s and t either both converge or both diverge.

12.38. Prove that, if the sum sequence $u + v$ converges, then u and v either both converge or both diverge.

12.39. Consider the rings $\mathfrak{F}(N,R)$ and R. Show that the function $\tilde{n}:\mathfrak{F}(N,R) \to R$, where $\tilde{n}(s) = s_n$ for $s \in \mathfrak{F}(N,R)$, is a ring homomorphism.

12.10 Infinite series

In each number system we studied we defined the sum of two numbers and saw that this could easily be extended to the sum of an n-tuple of numbers. Since addition satisfies the associative law, this statement about the sum of an n-tuple is unambiguous; we do not need to describe the way the terms are grouped. Since addition satisfies the commutative law, we can talk about the sum of a set of numbers, not necessarily an n-tuple. But what would we mean by the "sum of an infinite set of numbers" or the "sum of the terms of an infinite sequence"? These phrases have no meaning in terms of the addition we have just discussed, but they can be given a meaning in terms of our study of sequences.

Consider a sequence $(x_n)_{n \in N}$ of either real or complex numbers. From this form a new sequence $(s_n)_{n \in N}$, where

$$s_1 = x_1,$$
$$s_2 = x_1 + x_2,$$
$$\cdot$$
$$\cdot$$
$$\cdot$$
$$s_n = x_1 + x_2 + \cdots + x_n.$$

The sequence s is called the *sequence of partial sums* of the sequence x.

If the sequence s is convergent, we call its limit lim s *the sum of the series* whose general term is x_n. In this case we also say that the series with general term x_n *is convergent*. If the sequence s of partial sums does not converge, we say that the series with general term x_n *is divergent*, and *we no longer talk about its sum.*

We have now defined convergence for both real and complex series. Much of what we wish to say about series is true in exactly the same form for either real or complex series. Unless we specifically state otherwise our results will be true in both cases.

What we have done so far is to associate with each sequence x a new sequence s, called the sequence of partial sums, and to consider whether the new sequence is convergent. If we let S represent the set of all sequences (real or complex as the case may be), then this process of association is in fact a function $\Sigma : \mathsf{S} \to \mathsf{S}$, where $\Sigma(x) = s$ and $s_n = x_1 + x_2 + \cdots + x_n$.

It is customary in the calculus to represent a series whose general term is x_n by $\sum x_n$ or by $\sum_{n=1}^{\infty} x_n$ or by $x_1 + x_2 + \cdots + x_n + \cdots$. In keeping with this it is sometimes convenient to write the partial sum s_n as $\sum_{k=1}^{n} x_k$ instead of as $x_1 + x_2 + \cdots + x_n$.

We shall show that the function Σ is bijective. Let $s \in \mathsf{S}$ be any sequence. Define the sequence x, where $x_n = s_n - s_{n-1}$ for $n \geq 2$ and $x_1 = s_1$. Then $x_1 + x_2 + \cdots + x_n = s_1 + (s_2 - s_1) + \cdots + (s_n - s_{n-1}) = s_n,$

and hence $\Sigma(x) = s$. Therefore the function Σ is onto. Now consider $x \in S$, $x' \in S$ such that $\Sigma(x) = \Sigma(x') = s$. Then $x_1 + x_2 + \cdots x_n = s_n$ and $s_n - s_{n-1} = x_n$. Similarly, $s_n - s_{n-1} = x_n'$. Therefore $x_n = x_n'$, $x = x'$ and the function Σ is injective.

We are chiefly interested in convergent series, that is, series for which the sequence of partial sums has a limit, say $\lim s = a$. In this case we say that a is the sum of the series or that the series converges to a. We might write $a = \lim \sum_{k=1}^{n} x_k$ but this is usually replaced by $a = \sum_{k=1}^{\infty} x_k$ or simply $a = \sum x_k$.

EXAMPLE   12.19

Consider the infinite series

$$b_0 + \frac{b_1}{10} + \frac{b_2}{10^2} + \cdots + \frac{b_n}{10^n} + \cdots,$$

with $b_0 \in Z$ and $b_i \in \{0,1, \cdots ,9\}$ for $i \in N$. If s_n denotes the partial sum of the first n terms, we see that s_n is the rational number $b_0 \cdot b_1 b_2 \cdots b_{n-1}$. Consider the real number $l = b_0 \cdot b_1 b_2 b_3 \cdots$. Then

$$|l - s_n| = 0.00 \cdots 0 b_n b_{n+1} \cdots \leq 0.00 \cdots 0999 \cdots$$
$$= \frac{1}{10^n}.$$

For a given $\varepsilon > 0$ we choose for $n(\varepsilon)$ the smallest natural number such that $1/10^{n(\varepsilon)} < \varepsilon$. For $n > n(\varepsilon)$ we have $|l - s_n| < \varepsilon$ and hence l is the sum of the series.

12.11   Some criteria for convergence

There are two basic problems that may concern us in the study of a particular series. The first is the question of whether the series converges. If the series does converge, we can go on to the second question of what its sum is. We shall give some means by which the first question may be answered; we shall not consider the second, and usually more difficult, problem.

Since we shall apply Cauchy's theorem in many of our proofs, it will be convenient to restate it in terms of series rather than sequences. We do this in the following lemma.

LEMMA   12.3

The series $\sum x_n$ of real or complex numbers is convergent if and only if for each $\varepsilon > 0$ there is $n(\varepsilon) \in N$ such that

$$|x_m + x_{m+1} + \cdots + x_{m+k}| < \varepsilon$$

for all $m > n(\varepsilon)$, $k \geq 0$.

Proof

If $(s_n)_{n \in N}$ is the sequence of partial sums we know by the definition of convergence and Theorem 12.9 that $\sum x_n$ converges if and only if for each $\varepsilon > 0$ there is $n(\varepsilon) \in N$ such that $|s_{m+k} - s_{m-1}| < \varepsilon$ for all $m - 1 > n(\varepsilon)$, $k \geq 0$. But

$$|s_{m+k} - s_{m-1}| = |x_m + x_{m+1} + \cdots + x_{m+k}|,$$

and this completes the proof. •

We shall now prove a necessary condition for convergence of a series.

THEOREM 12.18

If the real or complex series $\sum x_n$ is convergent, then $\lim x_n = 0$.

Proof

If we take $k = 0$ in Lemma 12.3 we see that for each $\varepsilon > 0$ there is $n(\varepsilon) \in N$ such that $|x_m| < \varepsilon$ for all $m > n(\varepsilon)$. But this means that $\lim x_n = 0$. •

The reader is warned against misinterpreting this result. It gives a *necessary* condition for convergence, but not a *sufficient* condition. It can never be used to prove that a series converges, but if $\lim x_n \neq 0$, then this theorem proves that the series diverges.

While we are on the subject of warnings we might add that this theorem and the others in this section are concerned with the convergence of series, not of sequences.

EXAMPLE 12.20

Consider the series $\sum x_n$ where $x_n = 1/n$, that is, $\sum 1/n = 1 + \frac{1}{2} + \frac{1}{3} + \cdots + 1/n + \cdots$. The sequence of partial sums is s where $s_n = 1 + \frac{1}{2} + \frac{1}{3} + \cdots + 1/n$. In the example at the end of Section 12.7 it was shown that the sequence s is not convergent. Therefore the *series* is not convergent. If we consider the *sequence* x, where $x_n = 1/n$, then this sequence converges and $\lim x_n = 0$. We have thus an example in which the $\lim x_n = 0$ but the series diverges. This shows that the converse of Theorem 12.17 cannot be true. This series is called the *harmonic series*.

EXAMPLE 12.21

Consider the series $\sum n/(n + 1)$. Does this series converge? In Example 12.7 we saw that $\lim (n/(n + 1)) = 1$. Thus $\lim x_n \neq 0$ and hence the series diverges.

Some of the methods we want to develop for testing a series for convergence will be proved only for *positive term series*, that is, for series $\sum a_n$ where $a_n \in R$, $a_n \geq 0$ for all $n \in N$. It would be more precise to call these "series with nonnegative terms" but the use of the word "positive" is customary here and is also less awkward. But these results can sometimes be used in a more general way. To show how this can be done we associate with each series of complex terms a series of positive real terms as in the following definition.

DEFINITION

The series $\sum x_n$ is called *absolutely convergent* if the series $\sum |x_n|$ is convergent.

The reader may ask what connection there is between convergence and absolute convergence. We shall answer this by means of a theorem and an example.

THEOREM   12.19

Every absolutely convergent series is convergent.

Proof

If $\sum x_n$ is absolutely convergent, then for each $\varepsilon > 0$ there is $n(\varepsilon) \in N$ such that

$$|x_m| + |x_{m+1}| + \cdots + |x_{m+k}| < \varepsilon$$

for all $m > n(\varepsilon)$, $k \geq 0$, by Lemma 12.3. But

$$|x_m + x_{m+1} + \cdots + x_{m+k}| \leq |x_m| + |x_{m+1}| + \cdots + |x_{m+k}| < \varepsilon.$$

Therefore $\sum x_n$ is convergent by Lemma 12.3. •

EXAMPLE   12.22

Consider the series

$$\frac{\sum (-1)^{n+1}}{n} = 1 - \frac{1}{2} + \frac{1}{3} - \frac{1}{4} + \cdots + \frac{(-1)^{n+1}}{n} + \cdots.$$

Then

$$x_m + x_{m+1} + \cdots + x_{m+2k+1}$$

$$= (-1)^{m+1} \left[\frac{1}{m} - \frac{1}{(m+1)} + \cdots - \frac{1}{(m+2k+1)} \right].$$

But

$$\frac{1}{m} - \frac{1}{(m+1)} + \cdots - \frac{1}{(m+2k+1)}$$

$$= \frac{1}{m(m+1)} + \frac{1}{(m+2)(m+3)} + \cdots + \frac{1}{(m+2k)(m+2k+1)} \geq 0.$$

Also

$$\frac{1}{m} - \frac{1}{(m+1)} + \cdots - \frac{1}{(m+2k+1)} = \frac{1}{m} - \frac{1}{(m+1)(m+2)}$$

$$- \cdots - \frac{1}{(m+2k-1)(m+2k)} - \frac{1}{(m+2k+1)} < \frac{1}{m}.$$

Therefore

$$|x_m + x_{m+1} + \cdots + x_{m+2k+1}| < \frac{1}{m} < \varepsilon$$

for $m > 1/\varepsilon$, and

$$|x_m + x_{m+1} + \cdots + x_{m+2k+2}| < \frac{1}{m} + \frac{1}{(m+2k+2)} < \varepsilon$$

for $m > 2/\varepsilon$. Thus for $m > 2/\varepsilon$ we have

$$|x_m + x_{m+1} + \cdots + x_{m+k}| < \varepsilon,$$

and $\sum x_n$ is convergent.

But we saw in an earlier example that $\sum |x_n|$ is not convergent. This shows that a series may be convergent without being absolutely convergent.

12.12   Positive term series

In this section we shall present a few of the methods that are available for determining whether a series with positive terms converges. Our discussion is by no means complete. The reader can find additional methods in calculus texts and in specialized books on infinite series.

For a positive term series it is clear that the sequence of partial sums is nondecreasing and hence is convergent if and only if it is bounded above. In view of this we sometimes write $\sum x_n < \infty$ to indicate that the positive term series $\sum x_n$ is convergent and $\sum x_n = \infty$ to indicate that it is divergent.

Theorem 12.20 is the central test for convergence from which the others are derived.

THEOREM   12.20 (COMPARISON TEST)

Let $\sum x_n$ and $\sum y_n$ be two series of positive terms such that for all $n > n_0$, $x_n \leq y_n$. Then

    1. If $\sum y_n$ is convergent, so is $\sum x_n$.
    2. If $\sum x_n$ is divergent, so is $\sum y_n$.

Proof

1. If $\sum y_n$ is convergent, then by Lemma 12.3 for each $\varepsilon > 0$, there is $n(\varepsilon) \in N$ such that $y_m + y_{m+1} + \cdots + y_{m+k} < \varepsilon$ for all $m > n(\varepsilon)$, $k \geq 0$. Let n_1 be the larger of n_0 and $n(\varepsilon)$. Then for $m > n_1$ we have

$$x_m + x_{m+1} + \cdots + x_{m+k} \leq y_m + y_{m+1} + \cdots + y_{m+k} < \varepsilon.$$

Therefore $\sum x_n$ is convergent.

2. Suppose $\sum y_n$ is not divergent, that is, it is convergent. Then, by part 1, $\sum x_n$ is convergent. But this is a contradiction. Therefore our assumption is false and $\sum y_n$ is divergent. •

To use this theorem we try to find a series that is known to be convergent or to be divergent and with which we can compare the series we are studying. This indicates that we need a collection of convergent series and a collection of divergent series. The most fruitful series to have in such a list but also the most difficult to handle will be those that are near the borderline between convergent and divergent, that is convergent series that approach their sum "slowly" and divergent series that do not increase "too rapidly." We shall not attempt to make these ideas precise; the reader will develop an intuitive appreciation of them. The following examples provide us with a small collection of useful series for comparison purposes. The *geometric series* and the *p series* are particularly useful; the reader should be sure he understands these thoroughly.

EXAMPLE   12.23

The series $\sum r^{n-1} = 1 + r + \cdots + r^n + \cdots$ is called a *geometric series*. In the exercises in Chapter 5 the reader was asked to prove that $1 + r + \cdots + r^{n-1} = (1 - r^n)/(1 - r)$. If $|r| < 1$, Theorem 12.15 shows that the limit of the sequence of partial sums is $1/(1 - r)$, and the series has the sum $1/(1 - r)$. If $|r| \geq 1$ the sequence of partial sums is unbounded and hence the series diverges.

We can sum up our results as follows: The geometric series $\sum r^{n-1}$ is convergent if $|r| < 1$ and divergent if $|r| \geq 1$.

For $r > 0$ the geometric series is a positive term series and so can be used for comparison.

EXAMPLE   12.24

Suppose we find that we can use the geometric series $\sum r^n$ with $0 < r < 1$ in part 1 of Theorem 12.19. It is clear from the last example that $\sum r^n$ is convergent. We have $x_n \leq r^n < 1$, therefore, $\sqrt[n]{x_n} < r < 1$. This gives us *Cauchy's test* for convergence: A series of positive terms $\sum x_n$ converges if, for all $n > n_0, \sqrt[n]{x_n} < r < 1$ and diverges if, for all $n > n_0, \sqrt[n]{x_n} \geq 1$. To prove the last part we need only observe that $x_n \geq 1$ and hence $\lim x_n \neq 0$.

EXAMPLE   12.25

A series of the form $\sum 1/n^p$ is called a *p series*. We have already seen that, for $p = 1$, the series, which in this case is the harmonic series, is divergent. If $p < 1$ we have $1/n < 1/n^p$. Then by Theorem 12.19 the series $\sum 1/n^p$ is divergent.

We shall now show that the series $\sum 1/n^2$ is convergent. If we let s_n denote the partial sum of the first n terms we have

$$s_n = \frac{1}{1^2} + \frac{1}{2^2} + \frac{1}{3^2} + \cdots + \frac{1}{n^2}.$$

It is sufficient to show that s_n is bounded above. Since $1/n^2 < 1/n(n-1) = 1/(n-1) - 1/n$ for $n \geq 2$ we see that

$$s_n < 1 + \left(1 - \frac{1}{2}\right) + \left(\frac{1}{2} - \frac{1}{3}\right) + \left(\frac{1}{3} - \frac{1}{4}\right)$$
$$+ \cdots + \left(\frac{1}{n-2} - \frac{1}{n-1}\right) + \left(\frac{1}{n-1} - \frac{1}{n}\right) = 1 + 1 - \frac{1}{n} < 2.$$

Therefore the series is convergent.

If $p > 2$ we have $1/n^p < 1/n^2$ and hence $\sum 1/n^p$ converges for $p \geq 2$.

We have not considered the case in which $1 < p < 2$. The p series converges in this case, but we shall not prove this fact. The usual proof depends on the concept of the integral, which we shall introduce in Chapter 14, and also on a study of the exponential function, which we do not attempt. For the purposes of the exercises the reader may assume this result.

We can summarize these results as follows: The p series $\sum 1/n^p$ is convergent for $p > 1$ and divergent for $p \leq 1$.

EXAMPLE 12.26

Consider the series

$$\sum \frac{1}{n\sqrt{n+1}}.$$

We have $1/n\sqrt{n+1} < 1/n^{3/2}$. But $\sum 1/n^{3/2}$ is convergent; therefore by Theorem 12.20 $\sum 1/n\sqrt{n+1}$ is also convergent.

We shall use the comparison test together with a geometric series to prove theorem 12.21, which gives a test that is more easily applied in some cases.

THEOREM 12.21 (D'ALEMBERT'S RATIO TEST)

If $\sum x_n$ is a series of positive terms such that for $n > n_0$

(1) $$\frac{x_{n+1}}{x_n} \le q < 1,$$

then the series converges. If

(2) $$\frac{x_{n+1}}{x_n} \ge 1,$$

then the series diverges.

Proof

1. The condition can be expressed as

$$\frac{x_{n+1}}{x_n} \le \frac{q^{n+1}}{q^n},$$

or

$$\frac{x_{n+1}}{q^{n+1}} \le \frac{x_n}{q^n},$$

for $n > n_0$. This shows that x_n/q^n is a nonincreasing sequence and

$$\frac{x_n}{q^n} \le \frac{x_{n_0}}{q^{n_0}}$$

for all $n > n_0$. Therefore

$$x_n < \frac{x_{n_0}}{q^{n_0}} \cdot q^n = kq^n$$

for all $n > n_0$. But $\sum q^n$ is convergent and the reader can easily prove that $\sum kq^n$ also converges, that is, $\sum x_n$ is convergent.

2. The condition can now be expressed as

$$\frac{x_{n+1}}{x_n} \geq \frac{q^{n+1}}{q^n},$$

where $q \geq 1$. An argument similar to part 1 shows that $x_n > kq^n$. But $\sum q^n$ diverges, since $q \geq 1$, and hence $\sum x_n$ diverges. •

The reader will realize that this proof could be considerably simplified. We have put it in this form as a pattern for the more general result to be found in the exercises.

EXAMPLE 12.27

Consider the series

$$\sum \frac{z^n}{n!}$$

where z is a complex number. The ratio of the absolute values of consecutive terms is

$$\frac{|z^{n+1}|}{(n+1)!} \cdot \frac{n!}{|z^n|} = \frac{|z|}{n+1} < \frac{1}{2} < 1$$

for $n + 1 > 2|z|$. Therefore $\sum z^n/n!$ converges absolutely.

EXAMPLE 12.28

For the series $\sum 1/n$, we get the ratio

$$\frac{1}{n+1} \cdot \frac{n}{1} = \frac{n}{n+1}.$$

There is no $r < 1$ such that $n/(n+1) < r$ for all large values of n, and we do not have $x_{n+1}/x_n \geq 1$ for $n \geq n_0$. Thus the theorem does not apply. This shows that it is not enough to have $x_{n+1}/x_n < 1$ for $n > n_0$; we need a fixed number r between x_{n+1}/x_n and 1.

EXAMPLE 12.29

For the series $\sum 1/n^2$, which we have shown is convergent, we get the ratio

$$\frac{1}{(n+1)^2} \cdot \frac{n^2}{1} = \left(\frac{n}{n+1}\right)^2.$$

Again there is no $r < 1$ such that $x_{n+1}/x_n < r$ for all large values of n, nor do we have $x_{n+1}/x_n \geq 1$ for $n \geq n_0$. These two examples show that this situation may hold for either a convergent or a divergent series, and hence that no information can be obtained in this way.

EXERCISES

12.40. Write out the first four terms and the general term of the sequence of partial sums of the series

$$\sum \frac{1}{2^n}.$$

12.41. (a) What is the general term in the sequence of partial sums of the series

$$\sum \left(\frac{1}{n+1} - \frac{1}{n} \right)?$$

(b) Is this series convergent?

12.42. Is the series

$$\sum \frac{2^n - 5}{2^n}$$

convergent? Give reasons for your answer.

12.43. If k is a fixed complex number show that the series

$$\sum k u_n \quad \text{and} \quad \sum u_n$$

either both converge or both diverge.

12.44. Show that the series

$$\sum_{n=1}^{\infty} u_n \quad \text{and} \quad \sum_{n=1}^{\infty} u_{k+n}$$

either both diverge or both converge, where $k \in N$ is fixed.

12.45. Discuss the convergence of the series

$$\sum \frac{n!}{n^n}$$

by comparing it with

$$\sum \frac{2}{n^2}.$$

12.46. Does the series

$$\sum \frac{1}{\sqrt{n(n-1)}}$$

converge?

12.47. Consider the series $\sum (-1)^n a_n$, where $0 \le a_n \le a_{n-1}$ and $\lim_{n \to \infty} a_n = 0$. Use a method similar to Example 12.22 to prove that this series converges. This result is known as *Leibnitz's test* for the convergence of an alternating series.

12.48. Use the result of Exercise 12.47 to show that the series

$$\sum (-1)^n \frac{n^2}{n^3 + 1}$$

converges. Does it converge absolutely?

12.49. Does the series

$$\sum (-1)^n \frac{1}{(n+1)n^2}$$

converge? Does it converge absolutely?

12.50. Prove that the series

$$\sum \frac{a_n}{10^n},$$

where $0 \le a_n < 10$, is convergent.

12.51. Prove that the series

$$\sum \frac{a_n}{p^n},$$

where $p \in N$, $p > 1$, and $0 < a_n < p$, is convergent.

12.52. Is the series

$$\sum \frac{i}{\sqrt{n}}$$

convergent?

12.53. Does the series

$$\sum \frac{1}{\sqrt{n + \sqrt{n}}}$$

converge?

12.54. Prove that, if the series $\sum u_n$ and $\sum v_n$ both converge, then the series $\sum (u_n + v_n)$ also converges.

12.55. Prove that, if the series $\sum (u_n + v_n)$ converges, then the series $\sum u_n$ and $\sum v_n$ either both converge or both diverge.

12.56. Does the series

$$\sum \frac{n - \sqrt{n}}{n^2 + n}$$

converge?

12.57. Consider the series

$$\sum a_n x^n$$

where a_n and x are complex numbers. Use Cauchy's test to show that this series converges absolutely if

$$x < \frac{1}{\lim \sqrt[n]{|a_n|}}.$$

12.58. Use the result of Exercise 12.57 to find the values of x for which the series $\sum i^n x^n$ converges.

12.59. Do the series

$$\sum \frac{(n!)^3}{(2n)!} \quad \text{and} \quad \sum \frac{n!}{(2n)!}$$

converge or diverge?

12.60. Consider the series

$$\sum \frac{a^n}{n^n} \quad \text{and} \quad \sum \frac{a^n}{n!},$$

where a is a complex number. Are these series absolutely convergent?

12.61. Are the following series convergent?

(a) $\sum \frac{1}{n^2 + n}$,

(b) $\sum \frac{n!}{2^{2n}}$.

12.62. Does the series $\sum a_n$, where

$$a_{2n-1} = \frac{1}{n^2 + n},$$

$$a_{2n} = \frac{n!}{2^{2n}},$$

converge?

12.63. Consider the convergent series $\sum c_n$ and the divergent series $\sum d_n$, where $c_n \geq 0$, $d_n \geq 0$. Prove the following generalization of Theorem 12.20: The series $\sum x_n$, where $x_n \geq 0$, converges if

$$\frac{x_{n+1}}{x_n} \leq \frac{c_{n+1}}{c_n} \quad \text{for all } n > n_0,$$

and diverges if

$$\frac{x_{n+1}}{x_n} \geq \frac{d_{n+1}}{d_n} \quad \text{for all } n > n_0.$$

12.64. Show that neither d'Alembert's test nor Cauchy's test can be used to test the convergence of the p series.

12.65. Give a simpler proof for Theorem 12.20.

12.66. Prove that if the series $\sum x_n$ is divergent, the series

$$\sum \frac{x_n}{1 + x_n}$$

is also divergent. [*Hint:* Find an expression for $s_{n+m} - s_n$, where s_n is the nth partial sum, and apply Lemma 12.3.]

13

Limits and
Continuity

13.1   Introduction

In Section 3.3 we introduced the term *function of a real variable* to denote a function whose domain is a subset of the real numbers. We also pointed out that we use the word "variable" simply to denote elements chosen from the domain. In our study of the calculus we shall restrict our attention to functions of a real variable, that is, functions whose domain is a subset of the set of real numbers. We shall be concerned only with functions whose codomain is the set of real numbers (real functions) or the set of complex numbers (complex functions).

We are chiefly interested in functions whose domain is either the set R of real numbers or an interval, either open or closed, of R. The main ideas of the calculus are amply illustrated by such functions.

But our study of the calculus leads us to an even more restricted class of functions. To appreciate what this class is and why it plays so prominent a role, we shall consider briefly the history of the subject. The development of the calculus was motivated by geometric problems concerned with tangents, area, and volume, and by man's desire to describe the behavior of the physical world. These physical problems attracted attention to *motion* as a basic concept. In the study of motion man had a strong preference for situations where "jumps" were rare occurrences. This preference so dominated man's interpretation of the physical world that it gave rise to the slogan, "Natura non facit saltus" (nature does not jump). To express the absence of jumps, the notion of a *continuous* function was introduced. The first rigorous definition of continuity was given by A. L. Cauchy in 1821. Since his time a great deal of work has been done to put the calculus on a rigorous basis. It now appears that many physical phenomena are in fact discontinuous.

Mathematicians not only restricted their attention to motion without jumps, but also to "smooth" motion, or to motion where lack of smoothness was rare. This led to the notion of the *derivative* of a function, and to the study of a still narrower class of *differentiable functions*.

It was only with difficulty that mathematicians freed their thinking from the shackles of such restrictions. Charles Hermite, a famous French mathematician, is reported to have said, "Je me detourne avec effroi et horreur de cette plaie lamentable" (I turn away in fright and horror from this distressing plague) when he was told that Weierstrass in 1871 had given an example of a function that is continuous but has a derivative nowhere.

We now turn our attention to the important concepts of *continuity* and *derivatives*. To do this, we shall make use of our knowledge of sequences and their limits.

13.2   Continuity at a point

In this section we shall be concerned with the behavior of a function in the neighborhood of a point, that is, in an interval containing the point. Our goal is to provide a rigorous characterization of a function that has the property which we describe intuitively as "not having a jump at a particular point."

Suppose we consider the physical world and try to explain what we mean by saying that a certain physical state does not have a jump at the instant t. We might attempt to describe this by saying that the variation in the state is not too great or can be kept under control around the instant t. If we were pressed for further clarification we might say that we would represent the measurement of the state at the instant t by $f(t)$, an element from the real numbers, complex numbers, or vectors, depending on the case we are studying. We could then define the *variation* in the state between the instants t and t' by $f(t) - f(t')$. When we say this variation is under control we may mean that we can make $|f(t) - f(t')|$ as small as we want (that is, smaller than any predetermined positive number) by taking t' close enough to t.

Throughout this chapter and the next we shall consider functions $f:A \to B$, where *the domain A is either the set of real numbers or an interval of the reals* (including the infinite intervals $\{x|x \in R, x > a\}$ and $\{x|x \in R, x < a\}$). Also *the codomain B is a subset either of the set of real numbers or of the set of complex numbers.*

In most of what we shall do there is little difference between working with complex functions and real functions. We shall therefore work with the more general case, that is, complex functions. There is, however, a great difference in the facility with which we can draw the graph of a real function, which is a subset of $R \times R$, and the graph of a complex function, which is a subset of $R \times C$. In the latter case we can sometimes obtain a clear idea of the behavior of the function by looking at the range of the function as a subset of $R \times R$. Since it is easier to draw the graphs of real functions, we shall usually use them as examples.

Consider now the function of a real variable $f: A \rightarrow B$. Suppose that we select a real number $a \in A$ and that there is an interval[1] $]c,d[$ in which $c < d$ such that $a \in]c,d[\subset A$. The requirement that the function f "does not jump" at a is the condition that $|f(x) - f(a)|$ can be made as close to zero as we want (we sometimes say *arbitrarily small*) if x is not too far from a. This means that for an arbitrary positive real number ε we have $|f(x) - f(a)| < \varepsilon$, provided x does not differ from a by more than a certain real $\delta(\varepsilon)$ determined by the choice of ε; that is, provided $|x - a| < \delta(\varepsilon)$. This discussion would not include the cases $A = [a,b]$ or $A = [c,a]$. These are, however, included in the next definition.

DEFINITION

A function of a real variable $f: A \rightarrow B$ is *continuous at the point* $a \in A$ if, for every real number $\varepsilon > 0$, there is a real number $\delta(\varepsilon) > 0$ such that

$$|f(x) - f(a)| < \varepsilon,$$

provided $|x - a| < \delta(\varepsilon)$ and $x \in A$.

The reader should observe that, for f to be continuous at a, it is necessary for $f(a)$ to exist.

We emphasize that the number $\delta(\varepsilon)$ depends on the choice of ε. It also depends on the point $a \in A$. This is an important point, and will be illustrated in the exercises.

This definition presents in a rigorous form the intuitive idea that the variation of f in the neighborhood of a can be kept arbitrarily small by restricting ourselves to a sufficiently small interval about a.

We shall now give a number of examples to clarify the concept of continuity.

EXAMPLE 13.1

Consider the function $f: R \rightarrow R$, where $f(x) = x^2$. Take the point $a = 0$ and suppose $\varepsilon > 0$ is given. If we choose $\delta(\varepsilon) = \sqrt{\varepsilon}$, we see that $|f(x) - f(0)| < \varepsilon$ for $|x - 0| < \delta$. In particular for $\varepsilon = \frac{1}{4}$ we can choose $\delta(\frac{1}{4}) = \frac{1}{2}$. This is illustrated in Figure 13.1.

As we saw in the special case of sequences, a complex function $f: A \rightarrow C$ can be considered a pair of real functions $f_1: A \rightarrow R$, $f_2: A \rightarrow R$ such that $f(x) = f_1(x) + i f_2(x)$. Lemma 13.1 provides a useful connection between the continuity of a complex function and the continuity of the real functions.

[1] See Section 4.6 for the definition and notation for intervals.

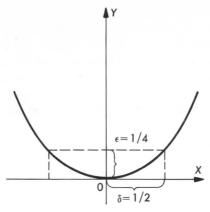

FIGURE 13.1

LEMMA   13.1

If $f: A \to C$, $f_1: A \to R$, and $f_2: A \to R$ are functions such that $f(x) = f_1(x) + if_2(x)$, then f is continuous at $a \in A$ if and only if f_1 and f_2 are continuous at $a \in A$.

Proof

1. Suppose f_1 and f_2 are continuous at $a \in A$. For each $\varepsilon > 0$ there are $\delta_1(\varepsilon/2)$ and $\delta_2(\varepsilon/2)$ such that

$$|f_1(x) - f_1(a)| < \frac{\varepsilon}{2} \quad \text{for } |x - a| < \delta_1\left(\frac{\varepsilon}{2}\right)$$

and

$$|f_2(x) - f_2(a)| < \frac{\varepsilon}{2} \quad \text{for } |x - a| < \delta_2\left(\frac{\varepsilon}{2}\right).$$

Let $\delta(\varepsilon)$ be the smaller of $\delta_1\left(\frac{\varepsilon}{2}\right)$ and $\delta_2\left(\frac{\varepsilon}{2}\right)$. Then

$$|f(x) - f(a)| = |f_1(x) + if_2(x) - f_1(a) - if_2(a)|$$
$$\leq |f_1(x) - f_1(a)| + |i|\,|f_2(x) - f_2(a)| < \frac{\varepsilon}{2} + \frac{\varepsilon}{2} = \varepsilon.$$

Therefore f is continuous at $a \in A$.

2. Suppose f is continuous at $a \in A$. For each $\varepsilon > 0$ there is $\delta(\varepsilon)$ such that

$$|f(x) - f(a)| < \varepsilon \quad \text{for } |x - a| < \delta(\varepsilon).$$

Then

$$|f_1(x) - f_1(a)| \leq |f(x) - f(a)| < \varepsilon.$$

Therefore f_1 is continuous at $a \in A$. Similarly, f_2 is continuous at $a \in A$. •

EXAMPLE   *13.2*

Consider the function $f: R \to C$, where $f(x) = \cos x + i \sin x$. We shall not attempt to draw the graph of f (although in this case it is not too difficult), but we shall draw its range. It is clear that $f(R)$ is represented as in Figure 13.2 by the circumference of a circle of radius 1 and center at the origin.

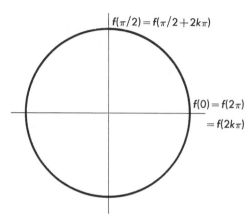

FIGURE 13.2

To show that f is continuous at $x = 0$ it is sufficient to show that the real functions f_1 and f_2, where $f_1(x) = \cos x$ and $f_2(x) = \sin x$, are continuous at $x = 0$. In particular for $\varepsilon = \frac{1}{2}$ we have

$$|f_1(x) - f_1(0)| < \frac{\varepsilon}{2} = \frac{1}{4} \qquad \text{for } |x - 0| < 0.7$$

$$|f_2(x) - f_2(0)| < \frac{\varepsilon}{2} = \frac{1}{4} \qquad \text{for } |x - 0| < 0.25.$$

From these results we obtain

$$|f(x) - f(0)| < \varepsilon = \frac{1}{2} \qquad \text{for } |x - 0| < 0.25.$$

EXAMPLE   *13.3*

We now give an example of a function that is *not* continuous. Consider the function $f: R \to R$, where

$$f(x) = \sin \frac{\pi}{x} \qquad \text{if } x \neq 0,$$

$$f(0) = 0.$$

The graph of this function is shown in Figure 13.3.

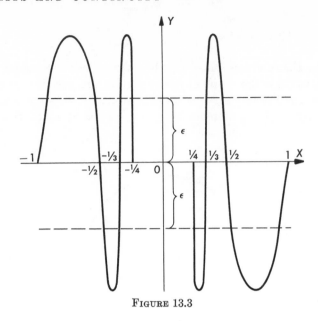

FIGURE 13.3

If we choose $\varepsilon > 1$, then for any $x \in R$ we have $|f(x) - f(0)| < \varepsilon$. But for $0 < \varepsilon < 1$ we see that, in any interval on the x axis with center at the origin, there are numbers x such that $|f(x) - f(0)| = |f(x)| > \varepsilon$. In terms of Figure 13.3 this means that there are values of x for which $f(x)$ lies outside the two horizontal lines drawn ε units above and below the x axis. From this we see that f is not continuous at $x = 0$. The function is, however, continuous at all other points.

EXAMPLE   13.4

As another example of a function that is not continuous, consider $f : R \rightarrow R$, where

$$f(x) = \cot x, \; x \neq k\pi,$$
$$f(k\pi) = 0.$$

The graph of f is shown in Figure 13.4.

To see that f is not continuous at $x = k\pi$, we observe that, if we draw horizontal lines ε units above and below the x axis, then in any interval containing $x = k\pi$ there are values of x such that $f(x)$ lies outside these lines, that is, $|f(x)| > \varepsilon$. But $|f(x) - f(k\pi)| = |f(x)|$. Therefore f is not continuous at $x = k\pi$.

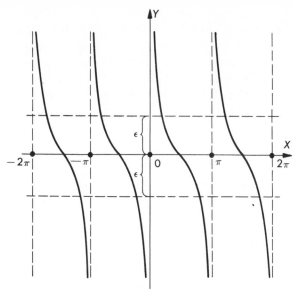

FIGURE 13.4

DEFINITION

A function that is not continuous at $x = a$ is said to be *discontinuous* at $x = a$.

We can restate the concept of continuity in different terms that may be useful in some cases and that may help the reader to visualize the idea. We consider a function $f: R \rightarrow R$ and a given $\varepsilon > 0$, as represented in Figure 13.5.

In studying the continuity of the function at $x = a$, we are interested in values of x such that $|f(x) - f(a)| < \varepsilon$. If we let $D_{a,\varepsilon} \subset R$ represent the set of all such x we see that, in Figure 13.5, this set consists of the three shaded

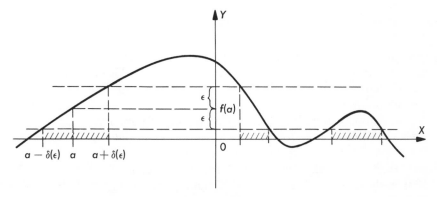

FIGURE 13.5

intervals on the x axis. If f is continuous at $x = a$, there must be an interval with center at a and contained in $D_{a,\varepsilon}$. If there is such an interval, then there is a $\delta(\varepsilon)$ such that the interval $]a - \delta(\varepsilon), a + \delta(\varepsilon)[$ is a subset of $D_{a,\varepsilon}$.

The function f is discontinuous at $x = a$ if there is some $\varepsilon > 0$ such that there is no interval $]a - \delta, a + \delta[\subset D_{a,\varepsilon}$ for $\delta > 0$.

Theorem 13.1 gives a characterization of continuity that could have been chosen as the definition.

THEOREM　13.1

A function $f: A \to B$ is continuous at $a \in A$ if and only if, for each sequence $(x_n)_{n \in N}$, $x_n \in A$ such that $\lim x_n = a$, we have $\lim f(x_n) = f(a)$, that is, $\lim f(x_n) = f(\lim x_n)$.

Proof

1. Suppose that f is continuous at a. Let $(x_n)_{n \in N}$ be any sequence such that $x_n \in A$ and $\lim x_n = a$. We want to show that $\lim f(x_n) = f(a)$, that is,

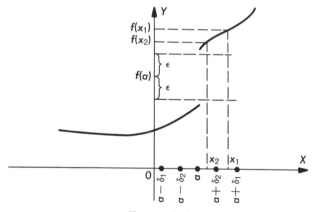

FIGURE 13.6

that $|f(x_m) - f(a)| < \varepsilon$ for $\varepsilon > 0$ provided $m > n(\varepsilon)$. But f is continuous at a; therefore $|f(x_m) - f(a)| < \varepsilon$ for $|x_m - a| < \delta(\varepsilon)$. Also $\lim x_n = a$; therefore there is a natural number $n(\varepsilon)$ such that $|x_m - a| < \delta(\varepsilon)$ for $m > n(\varepsilon)$. Therefore $\lim f(x_n) = f(a)$.

2. Suppose that $\lim f(x_n) = f(a)$ for every sequence $(x_n)_{n \in N}$, $x_n \in A$ such that $\lim x_n = a$. Assume that f is not continuous at $x = a$, that is, there is $\varepsilon > 0$ such that, in any interval $]a - \delta, a + \delta[$ with $\delta > 0$, there is an x such that $|f(x) - f(a)| > \varepsilon$. For a particular δ_1 choose x_1 as in Figure 13.6 such that $x_1 \in]a - \delta_1, a + \delta_1[$ and $|f(x_1) - f(a)| > \varepsilon$. Now choose $\delta_2 = |x_1 - a|/2$ and choose $x_2 \in]a - \delta_2, a + \delta_2[$ such that $|f(x_2) - f(a)| > \varepsilon$. In this way we can define δ_n and x_n by induction such that $\lim \delta_n = 0$. Thus we have $\lim x_n = a$ but $\lim f(x_n) \neq a$, since $|f(x_n) - f(a)| > \varepsilon$ for all $n \in N$.

Thus our assumption that f is discontinuous is false, and hence f is continuous. •

This theorem gives us an alternate, and equivalent, definition of continuity. Since they are equivalent, we can use the form that is more convenient in each situation we encounter.

Theorem 13.2 gives a property of the set of all functions that are continuous at the point a.

THEOREM 13.2

Let B be a subring of R or of C. Then the set of all functions $f: A \to B$ that are continuous at a given point $a \in A$ forms a ring with the usual addition, $(f + g)(x) = f(x) + g(x)$, and multiplication, $(fg)(x) = f(x)g(x)$.

Proof

We want to show that this set forms a subring of the ring of all functions $f: A \to B$. From Section 9.1 we know that it is sufficient to prove that, if f and g are in the subset, so are $f - g$ and fg.

Let $(x_n)_{n \in N}$, $x_n \in A$ be any sequence such that $\lim x_n = a$. Then by Theorem 12.10, $\lim (f - g)(x_n) = \lim (f(x_n) - g(x_n)) = \lim f(x_n) - \lim g(x_n) = f(a) - g(a) = (f - g)(a)$, and therefore $f - g$ is continuous at a; that is, $f - g$ is in the subset. Similarly, fg is continuous at a as a consequence of Theorem 12.11, and the theorem is proved. •

The next two theorems give useful ways of constructing new continuous functions from known continuous functions.

THEOREM 13.3

If $f: A \to B$, where $f(x) \neq 0$ for each $x \in A$ and f is continuous at $a \in A$, then the function $g: A \to B$, where $g(x) = 1/f(x)$, is also continuous at a.

Proof

Let $(x_n)_{n \in N}$, $x_n \in A$ be any sequence such that $\lim x_n = a$. Consider the sequence $(g(x_n))_{n \in N}$. Theorem 12.16 shows that $\lim g(x_n) = 1/\lim f(x_n) = 1/f(a) = g(a)$. Therefore g is continuous at a. •

For Theorem 13.4 we restrict our attention to real-valued functions rather than complex functions.

THEOREM 13.4

If $f: A \to B$ and $g: D \to E$, where A, B, D, E are subsets of R and $f(A) \subset D$ (for our purposes A and D are either R or intervals of R), if f is continuous at a and g is continuous at $f(a)$, then $g \cdot f: A \to E$ is continuous at a.

Proof

Let $(x_n)_{n \in N}$, $x_n \in A$ be any sequence such that $\lim x_n = a$. Since f is continuous at a we have $\lim f(x_n) = f(a)$. Then $(f(x_n))_{n \in N}$ is a sequence such that $\lim f(x_n) = f(a)$. Since g is continuous at $f(a)$ we have $\lim g(f(x_n)) = g(f(a))$. Therefore $g \cdot f$ is continuous at a. •

13.3   Local behavior of a function

In this section we shall be concerned with the behavior of a function in the neighborhood of a point a, but we shall not be concerned with the value $f(a)$ or even with whether a is an element of the domain. We do, however, require that some open interval with end point a is a subset of A, that is, $]b,a[\subset A$, or $]a,c[\subset A$, or $]b,a[\cup]a,c[\subset A$. It is not strictly necessary to state this third possibility, since we use "or" in the inclusive sense, but we want to emphasize that it is possible to have both intervals in A.

In Section 12.5 we defined the limit of a sequence, which we denoted by $\lim x_n$. We shall now use this idea of the limit of a sequence to define the limit of a function. If there is any danger of confusion we shall write $\lim_{n \to \infty} x_n$ for the limit of a sequence. The following three definitions provide us with the concept of the limit of a function.

DEFINITION

We say that the *left-hand limit of f at a* or the *limit of f as x approaches a from the left* exists if, for each sequence $(x_n)_{n \in N}$, $x_n \in A$, $x_n < a$ with $\lim x_n = a$, the sequence $(f(x_n))_{n \in N}$ converges and all these sequences have the same limit. We denote this common limit by $\lim_{x \to a, x < a} f(x)$.

DEFINITION

We say that the *right-hand limit of f at a* or the *limit of f as x approaches a from the right* exists if, for each sequence $(x_n)_{n \in N}$, $x_n \in A$, $x_n > a$ with $\lim x_n = a$, the sequence $(f(x_n))_{n \in N}$ converges and all these sequences have the same limit. We denote this common limit $\lim_{x \to a, x > a} f(x)$.

DEFINITION

We say that the *limit of f at a* or the *limit of f as x approaches a* exists if, for each sequence $(x_n)_{n \in N}$, $x_n \in A$, with $\lim x_n = a$, the sequence $(f(x_n))_{n \in N}$

converges and all these sequences have the same limit. We denote this common limit by $\lim_{x \to a} f(x)$.

The following two theorems provide us with an alternate, but equivalent, characterization of the limit of a function.

THEOREM 13.5

If the function $f: A \to B$ has a limit at the point a, then for each $\varepsilon > 0$ there is $\delta(\varepsilon) > 0$ such that

$$|\lim_{x \to a} f(x) - f(a)| < \varepsilon$$

for all $x \in A$ such that $|x - a| < \delta(\varepsilon)$.

Proof

Suppose the theorem is false, that is, $\lim_{x \to a} f(x)$ exists, but for some $\varepsilon > 0$ there is no $\delta(\varepsilon)$ with these properties. This means that in each interval with center a, there are elements $x \in A$ such that $|f(a) - \lim_{x \to a} f(x)| > \varepsilon$. We can now use the method used in proving Theorem 13.1 to find a sequence $(x_n)_{n \in N}$, $x_n \in A$, $\lim x_n = a$, such that $\lim f(x_n) \neq \lim_{x \to a} f(x)$. But this contradicts the existence of $\lim_{x \to a} f(x)$, and hence the theorem is proved. •

THEOREM 13.6

Let f be a function $f: A \to B$ and let a be a point such that $]b,a[\subset A$ or $]a,c[\subset A$. If there is a number k (real or complex) such that for each $\varepsilon > 0$ there is $\delta(\varepsilon) > 0$ such that $|f(x) - k| < \varepsilon$ provided $x \in A$ and $|x - a| < \delta(\varepsilon)$, then the limit of f at a exists, and $\lim_{x \to a} f(x) = k$.

Proof

Choose a sequence $(x_n)_{n \in N}$, $x_n \in A$, $\lim x_n = a$. Then for each $\varepsilon > 0$ there is $n(\varepsilon)$ such that $|x_n - a| < \delta(\varepsilon)$ for $n > n(\varepsilon)$. Also $x_n \in A$ and hence $|f(x_n) - k| < \varepsilon$ for $n > n(\varepsilon)$, that is, $\lim f(x_n) = k$. Then by the definition of the limit, $\lim_{x \to a} f(x) = k$.

From these two theorems we see that the limit of f as x approaches a exists if and only if there is a number k such that, for each $\varepsilon > 0$, there is a $\delta(\varepsilon) > 0$ such that $|f(x) - k| < \varepsilon$ for all $x \in A$ such that $|x - a| < \delta(\varepsilon)$. When this is true we have $\lim_{x \to a} f(x) = k$. •

The reader can use these results to prove the following theorem.

THEOREM   13.7

Let f be a function of a real variable. The limit of f at a exists and $\lim\limits_{x \to a} f(x) = k$ if and only if the right- and left-hand limits at a exist and $\lim\limits_{x \to a, x < a} f(x) = \lim\limits_{x \to a, x > a} f(x) = k$.

From Theorem 13.1 we obtain the following characterization of continuity at a point.

THEOREM   13.8

The function f is continuous at a if and only if $\lim\limits_{x \to a} f(x) = \lim\limits_{x \to a, x < a} f(x) = \lim\limits_{x \to a, x > a} f(x) = f(a)$.

We shall use these concepts of the limit of a function in our definitions of the derivative and the integral, but we can also give a more immediate example of their use. Consider two functions $f : A \to B$, $g : A \to B$, where $f(a) = 0$, $g(a) = 0$. If we define a function f/g, where $(f/g)(x) = f(x)/g(x)$, then a is not in its domain. It is possible, however, that $\lim\limits_{x \to a} f(x)/g(x)$ exists. If so, we can extend f/g to a domain including a by defining $(f/g)(a)$ as $\lim\limits_{x \to a} f(x)/g(x)$.

13.4   Functions continuous everywhere

In this section we shall be concerned with the class of functions $f : A \to B$ that are continuous at every point $a \in A$. Such a function is said to be *continuous on A* or, simply, *continuous*.

If we considered the set of all functions with domain $A \subset R$ and codomain $B \subset R$, very few would be continuous. On the other hand, most examples of functions of a real variable with which the reader is familiar are continuous. This suggests that the class of continuous functions is important.

We shall list several functions that are continuous on their domain. The reader should supply proofs for the continuity of several of them.

The *identity* $i_A : A \to A$, where $i_A(x) = x$, is a continuous function.

The *constant function* $f : A \to B$, where $f(x) = f(x')$ for all $x \in A$, $x' \in A$, is continuous on A.

The *linear map* $f : R \to R$, where $f(x) = cx$ for $c \in R$ (or $g : R \to C$ where $f(x) = kx$, $k \in C$), is continuous on R.

The *mth power* $f : R \to R$, where $f(x) = x^m$, is continuous on R for each $m \in R$.

The *trigonometric functions sine* and *cosine* are continuous on R. The other trigonometric functions are continuous on suitable open intervals.

The following theorems enable us to construct new continuous functions from these.

THEOREM 13.9

Let B be a subring of R or of C. Then the set of continuous functions $f: A \to B$ forms a ring with the addition $(f + g)(x) = f(x) + g(x)$ and the multiplication $(fg)(x) = f(x)g(x)$.

Proof

If f and g are continuous on A, they are continuous at every $a \in A$. Theorem 13.2 shows $f - g$ and fg are continuous at every $a \in A$ and hence are continuous on A. Therefore the continuous functions $f: A \to B$ form a subring of $\mathfrak{F}(A,B)$. •

THEOREM 13.10

If $f: A \to B$ is continuous on A, $g: D \to E$ is continuous on D, and $B \subset D$, then the composite $g \cdot f$ is continuous on A.

Proof

Theorem 13.4 shows that $g \cdot f$ is continuous at every $a \in A$ and hence is continuous on A. •

We can now start from a set of functions that are known to be continuous and construct new continuous functions by composition, addition, and multiplication. In particular the *polynomial functions* are continuous since they are constructed from linear functions and mth powers by composition and addition.

Among the many interesting and important properties of continuous functions we shall prove one that will be useful to us later.

THEOREM 13.11

Let $f: A \to B$ be a continuous, real-valued function and let $[a,b] \subset A$. Then for any k such that $f(a) < k < f(b)$ (or $f(b) < k < f(a)$), there is $x \in [a,b]$ such that $f(x) = k$.

Proof

Let $D_k = \{x | x \in [a,b], f(x) < k\}$. The shaded part of the x axis in Figure 13.7 represents D_k. Since $a \in D_k$ (or $b \in D_k$), we see that $D_k \neq \varnothing$. Since D_k

is bounded above by b, we know that D_k has a least upper bound, lub $D_k = c$, $a \leq c \leq b$. Since f is continuous at a, there is a $\delta > 0$ such that $|f(x) - f(a)| < k - f(a)$ for all $x \in [a, a + \delta]$, that is, $f(x) < k$ and hence $c \neq a$. Similarly, we see that $c \neq b$. A similar argument based on the continuity of f shows that, in every interval $[c - \delta_1, c]$, where $\delta_1 > 0$, there is a number x

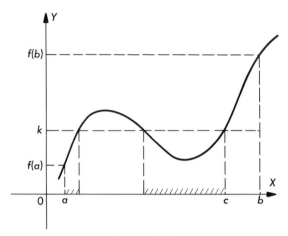

FIGURE 13.7

such that $f(x) < k$. Then we can find a sequence $(x_n)_{n \in N}$, $\lim x_n = c$, $f(x_n) < k$, and hence $\lim_{x \to c, x < a} f(x) \leq k$. But f is continuous at c, therefore $\lim_{x \to c,\ x < c} f(x) = f(c)$ and $f(c) \leq k$. Similarly, $\lim_{x \to c, x > c} f(x) \geq k$ and $f(c) \geq k$. From this it follows that $f(c) = k$. •

This theorem states that, if a continuous function takes two values, then it takes all intermediate values. This at one time was thought to characterize a function that has no jumps and hence to characterize continuous functions. Consider the function $f : [0,1] \to R$, where

$$f(x) = \begin{cases} x & \text{for } 0 \leq x < \dfrac{1}{2}, \\ x - \dfrac{1}{2} & \text{for } \dfrac{1}{2} \leq x \leq 1. \end{cases}$$

The graph of this function is shown in Figure 13.8. The range of f is $[0, \frac{1}{2}]$. It is clear that, if $f(a)$ and $f(b)$ are values of the function and $f(a) < c < f(b)$, then there is a point $x \in [0,1]$ such that $f(x) = c$. It is also clear that f is not continuous at $x = \frac{1}{2}$. Thus we have a function that assumes all intermediate values but is not continuous everywhere on its domain.

There are also examples of functions that assume all intermediate values on any arbitrary interval. These examples are beyond the scope of this book.

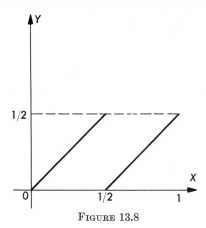

FIGURE 13.8

EXERCISES

13.1. Draw carefully on graph paper the graphs of the following real-valued functions:

(a) $f:[-3,3] \to R$, $f(x) = x^2$.
(b) $g:[-3,3] \to R$, $g(x) = |x|$.
(c) $h:[-3,3] \to R$, $h(x) = (x-2)(x+2)$.
(d) $k:[-3,3] \to R$, $k(x) = [x]$, where $[x]$ is as defined in Section 2.3.

13.2. For each function in Exercise 13.1 either find, by inspecting the drawing, the smallest $\delta(\varepsilon,a) > 0$ such that $|f(a) - f(x)| < \varepsilon$ if $|a - x| < \delta(\varepsilon,a)$, or show why no such $\delta(\varepsilon,a)$ exists, in the following cases:

(a) $\varepsilon = 1$, $a = 2$.
(b) $\varepsilon = \frac{1}{4}$, $a = 1$.

13.3. Find a positive number ε such that, for the function $f:R \to R$, where $f(x) = [x]$, and for any $\delta > 0$, we have $|f(0) - f(x)| > \varepsilon$ for some $x \in (0 - \delta, 0 + \delta)$.

13.4. Consider the functions $f:[-4,4] \to R$ and $g:[-4,4] \to R$, where

$$f(x) = \begin{cases} \sqrt{x^2 - 1} & \text{for } |x| \geq 1, \\ 0 & \text{for } |x| < 1, \end{cases}$$

and

$$g(x) = \begin{cases} \dfrac{1}{x} & \text{for } x \neq 0, \\ 0 & \text{for } x = 0. \end{cases}$$

By drawing the graph of these functions find, for each of them, $\delta(\varepsilon,a)$ for $\varepsilon = \frac{1}{4}$ and each of the values $-3, -2, -1, 1, 2, 3$, for a.

13.5. Draw carefully on graph paper the graph of the function $f:[-4,4] \to R$, where

$$f(x) = \begin{cases} \dfrac{x - 2}{x - 1} & \text{for } x \neq 1, \\ 1 & \text{for } x = 1. \end{cases}$$

Indicate on the diagram the sets

$$A = \{x|\ |f(x) - 1| < 1\}.$$
$$B = \left\{x|\ |f(x)| < \frac{1}{2}\right\}.$$

Indicate on the diagram the largest open interval I such that $I \subset A$ and $1 \in I$. Also indicate the largest open interval J such that $J \subset B$ and $2 \in J$. Is the function f continuous at $x = 1$? Is it continuous at $x = 2$?

13.6. Draw carefully the graph of the function $f : R \to R$, where

$$f(x) = \begin{cases} \dfrac{x}{|x|} & \text{for } x \neq 0, \\ 0 & \text{for } x = 0. \end{cases}$$

Indicate on the diagram the sets

$$A = \{x|\ |f(x)| < 1\}.$$
$$B = \left\{x|\ |f(x)| < \frac{1}{2}\right\}.$$

Do either or both of the sets A and B contain an interval containing 0? Is the function f continuous at $x = 0$?

13.7. For what values of x (if any) is the function $f : R \to R$ continuous if

$$f(x) = \begin{cases} x & \text{for } x \in Q, \\ -x & \text{for } x \in R - Q. \end{cases}$$

13.8. Draw on the complex plane the range of the function $f : [-3,3] \to C$, where

$$f(x) = \begin{cases} \dfrac{1}{x} + ix^2 & \text{for } x \neq 0, \\ 0 & \text{for } x = 0. \end{cases}$$

Indicate in the interval $[-3,3]$ of the real line the set $A = \{x|\ |f(x)| < 1\}$. Is there an interval $J \subset A$ such that $0 \in J$? Is f continuous at $x = 0$?

13.9. Draw on the complex plane the range of the function $f : [-3,3] \to C$, where $f(x) = x + i(x - [x])$ (with $[x]$ defined as in Section 2.3). For what values of x is this function not continuous?

13.10. Draw a portion of the graph of the function $f : R \to C$, where $f(x) = x - [x] + i(x - [x])$. For what values $x \in R$ is f not continuous?

13.11. We say that a real-valued function is bounded if its range is a bounded subset of the set R. Which functions in Exercises 13.5 to 13.7 are bounded?

13.12. We say that the complex-valued function $f = f_1 + if_2$ is bounded if the real-valued functions f_1 and f_2 are bounded. Prove that the complex function $f : R \to C$ is bounded if and only if the set $\{u|u = |f(x)|, x \in R\}$ is a bounded subset of R.

13.13. Which of the functions in Exercises 13.8 to 13.10 are bounded, where "bounded" is defined as in Exercise 13.12?

13.14. Prove that the set of all bounded real functions $f : R \to R$ is a subring of $\mathfrak{F}(R,R)$.

13.15. Prove that the set of all bounded complex functions $f : R \to C$ is a subring of $\mathfrak{F}(R,C)$.

13.16. (a) If $f: A \to R$, where $A \subset R$, is a bounded function, does $g: A \to R$, where $g(x) = 1/f(x)$, always exist? When the function g does exist is it always bounded? Give reasons for your answers.

(b) Give necessary and sufficient conditions on f for g to exist and be bounded.

13.17. Draw a portion of the graph of the function $f: R_+ \to R$, where $f(x) = 1/x - [1/x]$. Is f continuous at $x = 1$? For what values of x is it not continuous?

13.18. Give an example of functions $f: R \to R$, $g: R \to R$, and a real number a such that f is not continuous at $a \in R$, g is not continuous at $f(a) \in R$, but $g \cdot f$ is continuous at $a \in R$.

13.19. Draw a portion of the graph of the function $f: R \to R$, where

$$f(x) = \begin{cases} x & \text{for } x \geq 0, \\ \dfrac{1}{x} & \text{for } x < 0. \end{cases}$$

Prove that this function is not continuous at $x = 0$.

13.20. (a) Let $I = [a,b]$ and let $f_I: R \to \{0,1\}$ be the characteristic function of I as defined in Section 3.7. Prove that f_I is continuous for any $x \in R$ except $x = a$ and $x = b$.

(b) Are the results in (a) still true if I is replaced by $J = \,]a,b[$?

13.21. Prove that the function $f: R \to R$, where

$$f(x) = \begin{cases} \sin \dfrac{\pi}{x} & \text{for } x \neq 0, \\ 0 & \text{for } x = 0, \end{cases}$$

is continuous at $x = \frac{1}{2}$. If $\varepsilon = \frac{1}{2}$, find $\delta(\frac{1}{2},\frac{1}{2})$.

13.22. Is the function $f: R \to R$, where

$$f(x) = \begin{cases} \dfrac{x^2 - 1}{x^2 + x - 2} & \text{for } x \neq 1, \\ 0 & \text{for } x = 1, \end{cases}$$

continuous at $x = 1$? What is the value of $\lim\limits_{x \to 1} f(x)$?

13.23. Define a function $g: R \to R$ such that g is continuous at $x = 1$ and $g(x) = f(x)$ for $x \neq 1$, where f is the function in Exercise 13.22.

13.24. For each of the functions f listed below show that there is no function $g: R \to R$ such that g is continuous at every point $x \in R$ and $g(x) = f(x)$ for any $x \in A$ such that f is continuous at x.

(a) $f(x) = \begin{cases} \sin (1/x) & \text{for } x \neq 0, \\ 0 & \text{for } x = 0. \end{cases}$

(b) $f(x) = x - [x]$.

(c) $f(x) = \begin{cases} \sin |x| & \text{for } x \neq k\pi \text{ for any } k \in Z, \\ 1 & \text{for } x = k\pi \text{ for some } k \in Z. \end{cases}$

13.25. Show that for any $m \in N$ and any $x \in R$ the following limit exists:

$$\lim_{n \to \infty} (\cos m!\pi x)^{2n}.$$

13.26. The result of Exercise 13.25 shows that, for each $m \in N$, we can define a function $f_m : R \to R$, where

$$f_m(x) = \lim_{n \to \infty} (\cos m!\pi x)^{2n}.$$

At what points is the function f_m discontinuous?

13.27. Let f_m be the function defined in Exercise 13.26. Show that for each $x \in R$ the limit $\lim_{m \to \infty} f_m(x)$ exists. We can define the function $f : R \to R$, where $f(x) = \lim_{m \to \infty} f_m(x)$. What is the value $f(\frac{1}{2})$, $f(p/q)$ with p and q integers, $f(x)$ with x irrational? Of what subset of R is f the characteristic function?

13.28. Find the following limits:

(a) $\lim_{\{x \to k, x > k\}} [x] \cdot x$ for $k \in N \cup \{0\}$.

(b) $\lim_{x \to k, x < k} [x] \cdot x$ for $k \in N \cup \{0\}$.

(c) $\lim_{x \to 0, x > 0} x(x^{x/|x|})$.

(d) $\lim_{x \to 0, x < 0} x(x^{x/|x|})$.

13.29. Find the following limits:

(a) $\lim_{x \to 1, x > 1} \dfrac{\sqrt{x-1}}{\sqrt{x+1}}$.

(b) $\lim_{x \to -1, x < -1} \dfrac{\sqrt{x^2-1}}{\sqrt{x^2+1}}$.

(c) $\lim_{x \to 1, x > 1} \dfrac{\sqrt{x^2-1}}{\sqrt{x^2+1}}$.

13.30. Consider the following functions and the specified point a. Which ones have a limit at a, only a left-hand limit at a, only a right-hand limit at a, or no limit at a?

(a) $\dfrac{\sin x}{\cos (\pi - x)}$, $a = \pi$.

(b) $\cos \left(\dfrac{1}{x - \pi} \right) + \sin (x - \pi)$, $a = \pi$.

(c) $\log \cos (1/x)$, $a = 0$.

13.31. Let $f : A \to B$ be a function that is continuous at $a \in A$. Let $(x_n)_{n \in N}$ and $(y_n)_{n \in N}$ be two sequences such that $x_n \in A$, $y_n \in A$, and $\lim x_n = \lim y_n = a$. If the limits $\lim_{n \to \infty} f(x_n)$ and $\lim_{n \to \infty} f(y_n)$ exist, prove that they are equal.

13.32. Prove Theorem 13.7.

13.33. Prove Theorem 13.8.

13.34. Consider the function $f : R_+ \to R$, where $f(x) = 1/x$. Find $\delta(\varepsilon, x)$, the largest positive real number such that $|f(x') - f(x)| < \varepsilon$ for $|x' - x| < \delta(\varepsilon, x)$, for the four cases $\varepsilon = \frac{1}{10}$, $\varepsilon = \frac{1}{100}$, and $x = \frac{1}{2}$, $x = \frac{1}{4}$. This shows that δ depends on both ε and x.

13.35. For the function f of Exercise 13.34 show that there is no $\delta(\varepsilon)$ such that $|f(x') - f(x)| < \varepsilon$ for $|x - x'| < \delta(\varepsilon)$ for all $x \in R_+$.

13.36. For the function $g:[\frac{1}{100},10] \to R$, where $g(x) = 1/x$ and for $\varepsilon = \frac{1}{10}$ find a $\delta(\varepsilon) > 0$ such that $|f(x') - f(x)| < \varepsilon$ for all x in the domain and any x' in the domain such that $|x' - x| < \delta(\varepsilon)$.

13.37. Quote the appropriate results from Section 13.4 to show that the following functions are continuous everywhere in their domain:

(a) $f:R \to R$, $f(x) = \sin^2 x + 2 \cos x \sin x$.
(b) $g:R \to R$, $g(x) = x^2 \cos x^2$.
(c) $h:R \to R$, $h(x) = \cos(2x + x^2)$.
(d) $k:R_0 \to C$, $k(x) = \cos(\pi/3x) + i \sin x^3$.

13.38. If the functions $f:R \to R$ and $g:R \to C$ are continuous everywhere on R, prove that the functions $|f|:R \to R$ and $|g|:R \to R$, where $|f|(x) = |f(x)|$ and $|g|(x) = |g(x)|$, are also continuous everywhere on R.

13.39. Consider the function $f:R \to R$, where

$$f(x) = \begin{cases} x^2(x^{|x|/x}) & \text{for } x \neq 0, \\ 0 & \text{for } x = 0. \end{cases}$$

Draw a portion of the graph of this function. Is the function continuous everywhere on R? Give reasons for your answer.

13.40. Prove that the function $f:R \to C$, where $f(x) = |x|(\cos 2\pi/3 + i \sin 2\pi/3)$ is continuous everywhere on R. Draw the range of this function on the complex plane.

13.41. Consider a function $f:R \to B$, where $B = R$ or $B = C$, and the function $g:R_0 \to R$, where $g(x) = 1/x$. If $\lim_{x \to 0, x > 0} (f \cdot g)(x)$ exists, we say that $\lim_{x \to \infty} f(x)$ exists and we define

$$\lim_{x \to +\infty} f(x) = \lim_{x \to 0, x > 0} (fg)(x).$$

If $\lim_{x \to 0, x < 0} (fg)(x)$ exists we say that $\lim_{x \to -\infty} f(x)$ exists and we define

$$\lim_{x \to -\infty} f(x) = \lim_{x \to 0, x < 0} (fg)(x).$$

Find the following limits:

(a) $\lim_{x \to +\infty} \dfrac{x + 1}{x^2 - 2x}$.

(b) $\lim_{x \to -\infty} \dfrac{2 + ix}{x}$.

(c) $\lim_{x \to -\infty} \dfrac{x^3 - 2}{x \sin x}$.

13.42. Consider a function $f:R \to C$ that is not bounded on any interval of the domain containing a. It is convenient to consider various cases in which this is true:

(a) If $\lim_{x \to a} (1/f(x)) = 0$, we write $\lim_{x \to a} f(x) = \infty$.
(b) If $\lim_{x \to a, x > a} (1/f(x)) = 0$, we write $\lim_{x \to a, x > a} f(x) = \infty$.
(c) If $\lim_{x \to a, x < a} (1/f(x)) = 0$, we write $\lim_{x \to a, x < a} f(x) = \infty$.
(d) If $1/f(x)$ has neither a right nor a left limit, we say that $f(x)$ has neither a right nor a left limit at a.

Using this notation evaluate the following limits:

(a) $\lim\limits_{x\to 0} \left(\dfrac{1}{\sin x} + i \cot x \right).$

(b) $\lim\limits_{x\to 1, x>1} \left(\dfrac{x + 3i}{\sqrt{x^2 - 1}} \right).$

13.43. For a function $g : R \to R$ we can further modify the terminology of Exercise 13.42.

(a) If $\lim\limits_{x\to a} (1/f(x)) = 0$ and if $1/f(x) \geq 0$ for some δ and all x such that $|x - a| < \delta$, we write $\lim\limits_{x\to a} f(x) = +\infty$.

(b) If $\lim\limits_{x\to a} (1/f(x)) = 0$ and if $1/f(x) \leq 0$ for some δ and for all x such that $|x - a| < \delta$, we write $\lim\limits_{x\to a} f(x) = -\infty$.

The right and left limits can be modified similarly.

Evaluate the following limits.

(a) $\lim\limits_{x\to 0} \dfrac{1}{\sin^2 x}.$

(b) $\lim\limits_{x\to 0} \dfrac{1}{\sin (1/x)}.$

13.44. Consider the function $f : R_+ \to R$, where $f(x) = x^2$. For a given $\varepsilon > 0$, find the function whose value $\delta(\varepsilon, x)$ is the largest positive number such that $|f(x') - f(x)| < \varepsilon$ for $|x' - x| < \delta(\varepsilon, x)$. [*Hint:* The calculations give an expression for $\delta(\varepsilon, x)$ involving $\pm \varepsilon$. The proper sign can be chosen by examining a sketch of the graph of the function f.] Prove that $\lim\limits_{x\to +\infty} \delta(1, x) = 0$.

14

The Derivative and the Integral

14.1 Introduction

Study of the physical concept of motion leads to a consideration of velocity and acceleration. The need to represent these concepts mathematically was a major part of the motivation for developing the process of differentiation. This process associates with each function in a certain subset of the continuous functions—called the differentiable functions—a new function called the *derivative*. A study of the problem of constructing a tangent to a curve also leads to this concept.

The first part of this chapter will be devoted to the derivative and its properties, a study known as the *differential* calculus. We shall continue to emphasize concepts rather than the computational aspects found in most calculus books. As in the previous two chapters we shall deal with complex-valued functions of a real variable. Such complex functions introduce no additional difficulties since, we have already seen, they can be considered ordered pairs of real functions.

14.2 Definition of the derivative

In our study of the calculus we have restricted our attention to functions $f : A \rightarrow B$, where either $A = R$ or A is an interval contained in R, and either $B = R$ or $B = C$. In defining the derivative of the function f at the point x we shall for the present consider only those x for which there is a positive real number a such that $[x - a, x + a] \subset A$, that is, we shall not deal with the end points when A is a closed interval. We shall extend our definition to end points in Section 14.5.

We shall consider a function h with domain $[-a, a] - \{0\}$ and codomain

B such that

$$h(t) = \frac{f(x + t) - f(x)}{t}.$$

We call this function the *difference quotient of f at the point x*. It is customary to denote this function by $\Delta f/\Delta x$, a useful notation, since it emphasizes the important elements f and x.

Note that the difference quotient is not defined for $t = 0$. We are concerned with its limit as t approaches 0, as we shall see in the following definition.

DEFINITION

The function $f:A \to B$ as described previously, is said to be *differentiable* at $x \in A$ if the difference quotient $\Delta f/\Delta x$ has a (unique) limit at $t = 0$, that is, if

$$\lim_{t \to 0} \frac{f(x + t) - f(x)}{t}$$

exists. If the limit does exist it is called the *derivative of f at x*. (Note that t can be either positive or negative.)

14.3   Geometric interpretation

Consider a real-valued function $f:A \to R$ with graph as represented in Figure 14.1. The difference quotient $[f(x + t) - f(x)]/t$ is the slope of the chord between the points P_1 and P_2 with coordinates $(x, f(x))$ and $(x + t, f(x + t))$, respectively. If f is continuous at x we know that $\lim_{t \to 0} f(x + t) = f(x)$, and

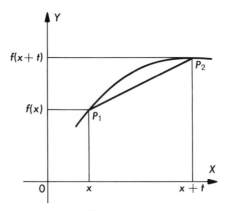

FIGURE 14.1

we say that the point P_2 approaches point P_1 as t approaches 0. If

$$\lim_{t \to 0} \frac{f(x + t) - f(x)}{t}$$

exists, then the chord P_1P_2 approaches the tangent at P_1, and the derivative of the function at x is equal to the slope of the tangent at P_1. The geometric statement that the curve has a tangent at $P_1(x,f(x))$ is thus equivalent to the analytic statement that the function f has a derivative at x.

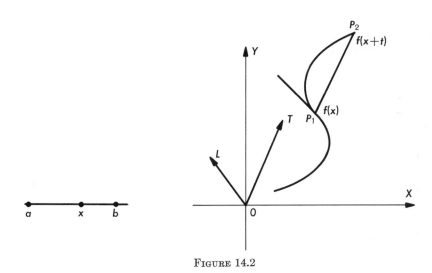

FIGURE 14.2

The geometric interpretation in the complex-valued case is a little more complicated. To avoid having to use a three-dimensional representation, we shall represent the domain and codomain of $f \colon A \to C$ on separate diagrams, as in Figure 14.2. The domain is R or a segment of R and the codomain is the plane.

We have simplified the diagram by representing an injective function, otherwise the range would be represented by a curve that intersected itself. The difference quotient

$$\frac{f(x + t) - f(x)}{t}$$

is a complex number that can be represented by a directed line segment OT, which is parallel to the chord P_1P_2, where P_1 and P_2 have coordinates $(f_1(x),f_2(x))$ and $(f_1(x + t),f_2(x + t))$, respectively [where $f(x) = f_1(x) + if_2(x)$]. If

$$\lim_{t \to 0} \frac{f(x + t) - f(x)}{t}$$

exists, it is a complex number represented by a directed line segment OL parallel to the tangent at P_1.

14.4 Notations for the derivative

There are various ways in which the derivative of f at x may be denoted. The traditional notations are $f'(x)$ and df/dx.

The definition of the derivative is frequently written in the form

$$\frac{df}{dx} = \lim_{\Delta x \to 0} \frac{\Delta f}{\Delta x}.$$

This does not agree with our earlier notation for limits. We have defined $\Delta f/\Delta x$ as a function and the derivative as the limit of this function. It would be more appropriate to write

$$\frac{df}{dx} = \lim_{t \to 0} \frac{\Delta f}{\Delta x}(t)$$

or, better still,

$$\frac{df}{dx} = \lim_{t \to 0} \frac{f(x + t) - f(x)}{t}.$$

It is possible to interpret Δf and Δx separately, but we shall not do so. The reader is warned against the fallacious idea that Δf and Δx represent "infinitely small quantities."

14.5 Differentiability and continuity

The reader who has had some experience in an approach to calculus where the computational aspects were emphasized may have received the impression that all functions are differentiable. It is important, if we are to understand the calculus, to realize that this is not so. There are important functions that are continuous but not differentiable at a point. It is still possible to form the difference quotient in these cases, but this function does not have a limit at $t = 0$.

We shall give several examples of functions that are not differentiable and shall also consider two new concepts that are closely related to the concept of derivative and that are useful in some of these cases.

EXAMPLE 14.1

We shall consider the function $f : R \to R$, where $f(x) = |x|$. This function is continuous on R. The graph of f is represented in Figure 14.3. It is clear that

$$\lim_{t \to 0, t > 0} \frac{f(0 + t) - f(0)}{t} = 1,$$

$$\lim_{t \to 0, t < 0} \frac{f(0 + t) - f(0)}{t} = -1.$$

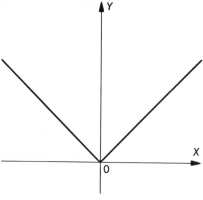

FIGURE 14.3

Thus we see that

$$\lim_{t \to 0} \frac{f(0 + t) - f(0)}{t}$$

does not exist, and hence f is not differentiable at $x = 0$.

The two limits we have considered in this example are given names in the following definition.

DEFINITION

If

$$\lim_{t \to 0, t > 0} \frac{f(x + t) - f(x)}{t}$$

exists, we call its value the *derivative at the right* (or the *right derivative*) of f at x.

If

$$\lim_{t \to 0, t < 0} \frac{f(x + t) - f(x)}{t}$$

exists, we call its value the *derivative at the left* (or the *left derivative*) of f at x.

In the geometric representation, we speak of the tangent at the left and the tangent at the right. If the left derivative and the right derivative are unequal, the tangent at the left and the tangent at the right are not on the same straight line. This can be seen in Figure 14.3.

The reader can prove that the function $f: A \to B$ is differentiable at a point $x \in A$ such that $[x - a, x + a] \subset A$ for some $a \in R$ if and only if the left and right derivatives at x exist and are equal. Furthermore this common value of the left and right derivatives is the derivative at x.

We mentioned at the beginning of Section 14.2 that we would defer the definition of the derivative at the end points of A, where A is a closed interval. If $A = [r, s]$, we say that $f: A \to B$ is differentiable at r if the right derivative exists at r, and we define the derivative as the value of the right derivative. Similarly, f is differentiable at s if the left derivative at s exists and the derivative at s is defined as the left derivative.

EXAMPLE   14.2

We shall consider the behavior of $f:A \to C$ at a point x, where the left and right derivatives exist but are not equal. In Figure 14.4 we represent the

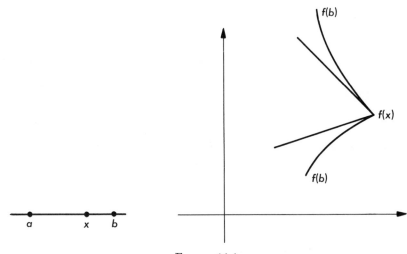

FIGURE 14.4

domain and codomain on separate diagrams. If the two limits

$$\lim_{t \to 0, t > 0} \frac{f(a + t) - f(a)}{t}, \qquad \lim_{t \to 0, t < 0} \frac{f(a + t) - f(a)}{t}$$

exist and are unequal, then the curve representing the range changes direction suddenly and the tangents obtained by approaching the point from the two sides do not coincide.

EXAMPLE   14.3

Consider the function $f:R \to R$, where

$$f(x) = \begin{cases} x \sin \dfrac{1}{x} & \text{for } x \neq 0, \\ 0 & \text{for } x = 0. \end{cases}$$

The graph of this function is represented in Figure 14.5. The function is continuous for all $x \in R$ and has a derivative at all $x \neq 0$.

The difference quotient at $x = 0$ represents the slope of the secant from $(0,0)$ to $(t, f(t))$. In any interval about $x = 0$ this slope will vary between $+1$ and -1. Therefore it does not have a limit. In this case the left- and right-hand limits do not exist either and hence f has neither a left nor a right derivative at $x = 0$.

Such examples of functions that are continuous but not differentiable at one or at a finite number of points were known as early as the eighteenth century, but the idea persisted that such points must always be separated

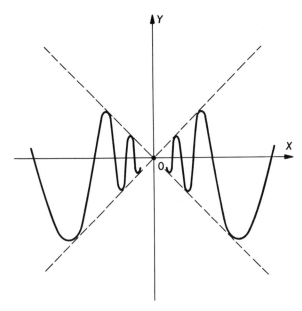

FIGURE 14.5

from each other by an interval. The example, given in 1871 by Weierstrass,[1] of a function that is continuous at all points of its domain but differentiable nowhere brought about the proper separation between continuity and differentiability.

We have sought to emphasize that continuity does not imply differentiability. The converse situation is examined in Theorem 14.1.

THEOREM 14.1

If a function f has a derivative at a point x, then f is continuous at x.

[1] Bolzano had discovered such an example before 1830, but it remained unknown until a century later.

Proof

It is sufficient to show that

$$\lim_{t \to 0} (f(x + t) - f(x)) = 0, \tag{1}$$

for then $\lim_{t \to 0} f(x + t) = f(x)$ and f is continuous at x. If this limit does not exist or if it is not equal to 0, then

$$\lim_{t \to 0} \frac{f(x + t) - f(x)}{t}$$

does not exist. But this contradicts the fact that f has a derivative at x. Therefore Eq. (1) is true and the theorem is proved. •

14.6   Rules for differentiation

The process of finding the derivative of a given function is known as differentiation. In this section we shall prove some simple rules for differentiation. Our procedure will be to find the derivative of a few functions, then to develop means of constructing (and differentiating) new differentiable functions from the known differentiable functions. We shall also consider the algebraic structure of a set of differentiable functions.

We shall denote by Dif (A,B,x) the set of functions $f: A \to B$ that have derivatives at x.

Theorems 14.2 and 14.3 deal with two of the simplest differentiable functions, the constant map and the identity map.

THEOREM   14.2

If $f: A \to B$ is a constant function, then f is differentiable at x and $f'(x) = 0$.

Proof

Since f is a constant function, $f(x) = f(x + t)$ for all $x \in A, x + t \in A$. Then

$$\lim_{t \to 0} \frac{f(x + t) - f(x)}{t} = 0.$$

Therefore f is differentiable at x and $f'(x) = 0$. •

THEOREM   14.3

The function $f: A \to B$, where $f(x) = x$ for all $x \in A$, is differentiable at x and $f'(x) = 1$.

Proof

If we consider the limit of the difference quotient we get

$$\lim_{t \to 0} \frac{f(x + t) - f(x)}{t} = \lim_{t \to 0} \frac{x + t - x}{t} = 1.$$

Therefore f is differentiable at x and $f'(x) = 1$. •

The next step in complexity is to consider the function $f(x) = x + c$ where c is constant. Rather than study this function directly we prove the following, more general, theorem.

THEOREM 14.4

Consider the functions $f \in \text{Dif } (A,B,x)$, $g \in \text{Dif } (A,B,x)$, and $f + g : A \to B$, where $(f + g)(x) = f(x) + g(x)$ for $x \in A$. Then $f + g$ is differentiable at x and its derivative at x is $f'(x) + g'(x)$.

Proof

We know that

$$\lim_{t \to 0} \frac{f(x + t) - f(x)}{t} = f'(x)$$

and

$$\lim_{t \to 0} \frac{g(x + t) - g(x)}{t} = g'(x).$$

Let $h = f + g$, that is $h(z) = f(z) + g(z)$ for all $z \in A$. Then

$$\lim_{t \to 0} \frac{h(x + t) - h(x)}{t} = \lim_{t \to 0} \frac{f(x + t) + g(x + t) - f(x) - g(x)}{t}$$

$$= \lim_{t \to 0} \frac{f(x + t) - f(x)}{t} + \lim_{t \to 0} \frac{g(x + t) - g(x)}{t}$$

$$= f'(x) + g'(x).$$

This proves both the existence and the form of the derivative. •

The proof of the following corollary is left as an exercise.

Corollary 1

If for each $n \in N$ the function $f_n : A \to B$ is differentiable at x, then the function $f_1 + f_2 + \cdots + f_k$ is differentiable at x for any $k \in N$ and its derivative at x is $f_1'(x) + f_2'(x) + \cdots + f_k'(x)$.

The reader can use his knowledge of group theory together with Theorem 14.4 to prove the next corollary.

Corollary 2

The set Dif (A,B,x) is an Abelian group under the addition of functions and the function D_x : Dif $(A,B,x) \rightarrow B$, where $D_x(f) = f'(x)$, is a group homomorphism.

EXAMPLE   14.4

We can use Theorems 14.2, 14.3, and 14.4 to find the derivative of the function $f : R \rightarrow R$, where $f(x) = x + c$. If $g(x) = x$ and $h(x) = c$, we have $f(x) = g(x) + h(x)$ and $f'(x) = g'(x) + h'(x) = 1 + 0 = 1$.

Theorem 14.5 gives us a means of obtaining the derivative of the product of two differentiable functions.

THEOREM   14.5

Consider the functions $f \in$ Dif (A,B,x), $g \in$ Dif (A,B,x), and their product $fg : A \rightarrow B$, where $(fg)(z) = f(z)g(z)$ for all $z \in A$. Then fg is differentiable at x and its derivative is $f'(x)g(x) + f(x)g'(x)$.

Proof

Let $h = fg$. Then

$$\lim_{t \to 0} \frac{h(x + t) - h(x)}{t} = \lim_{t \to 0} \frac{f(x + t)g(x + t) - f(x)g(x)}{t}$$

$$= \lim_{t \to 0} \frac{f(x + t)g(x + t) - f(x + t)g(x)}{t}$$

$$+ \lim_{t \to 0} \frac{f(x + t)g(x) - f(x)g(x)}{t}$$

$$= \lim_{t \to 0} f(x + t) \lim_{t \to 0} \frac{g(x + t) - g(x)}{t}$$

$$+ g(x) \lim_{t \to 0} \frac{f(x + t) - f(x)}{t}$$

$$= f(x)g'(x) + g(x)f'(x).$$

This proves the existence of the derivative and also its form. •

The reader can use this theorem together with Theorem 14.2 to prove the following corollary.

Corollary 1

Consider the functions $f \in$ Dif (A,B,x) and $cf : A \rightarrow B$, where $(cf)(z) = cf(z)$ for all $z \in A$, where $c \in B$ is constant. Then cf is differentiable at x and its derivative is $cf'(x)$.

EXAMPLE   14.5

Consider the function $f : A \to B$, where $f(x) = cx$ for $c \in B$, where c is constant. We know that the function $g : A \to B$, where $g(x) = x$ is differentiable at x and $g'(x) = 1$. Therefore f is differentiable and $f'(x) = cg'(x) = c$.

The following theorem is an important application of Theorem 14.5.

THEOREM   14.6

For each $n \in N$ the function $f_n : A \to B$, where $f_n(x) = x^n$ for $x \in A$ is differentiable at x and $f_n'(x) = nx^{n-1}$.

Proof

We shall prove the theorem by induction. Let $M = \{n | n \in N, f_n \in \text{Dif}\,(A, B, x), f_n'(x) = nx^{n-1}\}$. From Theorem 14.3 we see that $1 \in M$. If $n \in M$, then f_n is differentiable at x and $f_n'(x) = nx^{n-1}$. It is clear that $f_{n+1} = f_n f_1$. By Theorem 14.5, f_{n+1} is differentiable at x and

$$
\begin{aligned}
f_{n+1}'(x) &= f_n'(x) f_1(x) + f_n(x) f_1'(x) \\
&= nx^{n-1}x + x^n \\
&= (n+1)x^n.
\end{aligned}
$$

Therefore $n + 1 \in M$ and $M = N$. •

EXAMPLE   14.6

Consider the polynomial function $f : A \to B$, where $f(x) = a_0 x^n + a_1 x^{n-1} + a_2 x^{n-2} + \cdots + a_{n-1}x + a_n$ for $a_i \in B$ with a_i constant. If we use the notation of Corollary 2 to Theorem 14.4 for the derivative, we see that $D_x(a_k x^{n-k}) = (n - k)a_k x^{n-k}$ by Theorem 14.6 and Corollary 1 to Theorem 14.5. Then by Corollary 1 to Theorem 14.4 we have $f'(x) = na_0 x^{n-1} + (n - 1)a_1 x^{n-2} + \cdots + 2a_{n-2}x + a_{n-1}$.

We have now obtained the derivative of a polynomial function. Can we also obtain the derivative of a rational function, that is, a function $f : A \to B$, where $f(x) = p(x)/q(x)$ and $p : A \to B$ and $q : A \to B$ are polynomial functions? As a first step we consider the special case in which $f(x) = 1/x$.

THEOREM   14.7

The function $f : A \to B$, where $0 \notin A$ and $f(x) = 1/x$, is differentiable at $x \in A$ and its derivative at x is $-1/x^2$.

Proof

If $x \in A$ we can choose an interval in A that contains x (but does not contain 0, since $0 \notin A$). Then, provided $x + t$ is in this interval we have

$$\lim_{t \to 0} \frac{f(x + t) - f(x)}{t} = \lim_{t \to 0} \frac{1/(x + t) - 1/x}{t}$$

$$= \lim_{t \to 0} \frac{x - x - t}{t(x + t)x}$$

$$= \lim_{t \to 0} \frac{-1}{(x + t)x} = \frac{-1}{x^2}.$$

This proves both the existence and the form of the derivative. •

Instead of finding the derivative of $1/f(x)$ directly, we shall first prove the following general theorem, which is usually referred to as *the chain rule*.

THEOREM   14.8

Consider the functions $f \in \text{Dif}(A,R,x)$ and $g \in \text{Dif}(E,F,f(x))$, where $f(A) \subset E$ and $F \subset R$ or $F \subset C$. Let $g \cdot f$ be their composite. Then $g \cdot f$ is differentiable at x and its derivative is $g'(f(x)) \cdot f'(x)$.

Proof

We shall consider two cases. In the first for each sequence $(t_n)_{n \in N}$, with $\lim t_n = 0$, we have $f(x + t_n) \neq f(x)$ for sufficiently large n, that is, for all $n > n_0$. In the second case there is a sequence $(t_n)_{n \in N}$ with $\lim t_n = 0$ and $f(x + t_n) = f(x)$ for all $n \in N$.

1. If we define $s = f(x + t) - f(x)$ we see that $\lim_{t \to 0} s = 0$, but $s \neq 0$ for $t \neq 0$, provided we are working in a sufficiently small interval about x. Then

$$\lim_{t \to 0} \frac{g(f(x + t)) - g(f(x))}{t} = \lim_{t \to 0} \frac{g(f(x + t)) - g(f(x))}{f(x + t) - f(x)} \cdot \frac{f(x + t) - f(x)}{t}$$

$$= \lim_{t \to 0} \frac{g(f(x) + s) - g(f(x))}{s} \cdot \lim_{t \to 0} \frac{f(x + t) - f(x)}{t}$$

$$= \lim_{s \to 0} \frac{g(f(x) + s) - g(f(x))}{s} \cdot f'(x)$$

$$= g'(f(x))f'(x).$$

This completes the proof for the first case.

2. In the second case we have to consider two kinds of sequence $(t_n)_{n \in N}$, one in which $f(x + t_n) = f(x)$ for all t_n and one in which $f(x + t_n) \neq f(x)$ for sufficiently large n. If $f(x + t_n) = f(x)$, we have

$$\lim_{t_n \to 0} \frac{g(f(x + t_n)) - g(f(x))}{t_n} = 0.$$

If $f(x + t_n) \neq f(x)$ for large n, we can define $s_n = f(x + t_n) - f(x)$ as before.

Then

$$\lim_{t_n \to 0} \frac{g(f(x + t_n)) - g(f(x))}{t_n}$$

$$= \lim_{t_n \to 0} \frac{g(f(x) + t_n) - g(f(x))}{f(x + t_n) - f(x)} \cdot \frac{f(x + t_n) - f(x)}{t_n}$$

$$= \lim_{s_n \to 0} \frac{g(f(x) + s_n) - g(f(x))}{s_n} \cdot \lim_{t_n \to 0} \frac{f(x + t_n) - f(x)}{t_n}$$

$$= g'(f(x)) \cdot f'(x).$$

But

$$f'(x) = \lim_{t_n \to 0} \frac{f(x + t_n) - f(x)}{t_n}$$

for any sequence $(t_n)_{n \in N}$ such that $\lim t_n = 0$. If we choose a sequence such that $f(x + t_n) = f(x)$ for all $n \in N$, we see that $f'(x) = 0$.

This means that, for *any* sequence (t_n) with $\lim t_n = 0$, we have

$$\lim_{t_n \to 0} \frac{g(f(x + t_n)) - g(f(x))}{t_n} = 0.$$

Thus $g \cdot f$ is differentiable at x and, furthermore, its derivative is $g'(f(x)) f'(x)$. •

The second part of this proof is sometimes omitted, but it should be clear from the above proof that it is necessary.

The following theorem uses the chain rule to obtain the derivative of $1/g(x)$.

THEOREM   14.9

Consider the function $g \in \mathrm{Dif}\,(A,R,x)$, where $g(x) \neq 0$ for all $x \in A$, and the function $f : A \to R$, where $f(x) = 1/g(x)$ for all $x \in A$. Then f is differentiable at x and its derivative is $-g'(x)/[g(x)]^2$.

Proof

Consider the function $h \in \mathrm{Dif}\,(R - \{0\}, R, x)$, where $x \neq 0$ and $h(x) = 1/x$. Then f is the composite $h \cdot g$. Since $g(A) \subset R - \{0\}$, we can apply the chain rule to show that f is differentiable at x and $f'(x) = h'(g(x))g'(x) = [-1/(g(x))^2]g'(x) = -g'(x)/[g(x)]^2$. •

We can now combine the results of Theorems 14.5 and 14.9 to obtain the derivative of $f(x) = h(x)/g(x)$ of which a rational function is a special case.

THEOREM   14.10

Consider the functions $h \in \mathrm{Dif}\,(A,B,x)$, $g \in \mathrm{Dif}\,(A,B,x)$, where $g(x) \neq 0$ for all $x \in A$, and $f : A \to B$, where $f(x) = h(x)/g(x)$ for $x \in A$. Then f is differentiable at x, and its derivative is

$$f'(x) = \frac{g(x)h'(x) - g'(x)h(x)}{[g(x)]^2}.$$

Proof

We know from Theorem 14.9 that the function $k\colon A \to B$, where $k(x) = 1/g(x)$, is differentiable at x and $k'(x) = -g'(x)/[g(x)]^2$. Also $f(x) = h(x)k(x)$. Then Theorem 14.5 shows that f is differentiable at x and

$$\begin{aligned}
f'(x) &= h(x)k'(x) + h'(x)k(x) \\
&= \frac{-h(x)g'(x)}{[g(x)]^2} + \frac{h'(x)}{g(x)} \\
&= \frac{g(x)h'(x) - g'(x)h(x)}{[g(x)]^2}. \quad \bullet
\end{aligned}$$

EXAMPLE 14.7

We can now apply these various rules for differentiation to obtain the derivative at x of $f\colon A \to B$, where

$$f(x) = \frac{2x^3 + 3x + 2}{x + 3}$$

and $-3 \notin A$. The calculation is performed as follows:

$$\begin{aligned}
f'(x) &= \frac{(x + 3)D_x(2x^3 + 3x + 2) - (2x^3 + 3x + 2)D_x(x + 3)}{(x + 3)^2} \\
&= \frac{(x + 3)(6x^2 + 3) - (2x^3 + 3x + 2)}{(x + 3)^2} \\
&= \frac{4x^3 + 18x^2 + 7}{(x + 3)^2}.
\end{aligned}$$

The proofs of the following rules for differentiation are left as exercises.

$$\begin{aligned}
D_x(\sin x) &= \cos x, \\
D_x(\cos x) &= -\sin x, \\
D_x(\sec x) &= \tan x \sec x, \\
D_x(\csc x) &= -\cot x \csc x, \\
D_x(\tan x) &= \sec^2 x, \\
D_x(\cot x) &= -\csc^2 x.
\end{aligned}$$

14.7 Functions differentiable everywhere

In this section we shall consider functions that are differentiable at each point of their domain. We continue to restrict the domain to be either the set of real numbers R or an interval in R. If A is the domain we shall write

Dif (A,R) to represent the set of real-valued functions with domain A that are differentiable at every point of A, and Dif (A,C) for the similar set of complex-valued functions. We shall call Dif (A,R) the set of *real-valued functions differentiable on A*, and Dif (A,C) the set of *complex-valued functions differentiable on A*.

With each differentiable function $f \in$ Dif (A,R) we can associate a function $g \in \mathcal{F}(A,R)$, where $g(x) = f'(x)$. We usually denote this function by $f' : A \rightarrow R$. We can describe this by saying we have a function $D : $Dif $(A,R) \rightarrow \mathcal{F}(A,R)$, where $D(f) = f'$. We shall use the same notation for the complex-valued case, that is, we have a function $D : $Dif $(A,C) \rightarrow \mathcal{F}(A,C)$ where $D(f) = f'$.

We shall now consider the geometric or mechanical significance of the function f'. For the real-valued case we have seen in Section 14.3 that $f'(x)$ represents the slope of the tangent at $(x,f(x))$ of the curve representing the graph of the function f. In mechanical terms, if $f(t)$ represents the position of an object at time t, then $f'(t)$ represents its velocity at time t and f' is the velocity function.

EXAMPLE 14.8

For the function $f : R \rightarrow R$, where $f(x) = x^3 + 2x$, we have $f' : R \rightarrow R$, where $f'(x) = 3x^2 + 2$. A portion of the graphs of f and f' is shown in the two parts of Figure 14.6.

In Section 14.3 we saw that, instead of representing the graph of $f \in \mathcal{F}(A,C)$ as a subset of $R \times R \times R$, it is sometimes more convenient to represent the range of f in C. This representation can be linked with the idea of the motion of a point on the plane. If a point moves on the plane from

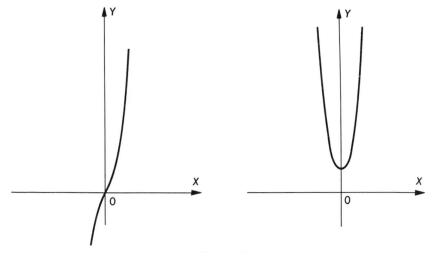

FIGURE 14.6

moment a to moment b its motion can be described as a complex-valued function $f:[a,b] \to C$, where, for $t \in [a,b]$, $f(t)$ indicates the position at time t. The path of motion is the range of the function f. The functions that occur in describing planar motion are usually differentiable at all points of the domain, that is, there is a function $f':[a,b] \to C$. The range of this function can also be represented in the complex plane $R \times R$. This representation is sometimes called a *hodograph* in mechanics. The vector representing the complex number $f'(t)$ is the velocity vector of the moving point at time t.

EXAMPLE   14.9

Consider the function $f:R \to C$, where

$$f(t) = t^3 + t + i(1 - t^6).$$

Then

$$f'(t) = 3t^2 + 1 - 6it^5.$$

Portions of the ranges of f and of f' are represented in Figure 14.7. We ob-

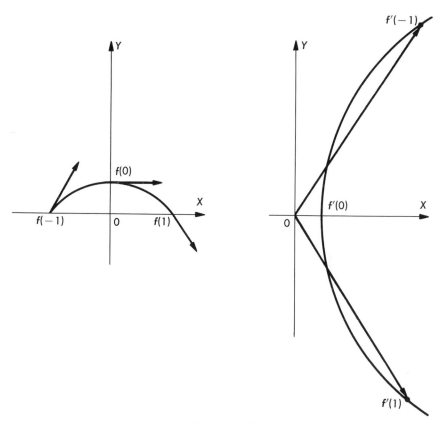

FIGURE 14.7

serve that the vector representing $f'(1)$ is parallel to the tangent vector to the curve representing $f(R)$ at $f(1)$.

14.8 Maximum and minimum values

In this section we shall consider the largest and smallest values of a function for points in its domain or for points in a subset of its domain. We shall distinguish between the concepts of relative maximum or minimum and absolute maximum or minimum.

DEFINITIONS

A real-valued function $f : A \to R$ is said to have a *relative maximum* at a point $x \in A$ if there is an interval $]x - \varepsilon, x + \varepsilon[\subset A$ with $\varepsilon > 0$ such that $f(x) \geq f(x')$ for all $x' \in]x - \varepsilon, x + \varepsilon[$.

Similarly, the function f has a *relative minimum* if there is an interval $]x - \varepsilon', x + \varepsilon'[\subset A$ with $\varepsilon' > 0$ such that $f(x) \leq f(x')$ for all $x' \in]x - \varepsilon, x + \varepsilon'[$.

We say that the function f has a *relative extremum* at $x \in A$ if f has either a relative maximum or a relative minimum at x.

For the function $f : A \to R$ there may be distinct elements x_1 and x_2 of A such that $f(x_1) \neq f(x_2)$ but $f(x_1)$ and $f(x_2)$ are both relative maxima. Similarly, there may be more than one relative minimum. These facts are in contrast with the properties of absolute extrema introduced in the following definition.

DEFINITION

The *absolute maximum* of a function $f : A \to R$ is the largest element in its range if there is a largest element; the *absolute minimum* is the smallest element in the range if there is a smallest element.

It is clear from this definition that, for any function, the absolute maximum and the absolute minimum must be unique. We may, however, have distinct elements x_1 and x_2 of the domain such that $f(x_1) = f(x_2)$ is the absolute maximum (or the absolute minimum).

An absolute extremum need not be a relative extremum. If $x \in A$ but no interval containing x is a subset of A, then $f(x)$ cannot be a relative extremum. It may, however, be an absolute extremum. For example, consider the function $f : [0,1] \to R$, where $f(x) = x^2$. Then $f(0) = 0$ is the absolute minimum, but there are no relative extrema. If, however, for the function $g : A \to R$ we have $g(x)$ an absolute extremum and there is an interval $]x - \varepsilon, x + \varepsilon[\subset A$, where $\varepsilon > 0$, then $f(x)$ is also a relative extremum.

For a real-valued function whose domain is a closed interval and that is continuous on its domain, there are always absolute extrema. This is stated in Theorem 14.11. The proof could have been given in the previous chapter on continuity but has been postponed to keep the discussion of extreme values in one place.

THEOREM   14.11

A real-valued continuous function $f : A \to R$ whose domain is a closed interval is a bounded function and has absolute extrema.

Proof

Suppose that f is not bounded above, that is, the range $f(A)$ has no upper bound. Then there is a sequence $(x_n)_{n \in N}$, $x_n \in A$ such that $f(x_n) > n$ for all $n \in N$. The sequence (x_n) is bounded because A is bounded. Theorem 12.7 shows that there is a convergent subsequence $(y_n)_{n \in N}$. Let $y = \lim y_n$, then $y \in A$, since A is a closed interval and hence contains the least upper bound and greatest lower bound of any subset. Since the function f is continuous, we know that $f(y) = \lim_{n \to \infty} f(y_n)$. On the other hand, $f(y_n) \geq f(x_n) > n$ and hence the sequence $(f(y_n))_{n \in N}$ has no limit. We have thus reached a contradiction and therefore our assumption that f is not bounded above is false. A similar proof shows that f is bounded below.

We shall now show that f has an absolute maximum. The range $f(A)$ is a subset of R and is bounded above, therefore it has a least upper bound. The definition of the least upper bound in Section 6.10 shows that, for each $n \in N$, there is $x_n \in A$ such that

$$\operatorname*{lub}_{x \in A} f(x) - \frac{1}{n} < f(x_n) \leq \operatorname*{lub}_{x \in A} f(x).$$

From this we see that the sequence $(f(x_n))_{n \in N}$ is convergent and

$$\lim_{n \to \infty} f(x_n) = \operatorname*{lub}_{x \in A} f(x).$$

The sequence $(x_n)_{n \in N}$ is bounded and hence has a convergent subsequence $(y_n)_{n \in N}$. If we let $y = \lim y_n$, we have $y \in A$. Since f is continuous, we have

$$f(y) = \lim_{n \to \infty} f(y_n) = \lim_{n \to \infty} f(x_n) = \operatorname*{lub}_{x \in A} f(x).$$

Therefore $f(y)$ is the absolute maximum. A similar proof shows the existence of an absolute minimum. •

We leave the proof of the following corollary as an exercise.

Corollary 1

A complex-valued continuous function $f : A \to C$, whose domain is a closed interval, is bounded.

We return to our study of relative extrema. If the function $f:A \to R$ is differentiable on A, Theorem 14.12 gives a useful method for looking for the relative extrema.

THEOREM   14.12

If the function $f:A \to R$ is differentiable on A and if $f(x)$ is a relative extremum of f, then $f'(x) = 0$, that is, the set $\{x|x \in A, f(x) \text{ a relative extremum of } f\}$ is a subset of $\{x|x \in A, f'(x) = 0\}$.

Proof

Consider $x \in A$ such that $f(x)$ is a relative maximum of f. With the help of Figure 14.8 we see that, in some neighborhood of x, we have $x + t_1 < x$ such that $f(x + t_1) - f(x) \le 0$ and $x + t_2 > x$ such that $f(x + t_2) - f(x) \le 0$. Then the difference quotient gives

$$\lim_{t_1 \to 0} \frac{f(x + t_1) - f(x)}{t_1} \le 0,$$
$$\lim_{t_2 \to 0} \frac{f(x + t_2) - f(x)}{t_2} \ge 0.$$

But f is differentiable on A, so that these limits must be the same. Therefore $f'(x) = 0$.

A similar proof can be used if $f(x)$ is a relative minimum. •

The converse of this theorem is not true, that is, we can have $f'(x) = 0$ without $f(x)$ being a relative extremum. For example, consider the function $f:R \to R$, where $f(x) = x^3$. The graph of f is represented in Figure 14.9. We see that $f'(x) = 3x^2$ and $f'(0) = 0$. But $f(0)$ is not a relative maximum, since $f(x) > f(0)$ for all $x > 0$, nor a relative minimum, since $f(x) < f(0)$ for all $x < 0$.

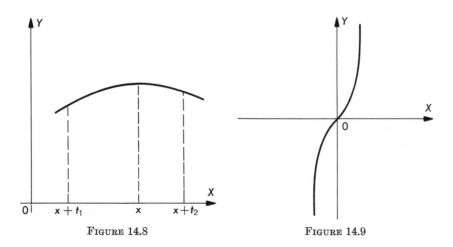

FIGURE 14.8   FIGURE 14.9

Methods for selecting from among the points x at which $f'(x) = 0$ those for which $f(x)$ is a relative extremum will be found in calculus books dealing with the computational aspects of the subject. We shall give one example in which we rely upon the accuracy of a diagram to obtain our results.

EXAMPLE 14.10

The graph of the function $f:[-2,3] \to R$, where $f(x) = (x-2)^2(x+1)^3$ is shown in Figure 14.10. We can calculate

$$f'(x) = 2(x-2)(x+1)^3 + 3(x-2)^2(x+1)^2$$
$$= (x-2)(x+1)^2(2x+2+3x-6)$$
$$= (x-2)(x+1)^2(5x-4).$$

Then $f'(x) = 0$ when $x = 2$, -1, or $\frac{4}{5}$. Also $f(2) = 0$, $f(-1) = 0$, $f(\frac{4}{5}) = 8.4$. From the diagram we see that $f(2)$ is a relative minimum, $f(\frac{4}{5})$ is a

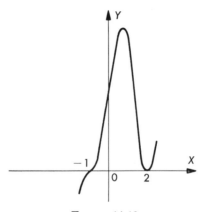

FIGURE 14.10

relative maximum, $f(-1)$ is not a relative extremum. We can also see that $f(-2) = -256$ is the absolute minimum and $f(3) = 64$ is the absolute maximum.

14.9 Some fundamental theorems

In this section we shall prove some of the most important results relating to the concept of the derivative.

THEOREM 14.13 (ROLLE'S THEOREM)

If the function $f:[a,b] \to R$ is continuous on its domain $[a,b]$ and differentiable in the open interval $]a,b[$, and if $f(a) = f(b)$, then $f'(c) = 0$ for some $c \in]a,b[$.

Proof

If f is a constant function, then $f'(x) = 0$ for all $x \in\,]a,b[$ and the theorem is proved. If f is not a constant function, either there is an $x_1 \in\,]a,b[$ such that $f(x_1) > f(a)$ or there is an $x_2 \in\,]a,b[$ such that $f(x_2) < f(a)$. We shall consider the case where $f(x_1) > f(a)$. Since f is continuous on the closed interval, it has an absolute maximum, say $f(c)$. But $c \neq a$ and $c \neq b$, since $f(x_2) > f(a) = f(b)$ and hence $f(a) = f(b)$ is not the absolute maximum. Therefore $f(c)$ is also a relative maximum and $f'(c) = 0$. A similar proof applies to the case in which $f(x_2) < f(a) = f(b)$. •

Rolle's theorem provides us with a means for proving the following important theorem.

THEOREM 14.14 (MEAN-VALUE THEOREM)

If the function $f:[a,b] \to R$ is continuous on $[a,b]$ and differentiable on $]a,b[$, then there is an element $c \in\,]a,b[$ such that

$$f'(c) = \frac{f(b) - f(a)}{b - a}.$$

Proof

We want to define a new function $g:[a,b] \to R$ to which we can apply Rolle's theorem. We want g to be continuous on $[a,b]$ and differentiable on $]a,b[$. Also we want $g(a) = g(b)$. It is clear that, if we define

$$g(x) = f(x) - \frac{f(b) - f(a)}{b - a}(x - a),$$

g has the required properties. Thus by Rolle's theorem there is an element $c \in\,]a,b[$ such that $g'(c) = 0$. But

$$g'(c) = f'(c) - \frac{f(b) - f(a)}{b - a}.$$

Therefore we have

$$f'(c) = \frac{f(b) - f(a)}{b - a},$$

the required result. •

The geometric interpretation of this theorem is represented in Figure 14.11. The theorem states that there is a point on the curve between the points $(a,f(a))$ and $(b,f(b))$ at which the tangent is parallel to the chord between these two points.

There is a corollary to the mean-value theorem that is of great importance for our work with integrals in the next few sections.

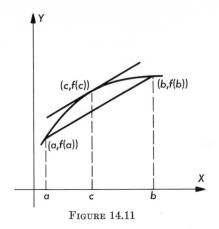

FIGURE 14.11

Corollary 1

If the function $f:[a,b] \to R$ is continuous on $[a,b]$ and differentiable on $]a,b[$ and if $f'(x) = 0$ for all $x \in]a,b[$, then f is a constant function.

Proof

For any point $x \in]a,b]$ the mean value theorem shows that

$$f(x) - f(a) = (x - a)f'(c) = 0.$$

Therefore $f(x) = f(a)$ for all $x \in [a,b]$. •

Corollary 2 gives a useful connection between the derivative and monotone functions.

Corollary 2

If the function $f:[a,b] \to R$ is continuous on $[a,b]$ and differentiable on $]a,b[$ and if $f'(x) > 0$ for all $x \in]a,b[$, then f is an increasing function.

Proof

If we choose $x \in [a,b]$, $x' \in [a,b]$ such that $x < x'$, the mean-value theorem shows that

$$f(x') - f(x) = (x' - x)f'(c)$$

for some $c \in [x,x']$. But $f'(c) > 0$ and $x' - x > 0$, therefore $f(x') - f(x) > 0$ and f is an increasing function. •

The reader can prove a similar result relating a negative derivative to a decreasing function.

The converse of this theorem is not true, although a similar result is true. The function $f:[-1,1] \to R$, where $f(x) = x^3$, is differentiable on $[-1,1]$ and is an increasing function. But $f'(0) = 0$.

It is easily seen that, if $f:[a,b] \to R$ is continuous on $[a,b]$, differentiable on $]a,b[$, and increasing, then $f'(x) \geq 0$ for all $x \in]a,b[$.

Corollary 1 can easily be extended to complex valued functions. We state the result as a further corollary.

Corollary 3

If the function $f:[a,b] \to C$ is continuous on $[a,b]$ and differentiable on $]a,b[$, then $f'(x) = 0$ for all $x \in]a,b[$ if and only if f is a constant function.

Proof

If f is a constant function, then Theorem 14.2 shows that $f'(x) = 0$ for all $x \in]a,b[$. Let $f(x) = f_1(x) + if_2(x)$, where $f_j:[a,b] \to R$ for $j = 1,2$. Then $f'(x) = f_1'(x) + if_2'(x)$ and $f'(x) = 0$ implies that $f_1'(x) = 0$, $f_2'(x) = 0$ for all $x \in]a,b[$. Then by Corollary 1, f_1 and f_2 are constant functions. Therefore f is a constant function. •

We have seen that all differentiable functions are continuous, that is, the set of differentiable functions is a proper subset of the set of continuous functions. We have also seen that, with each differentiable function $f: A \to B$, the process of differentiation associates a function $f': A \to B$, called the derivative. What is the connection between the set of derivatives with domain A and the set of continuous functions on A? An example will be found in the exercises to show that the derivative need not be continuous. We shall now turn to a consideration of the integral calculus. Our main theorem on this subject is that every continuous function is the derivative of some function.

EXERCISES

Note: Throughout these exercises $[x]$ denotes the integer n such that $n \leq x < n + 1$.

14.1. Write the difference quotient at $x = 0$ for each of the following functions:

(a) $f:R \to R$, $f(x) = x \sqrt{x}$.
(b) $g:R \to R$, $g(x) = x^2 \sin x$.
(c) $h:R \to R$, $h(x) = x \cos x$.

14.2. Find the limit of the difference quotient at $x = 0$ for each of the functions in Exercise 14.1.

14.3. Write out the difference quotient at $x = \frac{1}{2}$ for each of the following functions:

(a) $f:R_+ \to R$, $f(x) = |x|/x$.
(b) $g:R_+ \to R$, $g(x) = 1/x^2$.
(c) $h:R \to R$, $h(x) = x - [x]$.

14.4. Find the limit of the difference quotient at $x = \frac{3}{2}$ for each of the functions in Exercise 14.3.

14.5. Write out the difference quotient at $x = 0$ for each of the following functions:

(a) $f:R \to C$, $f(x) = \cos x + i \sin x$.
(b) $g:]-\pi/2,\pi/2[\to C$, $g(x) = \cos x + i \tan x$.
(c) $h:R_+ \to C$, $h(x) = x^2 + i/(x^2 + 1)$.

14.6. (a) Prove that the function $f:A \to B$ is differentiable at $x \in A$ such that $[x - a, x + a] \subset A$ for some $a > 0$ if and only if the left and right derivatives at x exist and are equal.

(b) Prove that when the left and right derivatives at x exist and are equal their common value is equal to the derivative at x.

14.7. Prove Corollary 1 to Theorem 14.4.

14.8. Prove Corollary 2 to Theorem 14.4.

14.9. Prove Corollary 1 to Theorem 14.5.

14.10. If B is a ring ($B = R$ or $B = C$), prove that Dif (A,B,x) is a ring for any $x \in A$.

14.11. Is the function $D_x:$ Dif $(A,B,x) \to B$ as defined in Section 14.6 a ring homomorphism? Give reasons for your answer.

14.12. Draw the following diagram. Let A be the point $(1,0)$ and let B be a point on the unit circle such that $\angle BOA$ is less than $\pi/2$. Let C be the point on the x axis such that OA is perpendicular to CB. Let D be the point on OB extended such that AD is perpendicular to OA. If the measure of $\angle BOA$ is θ radians, then the length of arc BA is θ, the length of CB is $\sin \theta$, and the length of AD is $\tan \theta$. Show that

$$\frac{1}{\cos \theta} < \frac{\sin \theta}{\theta} < 1.$$

Hence show that

$$\lim_{\theta \to 0} \frac{\sin \theta}{\theta} = 1.$$

14.13. By expressing $\cos \theta - 1$ in terms of $\sin (\theta/2)$ and using the result of Exercise 14.12, show that

$$\lim_{\theta \to 0} \frac{\cos \theta - 1}{\theta} = 0.$$

14.14. Use the results of Exercises 14.12 and 14.13 to prove that $D_x(\sin x) = \cos x$ for any x.

14.15. Use the results of Exercises 14.12 and 14.13 to prove that $D_x(\cos x) = -\sin x$.

14.16. Use the results of Exercises 14.14 and 14.15 to prove that $D_x(\sec x) = \tan x \sec x$ and $D_x(\csc x) = -\cot x \csc x$.

14.17. Use the results of Exercises 14.14 and 14.15 to prove that $D_x(\tan x) = \sec^2 x$ and $D_x(\cot x) = -\csc^2 x$.

14.18. Find the right and left derivatives at $x = 0$ (if they exist) for the following functions. Do these functions have a derivative at $x = 0$?

(a) $f:R \to R$, $f(x) = x - [x]$.
(b) $g:R \to R$, $g(x) = x|x|$.
(c) $h:R \to R$, $h(x) = x - |x|$.

14.19. Find the difference quotient and the derivative at $x = 0$ for each of the following functions:

    (a) $f: R \to R$, $f(x) = \sin 2x$.
    (b) $g: R \to R$, $g(x) = \sin^2 x + \cos^2 x$.
    (c) $h: R \to C$, $h(x) = \sin^2 x + i \cos^2 x$.

14.20. Let Dif (A,R) be defined as in Section 14.7. Prove that Dif (A,R) is a group under addition.

14.21. Prove that the function $D:$ Dif $(A,R) \to \mathfrak{F}(A,R)$ as defined in Section 14.7 is a group homomorphism.

14.22. Which of the following functions have derivatives at all points in $]0,1[$? Which have a right derivative at $x = 0$? Which have a left derivative at $x = 1$?

    (a) $f: R \to R$, $f(x) = [x + \frac{1}{2}]$.
    (b) $g: R \to R$, $g(x) = x - [x]$.
    (c) $h: R \to R$, $h(x) = |x| - [x]$.

14.23. Draw the hodographs (see Section 14.7) of the following complex-valued functions:

    (a) $f: R \to C$, $f(x) = x + ix^2$.
    (b) $g: R \to C$, $g(x) = \cos x + i \sin x$.
    (c) $h: R \to C$, $h(x) = \cos^2 x + i \sin^2 x$.

14.24. Prove that the function f in Theorem 14.11 is bounded below.

14.25. Prove that the function f in Theorem 14.11 has an absolute minimum.

14.26. Give the proof of Theorem 14.12 for the case where $f(x)$ is a relative minimum.

14.27. Consider the set of all rectangles of fixed perimeter, l. Show that the square has the largest area among these.

14.28. Consider the set of triangles of fixed area a. Which one has the shortest perimeter?

14.29. Find all the relative maxima and relative minima of the function $f: R \to R$, where $f(x) = (x - 1)^2(x + 2)^3$. Does this function have an absolute maximum or an absolute minimum? Sketch the graph of f.

14.30. Find the relative maxima and relative minima of the function $f: R \to R$, where $f(x) = x/(x^2 + 1)$. Find the absolute maximum and the absolute minimum if these exist. Sketch the graph of f.

14.31. Prove Theorem 14.13 for the case where $f(x_2) < f(a)$.

14.32. Prove the analogue of Corollary 2 to Theorem 14.14 in the case where $f'(x) < 0$.

14.33. Prove that, for any polynomial function f whose degree is odd, there is a real number c such that $f(c) = 0$. We call c a *zero of the function f*.

14.34. Let $f: A \to R$ be differentiable everywhere on A. Prove that between two consecutive zeros of the derivative function f' there is at most one zero of f.

14.35. By drawing the graphs of the following functions on graph paper find the real number c required in the mean value theorem if $a = 0$, $b = 1$.

    (a) $f: R \to R$, $f(x) = x^2$.
    (b) $g: R \to R$, $g(x) = \sin x\pi/2$.

14.36. Draw on graph paper the graph of the function $f: R \to R$, where $f(x) = x/(x^4 + 1)$. Indicate the intervals of the domain for which this function is increasing and those for which it is decreasing.

14.37. (a) Show that the function $f: R \to R$, where

$$f(x) = x^2 \sin (1/x) \qquad \text{for } x \neq 0,$$
$$f(x) = 0 \qquad \text{for } x = 0,$$

is differentiable everywhere. [*Hint:* Apply formulas for the derivative for $x \neq 0$ and the difference quotient technique for $x = 0$.]

(b) Show that the derivative f' is not continuous at $x = 0$.

14.10   The integral

We have seen that a study of velocity or of geometric tangents leads to the concept of the derivative. In a similar way a study of length, area, and volume leads to the other major concept of the calculus, namely, the integral. The method that is used to introduce the integral is similar to the device used by the Greeks two thousand years earlier to study lengths, areas, and volumes, but whereas the Greeks emphasized solutions of particular problems, the calculus emphasizes the method itself and so reaches a much more general concept than that attained by the ancient Greeks.

We shall continue to emphasize the concepts rather than the methods of computation that can be found in any calculus text. Our main result is the theorem that every continuous function is the derivative of a differentiable function. This is sometimes called the *fundamental theorem of the calculus.*

14.11   Area and the definite integral

We shall begin a study of area in a way similar to that of the Greeks. Out of this we shall obtain the idea of the definite integral of a real-valued function whose domain is a closed interval and which is continuous on its domain. These ideas can be extended to functions that have some discontinuities, to functions whose domain is not a closed interval, and to functions that are not bounded. Although these generalizations are not difficult, we shall not treat them. At the end of the nineteenth century the concept of the integral was improved to make it a much more powerful mathematical instrument. We shall not attempt to describe these interesting developments. We shall, however, include a consideration of the integral of a complex-valued function.

In studying the area of a circle the Greek mathematicians observed that the difference in area between an inscribed regular[2] polygon of n sides and a circumscribed regular polygon of n sides becomes smaller as n is increased. This difference is represented by the shaded region in Figure 14.12. The fact that this difference approaches 0 means that the sequence $(c_n)_{n \in N}$, where c_n is the area of a circumscribed regular polygon of n sides, is nonincreasing and is bounded below by any i_m, where i_m is the area of an inscribed polygon of m sides. Also the sequence $(i_m)_{m \in N}$ is nondecreasing and is bounded

[2] Regularity is not necessary, but it simplifies the ideas.

above by any c_n. It follows that both sequences converge and $\lim c_n = \lim i_n$. This common limit was called the area of the circle.

We shall apply a similar method to a more general situation. Consider the continuous function $f:[a,b] \to R$ and let A be the set of points in the region of the plane bounded by the x axis, vertical lines at a and b, and the graph of the function f. This area is represented by the shaded region in Figure 14.13.

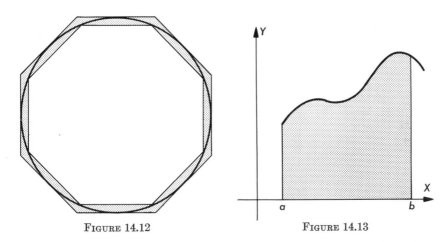

FIGURE 14.12   FIGURE 14.13

Just as we obtained two estimates—one too large and one too small—for the area of the circle in terms of polygons of n sides, we can obtain two estimates—one too large and one too small—for the area of A in terms of the areas of rectangles that we know how to calculate. We choose a set of $n + 1$ points $\{x_i | 1 \le i \le n + 1\}$ in $[a,b]$ such that $a = x_1 < x_2 < \cdots < x_k < \cdots < x_{n+1} = b$. On each subinterval $[x_k, x_{k+1}]$ we construct a rectangle whose height is

$$\sup_{x_k \le x \le x_{k+1}} f(x).$$

This set of rectangles is represented in Figure 14.14. It is clear that each rectangle is just high enough for the set A to be included in the union of these rectangles. The area of the union of these rectangles, which we denote by u, depends on the number of subintervals n and also on the location of the points x_k.

In a similar way we can construct a set of rectangles completely contained in the set A by choosing for the rectangle whose base is $[x_k, x_{k+1}]$ the height

$$\inf_{x_k \le x \le x_{k+1}} f(x).$$

This set of rectangles is represented in Figure 14.15. The area of the union of these rectangles, which we denote by l, also depends on the choice of subintervals, that is, the location of the points x_k.

We let L denote the set of all possible areas l of the unions of such "lower" rectangles and U the set of all possible areas u of unions of such "upper" rectangles. It is clear that $l \leq u$ for any $l \in L$ and $u \in U$. Also U is bounded below by any $l \in L$ and L is bounded above by any $u \in U$. Therefore sup L and inf U exist and sup $L \leq$ inf U. If the function f is such that sup $L =$ inf U, we call their common value the area of the set A.

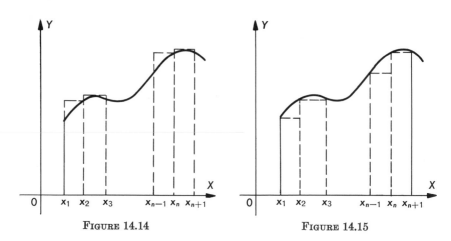

FIGURE 14.14   FIGURE 14.15

If we return to the construction of the rectangles, we see that

$$u = \sum_{i=1}^{n} (x_{i+1} - x_i) \sup_{x_i \leq x \leq x_{i+1}} f(x)$$

and

$$l = \sum_{i=1}^{n} (x_{i+1} - x_i) \inf_{x_i \leq x \leq x_{i+1}} f(x).$$

Whenever we have sup $L =$ inf U we call this common value *the definite integral of f* on $[a,b]$. It is traditionally denoted

$$\int_a^b f(x) \, dx,$$

a convenient notation since the symbol $\int$, an elongated S, suggests the sums from which it is defined, the product $f(x) \, dx$ suggests the terms in the sums, and the presence of f and a, b indicate the graph and domain of the function on which the value of the definite integral depends.

14.12   The existence of the definite integral

In the proof of Theorem 14.15 we shall make an assumption that is not proved until Theorem 14.16. The argument is not circular since we do not use Theorem 14.15 in the proof of Theorem 14.16. The reader who wishes to do so can reverse the arrangement of these two theorems. We have chosen this arrangement to provide motivation for the more subtle Theorem 14.16.

THEOREM   14.15

If the function $f:[a,b] \to R$ is continuous on $[a,b]$, then sup $L = $ inf U, where L, U are defined as in Section 14.11.

Proof

Let l, u be defined using the same subintervals. Then

$$l = \sum_{i=1}^{n} (x_{i+1} - x_i) \inf_{x_i \le x \le x_{i+1}} f(x)$$

and

$$u = \sum_{i=1}^{n} (x_{i+1} - x_i) \sup_{x_i \le x \le x_{i+1}} f(x).$$

From this we obtain

$$u - l = \sum_{i=1}^{n} (x_{i+1} - x_i)(\sup_{x_i \le x \le x_{i+1}} f(x) - \inf_{x_i \le x \le x_{i+1}} f(x)).$$

We now *assume* (see Theorem 14.16) that, for given $\varepsilon > 0$, there is a set of subintervals $[x_k, x_{k+1}]$ such that

$$\sup_{x_i \le x \le x_{i+1}} f(x) - \inf_{x_i \le x \le x_{i+1}} f(x) < \frac{\varepsilon}{b-a}$$

for each i.

Then $u - l < \varepsilon$ and, since $l \le \sup L \le \inf U \le u$, we have sup $L = $ inf U. •

It remains for us to prove what we assumed in the above proof, that is, that for some choice of the points x_i we have

$$\sup_{x_i \le x \le x_{i+1}} f(x) - \inf_{x_i \le x \le x_{i+1}} f(x) < \frac{\varepsilon}{b-a}$$

for all i. This is proved in the following theorem.

THEOREM   14.16

If the function $f:[a,b] \to R$ is continuous on $[a,b]$, then for each real $\varepsilon > 0$ there is a real $\delta(\varepsilon) > 0$ such that $|f(x) - f(x')| < \varepsilon$ whenever $|x - x'| < \delta(\varepsilon)$ and x, $x' \in [a,b]$.

Before proving this theorem we must be clear as to the exact meaning of the statement. Unless the reader has been very careful, he probably sees no difference between this condition and the definition of continuity. If he will refer to Section 13.2 he will see that $\delta(\varepsilon,x)$ in the definition of continuity depends on both ε and x. If $\inf\limits_{a<x<b} \delta(\varepsilon,x) \neq 0$, we could use this value for δ for each value of x. Theorem 14.16 uses this technique to show that there is $\delta(\varepsilon)$ dependent on ε but independent of x, that is, $\delta(\varepsilon)$ may be used at any point $x \in [a,b]$. Since the same $\delta(\varepsilon)$ may be used at all points, we say that a function with the property described in the theorem is *uniformly continuous* on $[a,b]$. The theorem may be stated: *A function that is continuous on a closed interval is uniformly continuous on that interval.* We shall now prove the theorem.

Proof

Suppose $\varepsilon > 0$ is given. Since the function $f:[a,b] \to R$ is continuous, there are, for each $x \in [a,b]$, intervals $[x - \delta, x + \delta] \subset [a,b]$ such that

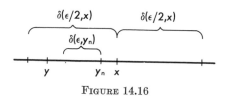

FIGURE 14.16

$|f(x) - f(x')| < \varepsilon$ for all $x' \in [x - \delta, x + \delta]$. Clearly the set of all such real numbers δ is bounded above by $b - a$. This set has a least upper bound, which we denote by $\delta(\varepsilon,x)$. This gives us a function $g:[a,b] \to R$, where $g(x) = \delta(\varepsilon,x)$. The range of this function is bounded below by 0, so that it has a greatest lower bound. We shall show that this greatest lower bound is not 0.

If $\inf \delta(\varepsilon,x) = 0$, there is a sequence $(x_n)_{n \in N}$, $x_n \in [a,b]$ such that $\lim \delta(\varepsilon,x_n) = 0$. Since the sequence (x_n) is bounded, it has a convergent subsequence $(y_n)_{n \in N}$. Then $\lim \delta(\varepsilon,y_n) = 0$. If we let $\lim y_n = x$, we see that $x \in [a,b]$. We shall now refer to Figure 14.16 to demonstrate a contradiction.

With x we associate $\delta(\varepsilon/2,x)$ and choose y_n such that $\delta(\varepsilon,y_n) < \delta(\varepsilon/2,x)/2$ and also $|x - y_n| < \delta(\varepsilon/2,x)/2$. For each y such that $|y - x| < \delta(\varepsilon/2,x)$, we have $|f(y) - f(x)| < \varepsilon/2$. Also $|x - y_n| < \delta(\varepsilon/2,x)/2$ and so $|f(x) - f(y_n)| < \varepsilon/2$. Then $|f(y) - f(y_n)| \leq |f(y) - f(x)| + |f(x) - f(y_n)| < \varepsilon$ for all

$$y \in (x - \delta(\varepsilon/2,x), x + \delta(\varepsilon/2,x)).$$

This shows that

$$\delta(\varepsilon,y_n) \geq \delta(\varepsilon/2,x) - |x - y_n| > 2 = \frac{\delta(\varepsilon/2,x)}{2}.$$

But this contradicts $\lim y_n = x$ and hence our assumption that $\inf \delta(\varepsilon,x) = 0$ is false.

We denote by $\delta(\varepsilon)$ the greatest lower bound,

$$\inf_{x \in [a,b]} \delta(\varepsilon, x).$$

We have shown that $\delta(\varepsilon) \neq 0$. It is now clear that, for $x \in [a,b]$ and

$$x' \in [a,b]$$

such that $|x - x'| < \delta(\varepsilon)$, we have $|f(x) - f(x')| < \varepsilon$. This completes the proof of the theorem. •

The following corollary states a similar result for complex-valued functions.

Corollary 1

If the complex-valued function $f:[a,b] \to C$ is continuous on $[a,b]$, then for each $\varepsilon > 0$ there is a real $\delta(\varepsilon) > 0$ such that $|f(x) - f(x')| < \varepsilon$ for

$$x \in [a,b], x' \in [a,b]$$

such that $|x - x'| < \varepsilon$.

Proof

We can write the function f as $f_1 + if_2$, where f_1 and f_2 are real-valued functions, continuous on $[a,b]$. For a given $\varepsilon > 0$ there are $\delta_1(\varepsilon/2)$ and $\delta_2(\varepsilon/2)$ such that $|f_1(x) - f_1(x')| < \varepsilon/2$ and $|f_2(x) - f_2(x')| < \varepsilon/2$ for $x \in [a,b], x' \in [a,b]$ such that $|x - x'| < \delta_1(\varepsilon/2)$ and $|x - x'| < \delta_2(\varepsilon/2)$. Choose $\delta(\varepsilon) = \min(\delta_1(\varepsilon/2), \delta_2(\varepsilon/2))$. Then

$$|f(x) - f(x')| = |f_1(x) + if_2(x) - f_1(x') - if_2(x')| \leq |f_1(x) - f_1(x')| \\ + |f_2(x) - f_2(x')| \leq \varepsilon$$

for $|x - x'| < \delta(\varepsilon)$. •

The main result of this section and the preceding one may be summarized as follows: *For any continuous function $f:[a,b] \to R$, there is a real number, denoted $\int_a^b f(x)\,dx$, which we call the definite integral of f on the interval $[a,b]$.*

14.13 Properties of the definite integral

We shall now consider some important properties of the definite integral. The first of these is referred to as the *law of the mean*, or the *mean-value theorem for integrals*.

THEOREM   14.17

If the function $f:[a,b] \to R$ is continuous on $[a,b]$, then there is a number $t \in [a,b]$ such that

$$\int_a^b f(x) \, dx = f(t)(b - a).$$

Proof

From the definition of the integral, we see that $\inf_{a \leq x \leq b} f(x)(b - a) \leq \int_a^b f(x) \, dx \leq \sup_{a \leq x \leq b} f(x)(b - a)$. This means that there is some number c such that $\inf f(x) \leq c \leq \sup f(x)$ and

$$c(b - a) = \int_a^b f(x) \, dx.$$

We must now show that $f(t) = c$ for some $t \in [a,b]$. Theorem 14.11 shows that the continuous function f has an absolute minimum

$$f(u) = \inf_{a \leq x \leq b} f(x)$$

and an absolute maximum

$$f(v) = \sup_{a \leq x \leq b} f(x).$$

Then $f(u) \leq c \leq f(v)$ and Theorem 13.11 shows that $f(t) = c$ for some $t \in [a,b]$. •

In Theorem 14.18 we shall write f to represent a real-valued function with domain $[a,c]$ and also the restriction of f to $[a,b]$ and the restriction to $[b,c]$, where $a \leq b \leq c$. This departure from our earlier notation for restricted functions simplifies the statement and should not cause any confusion.

THEOREM   14.18

If the function $f:[a,c] \to R$ is continuous on $[a,c]$ and if $a \leq b \leq c$, then

$$\int_a^c f(x) \, dx = \int_a^b f(x) \, dx + \int_b^c f(x) \, dx.$$

Proof

We have defined

$$\int_a^c f(x) \, dx = \inf U = \sup L,$$

where

$$U = \left\{ u \middle| u = \sum_{i=1}^n \sup_{x_i \leq x \leq x_{i+1}} f(x)(x_{i+1} - x_i), \, a = x_1 < x_2 < \cdots < x_{n+1} = c \right\}$$

and

$$L = \left\{ l \,\middle|\, l = \sum_{i=1}^{n} \inf_{x_i \leq x \leq x_{i+1}} f(x)(x_{i+1} - x_i), a = x_1 < x_2 < \cdots < x_{n+1} = c \right\}.$$

Also

$$\int_a^b f(x)\,dx = \inf U' = \sup L'$$

and

$$\int_b^c f(x)\,dx = \inf U'' = \sup L'',$$

where

$$U' = \left\{ u' \,\middle|\, u' = \sum_{i=1}^{n} \sup_{x_i \leq x \leq x_{i+1}} f(x)(x_{i+1} - x_i), a = x_1 < x_2 < \cdots < x_{n+1} = b \right\};$$

and similar definitions can be supplied for L', U'', and L''.

We observe that all $u' + u''$ are in U and all $l' + l''$ are in L, since we may choose $x_k = b$ for some k. Then

$$\inf U \leq \inf U' + \inf U'',$$

that is,

$$\int_a^c f(x)\,dx \leq \int_a^b f(x)\,dx + \int_b^c f(x)\,dx$$

and

$$\sup L \geq \sup L' + \sup L'',$$

that is,

$$\int_a^c f(x)\,dx \geq \int_a^b f(x)\,dx + \int_b^c f(x)\,dx.$$

From these two inequalities it is clear that

$$\int_a^c f(x)\,dx = \int_a^b f(x)\,dx + \int_b^c f(x)\,dx. \; \bullet$$

The next property deals with the integral of the sum of two functions.

THEOREM   14.19

If the functions $f:[a,b] \to R$ and $g:[a,b] \to R$ are continuous on $[a,b]$, then

$$\int_a^b (f(x) + g(x))\,dx = \int_a^b f(x)\,dx + \int_a^b g(x)\,dx.$$

Proof

We know that

$$\int_a^b f(x)\,dx = \sup L_f = \inf U_f$$

and

$$\int_a^b g(x)\,dx = \sup L_g = \inf U_g,$$

where

$$L_f = \left\{ l \mid l = \sum_{i=1}^n \inf_{x_i \le x \le x_{i+1}} f(x)(x_{i+1} - x_i), \ a = x_1 < \cdots < x_{n+1} = b \right\},$$

and L_g, U_f, U_g are defined similarly. If we define

$$U_{f+g} = \left\{ u \mid u = \sum_{i=1}^n \sup_{x_i \le x \le x_{i+1}} (f(x) + g(x))(x_{i+1} - x_i), \right.$$

$$\left. a = x_1 < \cdots < x_{n+1} = b \right\}$$

and define L_{f+g} similarly; then inf $U_{f+g} \le$ inf $U_f +$ inf U_g, since sup $(f(x) + g(x)) \le$ sup $f(x) +$ sup $g(x)$, and sup $L_{f+g} \ge$ sup $L_f +$ sup L_g, since inf $(f(x) + g(x)) \ge$ inf $f(x) +$ inf $g(x)$.

Also sup $L_{f+g} \le$ inf U_{f+g} and thus we have

$$\text{sup } L_{f+g} = \text{inf } U_{f+g} = \text{sup } L_f + \text{sup } L_g,$$

that is,

$$\int_a^b (f(x) + g(x)) \, dx = \int_a^b f(x) \, dx + \int_a^b g(x) \, dx. \ \bullet$$

14.14   Fundamental theorem of the calculus

We turn now to the question of the relation between the process of differentiation and the process of finding the definite integral, usually called *integration*. We can make the question more precise by asking whether every continuous function is the derivative of some function.

DEFINITION

A function $\varphi : A \to R$ is called an *antiderivative* or a *primitive* of the function $f : A \to R$ if $\varphi' = f$.

The primitive of a function, if it exists, is not unique. Theorem 14.20 gives an important relation between primitives.

THEOREM   14.20

If φ_1 and φ_2 are primitives of the function f, then the function $\varphi_1 - \varphi_2$ is a constant.

Proof

If we let $\varphi = \varphi_1 - \varphi_2$, then $\varphi' = \varphi_1' - \varphi_2' = f - f = 0$. Then by Corollary 1 (or 3 for the complex case) to Theorem 14.14 we know that φ is a constant function. $\bullet$

We shall now prove the fundamental theorem.

THEOREM   14.21 (FUNDAMENTAL THEOREM OF THE CALCULUS)

For every continuous function there are primitives.

Proof

We shall consider the continuous function $f:[a,b] \to R$ and write f also to represent the restriction of f to $[a,u]$, where $u \in [a,b]$. Then the integral $\int_a^u f(x)\, dx$ (sometimes called the *indefinite integral*) exists for all $u \in [a,b]$.

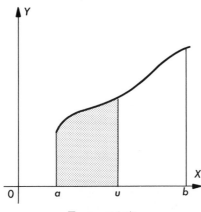

FIGURE 14.17

This integral is represented by the shaded area in Figure 14.17. We can now define a function $\varphi:[a,b] \to R$, where

$$\varphi(u) = \int_a^u f(x)\, dx.$$

We shall now prove that $\varphi'(u) = f(u)$ for each $u \in [a,b]$. The difference quotient is

$$\frac{\varphi(u+t) - \varphi(u)}{t} = \frac{1}{t}\left(\int_a^{u+t} f(x)\, dx - \int_a^u f(x)\, dx \right)$$
$$= \frac{1}{t} \int_u^{u+t} f(x)\, dx,$$

by Theorem 14.18. Then Theorem 14.17 shows that this is

$$\frac{f(s)(u+t-u)}{t} = f(s)$$

for some $s \in [u, u+t]$. This gives us

$$\varphi'(u) = \lim_{t \to 0} f(s) = f(u).$$

Thus φ is the primitive of f. •

The fundamental theorem guarantees the existence of a primitive for any continuous function, but it does not provide us with a convenient method for finding the primitive. It does, however, provide us with a means of calculating the definite integral if the primitive is known. If $f:[a,b] \to R$ is a continuous function and ψ is a primitive of f, then by Theorem 14.20 $\varphi - \psi$ is a constant, where φ is defined as in the proof of Theorem 14.21, that is, $\varphi(u) = \psi(u) + c$ for all $u \in [a,b]$ and some constant c. Then

$$\int_a^b f(x)\, dx = \varphi(b) = \psi(b) + c.$$

Also $\psi(a) + c = \varphi(a) = 0$ and hence $c = -\psi(a)$. Therefore

$$\int_a^b f(x)\, dx = \psi(b) - \psi(a).$$

EXAMPLE   14.11

Find the value of the definite integral

$$\int_0^5 x^n\, dx.$$

It is easily verified that $\varphi:[a,b] \to R$, where $\varphi(x) = x^{n+1}/(n+1)$, is a primitive of $f:[a,b] \to R$, where $f(x) = x^n$, for $n \in Z - \{-1\}$. Then

$$\int_0^5 x^n\, dx = \varphi(5) - \varphi(0)$$

$$= \frac{5^{n+1}}{(n+1)} - 0.$$

14.15   Definite integral for complex functions

We know that a complex-valued function $f:[a,b] \to C$ can be considered an ordered pair of real-valued functions, $f = f_1 + if_2$. If f is continuous on $[a,b]$, then so are f_1 and f_2. In this case we call the number

$$\int_a^b f_1(x)\, dx + i \int_a^b f_2(x)\, dx$$

the definite integral of f on the interval $[a,b]$ and denote it by $\int_a^b f(x)\, dx$. Theorem 14.15 guarantees the existence of this integral without any additional proof.

Any methods available for the integration of real-valued functions can now be used to find the definite integral of a complex-valued function.

EXAMPLE 14.12

$$\int_1^3 \left(\frac{1}{x^2} + ix \right) dx = \int_1^3 \left(\frac{1}{x^2} \right) dx + i \int_1^3 x \, dx$$

$$= \frac{1}{-1} \frac{1}{x} \Big|_{x=3} - \frac{1}{-1} \frac{1}{x} \Big|_{x=1} + \frac{ix^2}{2} \Big|_{x=3} - \frac{ix^2}{2} \Big|_{x=1}$$

$$= -\frac{1}{3} + 1 + \frac{i9}{2} - \frac{i}{2}$$

$$= \frac{2}{3} + 4i.$$

Some practice in calculating definite integrals will be given in the exercises, but for all but the simplest computational devices the student is referred to the specialized calculus texts.

EXERCISES

14.38. Apply the construction used in the definition of the definite integral to the function $f:[0,1] \to R$, where

$$f(x) = 1 \quad \text{for } x \text{ rational,}$$
$$f(x) = 0 \quad \text{for } x \text{ irrational.}$$

Show that

$$\sup \sum_{i=1}^n \inf f(x_i)(x_{i+1} - x_i) = 0,$$

$$\inf \sum_{i=1}^n \sup f(x_i)(x_{i+1} - x_i) = 1.$$

14.39. (a) Show that the function $f:]0,1] \to R$, where $f(x) = 1/x$, is not uniformly continuous.

(b) The restriction f_1 of f to the domain $[\varepsilon,1]$ for any ε such that $0 < \varepsilon < 1$ is uniformly continuous. Find $\delta(\frac{1}{10})$ such that $|f_1(x) - f_1(x')| < \frac{1}{10}$ whenever $x \in [\varepsilon,1], x' \in [\varepsilon,1]$, and $|x - x'| < \delta(\frac{1}{10})$.

14.40. Prove that the function $\varphi:R \to R$ where $\varphi(x) = x^{n+1}/(n+1)$ is a primitive of the function $f:R \to R$ where $f(x) = x^n$ for $n \in N$.

14.41. Use the result of Exercise 14.40 to evaluate the following integrals:

(a) $\int_{-1}^3 3x^2 \, dx.$

(b) $\int_0^2 (2x^3 + 3x + 1) \, dx.$

14.42. (a) Prove that the function $\varphi:R_+ \to R$, where $\varphi(x) = x^{n+1}/(n+1)$, is a primitive of the function $f:R_+ \to R$, where $f(x) = x^n$ for $n \in Z, n < -1$.

(b) Prove a similar result with R_+ replaced by R_-, the set of all negative real numbers.

14.43. Use the results of Exercises 14.40 and 14.42 to evaluate the following integrals.

(a) $\int_2^3 (1/x^2)\, dx.$

(b) $\int_1^2 (2x + 3 - 1/x^3)\, dx.$

(c) $\int_{-5}^{-1} (2/x^3)\, dx.$

14.44. (a) Prove that the function $\varphi : R \to R$, where $\varphi(x) = -\cos x$, is a primitive for the function $f : R \to R$, where $f(x) = \sin x$.

(b) Prove that the function $\psi : R \to R$, where $\psi(x) = \sin x$, is a primitive for the function $g : R \to R$, where $g(x) = \cos x$.

14.45. Find primitives for the following functions:

(a) $f :]-\pi/2, \pi/2[\to R,\ f(x) = \sec^2 x.$
(b) $g :]0, \pi[\to R,\ g(x) = \csc^2 x.$
(c) $h :]-\pi/2, \pi/2[\to R,\ h(x) = \tan x \sec x.$
(d) $k :]0, \pi[\to R,\ k(x) = \cot x \csc x.$

14.46. Use the results of Exercises 14.44 and 14.45 to evaluate the following integrals:

(a) $\int_0^\pi \sin x\, dx.$

(b) $\int_{\pi/4}^{\pi/2} \cot x \csc x\, dx.$

(c) $\int_0^{2\pi} \cos x\, dx.$

(d) $\int_0^{2\pi} |\cos x|\, dx.$

14.47. Use the results of Exercises 14.40, 14.42, 14.44, and 14.45 to evaluate the following integrals.

(a) $\int_{-2}^4 8\, dx.$

(b) $\int_0^{\pi/4} \tan^2 x\, dx.$

(c) $\int_{-1}^1 |x|\, dx.$

(d) $\int_{-2}^2 (x - |x|)\, dx.$

(e) $\int_0^4 (x - [x])\, dx.$

14.48. If f is continuous on the open interval $]a,b[$, then it is continuous on the closed interval $[a + \varepsilon, b - \varepsilon]$ for $0 < \varepsilon < (b - a)/2$. Then the integral $\int_{a+\varepsilon}^{b-\varepsilon} f(x)\, dx$ exists. We define

$$\int_a^b f(x)\, dx = \lim_{\varepsilon \to 0} \int_{a+\varepsilon}^{b-\varepsilon} f(x)\, dx$$

if the limit exists. We define

$$\int_a^b f(x)\, dx = \lim_{\varepsilon \to 0} \int_a^{b-\varepsilon} f(x)\, dx,$$

if f is continuous on $[a,b[$ and if the limit exists; we also define

$$\int_a^b f(x)\ dx = \lim_{\varepsilon \to 0} \int_{a+\varepsilon}^b f(x)\ dx$$

if f is continuous on $]a,b]$ and if the limit exists. Use these definitions to evaluate the following integrals:

(a) $\int_0^1 (1/x^2)\ dx.$

(b) $\int_{-2}^0 (x - 2 + 1/x^3)\ dx.$

14.49. Show that the method of Exercise 14.48 does not give a value for $\int_0^{\pi/2} \tan x\ dx.$

14.50. Let a be a fixed real number. If the function $f:R \to R$ is continuous on $[a,b]$ for all $b > a$, we can define a function $g:\{x|x \in R, x \geq a\} \to R$, where

$$g(x) = \int_a^x f(y)\ dy.$$

If $\lim_{x \to \infty} g(x)$ exists, we call it the *improper integral of f* over the interval $[a, \infty[$ and write

$$\int_a^\infty f(y)\ dy = \lim_{x \to \infty} \int_a^x f(y)\ dy = \lim_{x \to \infty} g(x).$$

If f is continuous on $[c,a]$ for all $c < a$, we write

$$\int_{-\infty}^a f(y)\ dy = \lim_{x \to -\infty} \int_x^a f(y)\ dy.$$

If f is continuous on R we write

$$\int_{-\infty}^\infty f(y)\ dy = \lim_{x \to \infty} \int_{-x}^x f(y)\ dy.$$

Use these ideas to evaluate the following integrals:

(a) $\int_1^\infty (1/x^2)\ dx.$

(b) $\int_{-\infty}^{-1} (1/x^3)\ dx.$

(c) $\int_{-\infty}^\infty f(x)\ dx$, where $f:R \to R$ and $f(x) = 1/x^2$ for $|x| > 1$, $f(x) = x$ for $|x| \leq 1$.

14.51. If $f:R_+ \to R_+$ is a nondecreasing continuous function, show that

$$\int_n^{n+1} f(x)\ dx \leq f(n) \leq \int_{n-1}^n f(x)\ dx.$$

14.52. Let f be the function in Exercise 14.51. Use the result of Exercise 14.51 to prove that the series $\sum_{n=1}^\infty f(n)$ converges if and only if the improper integral $\int_1^\infty f(x)\ dx$ exists and is finite in the sense of Exercise 14.50. This is known as the *integral test for the convergence of series.*

14.53. Use the result of Exercise 14.52 to prove that the series $\sum 1/n^2$ converges.

14.54. For the function f in Exercise 14.51 define a function $g:N \to R$ with

$$g(n) = \sum_{k=1}^{n} f(k) - \int_{1}^{n} f(x)\, dx.$$

Use the result of Exercise 14.51 to prove that $g(n) \geq 0$ and $g(n) \geq g(n+1)$.

14.55. Let $f:]a,b[\to R$ be a continuous, bounded function and let $K = \sup|f(x)|$. For $n \in N$, $m \in N$ prove that

$$\left| \int_{a+1/n}^{b-1/n} f(x)\, dx - \int_{a+1/(n+m)}^{b-1/(n+m)} f(x)\, dx \right| \leq 2K/n,$$

and hence that $\displaystyle\lim_{n \to \infty} \int_{a+1/n}^{b-1/n} f(x)\, dx$ exists. [We denote the value of this limit by

$\displaystyle\int_{a}^{b} f(x)\, dx.$]

14.56. Show that we can define a function $f:R_+ \to R$, where $f(x) = \int_{1}^{x} (1/t)\, dt$.

14.57. What is the derivative of the function f in Exercise 14.56?

14.58. (a) Let f be the function defined in Exercise 14.56, and let a be a fixed real number. Prove that the functions $\varphi:R \to R_+$ where $\varphi(x) = f(x)$, and $\psi:R \to R_+$, where $\psi(x) = f(ax)$, have the same derivative.

(b) Use the result of part (a) and Theorem 14.20 to prove that $f(ax) = f(a) + f(x)$. [This is the characteristic property of the logarithm function. The function f is called the *natural logarithm*. The value is often written $f(x) = \ln x$.]

Selected Answers
to Exercises

Introduction

I.1. If the weather is fair, then we shall go on a picnic.   **I.6.** If we fight for our freedom, then it is necessary.   **I.10.** We come to no conclusion since the implication does not tell us anything about a diligent student.   **I.14.** Whenever it rains we have a picnic.   **I.19.** Tom works hard but does not get good marks.   **I.22.** Either John or Mary was absent.   **I.27.** There is at least one man who cannot be happily married to any woman or who can be happily married to more than one woman. (The student should recognize the parallel with Playfair's form of parallel postulate.)   **I.30.** $A \Leftrightarrow B$.   **I.32.** $B \Rightarrow A$.   **I.37.** The contrapositive.

Chapter 1

1.4. $A = B$.   **1.7.** $\mathcal{O}(E) = \{\varnothing, \{a\}, \{b\}, \{c\}, \{a,b\}, \{a,c\}, \{b,c\}, \{a,b,c\}\}$.   **1.12.** $X \cap Y = \{3,5\}$, $X \cup Z = \{\{1,2,3\}, 1,2,3,4,5\}$ $X - Z = \{\{1,2,3\},4,5\}$.   **1.14.** (a) and (c) are true.   **1.17.** Only (ii).   **1.21.** *Hint:* Observe that each $A_i \cap B_i$ is a subset of each of A_3, B_1, $A_1 \cup B_2$, $A_2 \cup B_3$.   **1.28.** $j \in M$, $M \subset S \Rightarrow j \in S$ where j is John, M the set of men and S the set of mortal beings.   **1.32.** (a) $\{(a,0),$ $(a,1)$, $(a,2)$, $(b,0)$, $(b,1)$, $(b,2)\}$; (d) $\varnothing$.   **1.35.** *Hint:* On both sides we are interested in an element (x,y) of $A \times B$. We must show that the two sides impose the same conditions on this (x,y).

Chapter 2

2.3. (a) $(1,\{1,2\})$, $(1, \{1,2,3\})$, $(2, \{1,2\})$, $(2,\{1,2,3\})$, $(3, \{1,2,3\})$. (b) $(\{1,2\},$ $\{1,2\})$, $(\{1,2\}, \{1,2,3\})$, $(\{1,2,3\}, \{1,2,3\})$.   **2.5.** Not transitive (consider $x = 1$, $y = \frac{3}{2}$, $z = \frac{9}{4}$).   **2.7.** Only (c).   **2.15.** Symmetric and transitive, but not reflexive.   **2.18.** Only (a).   **2.21.** Symmetric, but not reflexive or transitive. **2.28.** Symmetric, but not reflexive or transitive.   **2.30.** The equivalence class containing E consists of all subsets X such that $\complement X \subset C$. The equivalence classes of $\varnothing$ and C are the same and consist of all subsets of C.   **2.32.** (a) Reflexive, transitive, not symmetric. (b) Reflexive, symmetric, transitive. (c) Reflexive, transitive,

377

not symmetric. (d) Reflexive, symmetric, transitive. **2.37.** (a) $G_\rho(d) = \{\{b,c,d\},$
$\{d\}\}$; (b) $G_\rho(\{\varnothing\}) = \{\{\varnothing,1,2\}, \{\{1\}, \varnothing\}\}$; (c) $G_\rho(\frac{1}{2}) = \{\sqrt{3}/2, -\sqrt{3}/2\}$,
$G_\rho(2) = \varnothing$; (d) $G_\rho(5) = \{\cdots -5n, \cdots, -5,0,5, \cdots, 5n \cdots\}$. **2.41.** Not
the same relation.

Chapter 3 (First Set of Exercises)

3.1. Only (b). **3.3.** No. **3.5.** Only (a) and (c). **3.9.** (a) $A = R - \{2\}$,
(c) $R - \{1\}$, (d) Yes. (e) No. **3.12.** Injective and onto. **3.16.** (a) Injective.
Onto if there is no border or margin on the map. (b) No. **3.20.** No. **3.24.**
$f = g$.

Chapter 3 (Second Set of Exercises)

3.25. (a) and (b) are involutions. **3.27.** (a) $\{(a,0), (b,1), (c,0), (d,1), (e,1)\}$; (b)
$\{(b,5), (d,16), (e,2)\}$; (c) Domain: A, Codomain: $\{2,5,10,16\}$, Graph: G_f. **3.33.**
(a) No, (b) $n + 1$. **3.44.** $(g \cdot f)(x,y) = xy + 1$. **3.46.** 5.

Chapter 4

4.2. No. **4.6.** The graph must be the diagonal. **4.12.** No. **4.14.** Statements
(b) and (c) are true. **4.19.** 3, 9. **4.24.** $A = \{x|0 \le x\}$. **4.26.** 36. **4.30.**
The prime numbers. **4.42.** No. **4.51.** $n = 2k - 1, k \in N$.

Chapter 5 (First Set of Exercises)

5.15. $f(n) = 2^{n-1}f(1)$.

Chapter 5 (Second Set of Exercises)

5.43. The class containing $(a + 2, a)$.

Chapter 6 (First Set of Exercises)

6.20. No.

Chapter 7

7.9. (a) $\frac{1}{5} + i\frac{3}{5}$; (b) $-3 - 2i$; (c) $1\frac{1}{5} - i\frac{2}{5}$. **7.13.** The points representing
z_1 and z_2 lie on the same straight line through the origin and lie on the same side of
the origin. **7.15.** (a) The points representing z_1 and z_2 are two units apart. (b)
The points representing z lie on the ellipse with foci at the points representing ± 2.
(c) The points representing z lie on a hyperbola with foci at the points representing $\pm 3i$. **7.21.** A circle with center at the origin. **7.23.** (a) $\cos 0 + i \sin 0$;
(c) $\sqrt{13} (\cos \theta + i \sin \theta)$ where θ is such that $\cos \theta = 2/\sqrt{13}$, $\sin \theta = -3/\sqrt{13}$;
(e) $6(\cos \pi/6 + i \sin \pi/6)$. **7.25.** (a) $6(\cos \pi/2 + i \sin \pi/2) = 6i$. (c) $24(\cos \pi$
$+ i \sin \pi) = -24$. **7.28.** (a) $16 + 16i$; (c) $-i$. **7.33.** (a) ± 2, $\pm 2i$; (c)
$\pm(1/\sqrt{2} + i/\sqrt{2})$. **7.35.** (a) $\pm 1 \sqrt{2}$; (c) 0, $\pm(3/\sqrt{2} \pm i/\sqrt{2})$. **7.37.**
(a) $[x - (\sqrt{3} + i)][x - i][x - (-\sqrt{3} + i)][x - (-\sqrt{3} - i)][x + i][x - (\sqrt{3}$
$- i)]$; (b) $[x - (\frac{1}{2})(\cos \pi/5 + i \sin \pi/5)][x - (\frac{1}{2})(\cos 3\pi/5 + i \sin 3\pi/5)][x -$
$(\frac{1}{2})(\cos \pi + i \sin \pi)][x - (\frac{1}{2})(\cos 7\pi/5 + i \sin 7\pi/5)][x - (\frac{1}{2})(\cos 9\pi/5 +$
$i \sin 9\pi/5)]$. **7.40.** $\pm i, \pm \sqrt{2} i$.

Chapter 8 (First Set of Exercises)

8.2. No. **8.12.** No. **8.22.** $\{f_1\}, \{f_1,f_2\}, \{f_1,f_3\}, \{f_1,f_6\}, \{f_1,f_4,f_5\}, S_3.$ **8.27.** (b) Each coset is a set of complex numbers all with the same amplitude. **8.36.** The largest element is Z and the smallest is $\{0\}$.

Chapter 8 (Second Set of Exercises)

8.40. The left and right cosets are the same: $\{I,R_2,H,V\}, \{R_1,R_3,D_+,D_-\}$. The subgroup is normal. **8.45.** **8.49.** Yes.

	I	R_2	H	V
I	I	R_2	H	V
R_2	R_2	I	V	H
H	H	V	I	R_2
V	V	H	R_2	I

8.57. The group must be Abelian.

Chapter 9

9.1. Z, Q, R, C. **9.3.** It is commutative and has an identity. **9.9.** No. **9.15.** (a) 2; (c) 12; (d) 0; (f) 10. **9.19.** The set of all polynomial functions. **9.24.** (a) $\begin{bmatrix} 12 & 6 & 3 \\ 16 & 8 & 5 \\ 14 & 9 & 1 \end{bmatrix}$; (b) $\begin{bmatrix} 7 & 10 \\ 36 & 31 \end{bmatrix}$; (e) $\begin{bmatrix} 10 & 3 & 10 \\ 7 & 1 & 6 \\ 7 & 1 & 5 \end{bmatrix}$. **9.26.** Yes. **9.28.** No. **9.45.** (a) $3 = 2(15) - 27$; (c) $1 = 6(11) - 5(13)$. **9.47.** (a) $(x-1)$ $(x+1)(x-3)(x+3)(x-4)(x+4)$; (c) $(x-1)(x+1)(x-3)(x+3)(x-2)$ $(x+2)$.

Chapter 10 (First Set of Exercises)

10.3. $OB - OA$. **10.9.** $x = \frac{1}{4}, \ y = \frac{1}{2}, \ z = \frac{1}{4}$. **10.12.** (a) $(3/\sqrt{43})i +$ $(3/\sqrt{43})j - (5/\sqrt{43})k$; (c) $(-4/\sqrt{33})i + (1/\sqrt{33})j + (4/\sqrt{33})k$. **10.15.** $i + 5j - 3k; \sqrt{35}$. **10.20.** (a) $\pi/3$; (c) $\pi/4$. **10.22.** (a) No.

Chapter 10 (Second Set of Exercises)

10.31. 0. **10.33.** (a), (b), (d) are equal. **10.35.** (a) -15. **10.39.** $\sqrt{42}$. **10.41.** $(-7\sqrt{3}/15)i + (\sqrt{3}/15)j + (5\sqrt{3}/15)k$. **10.46.** (b), (c), (f).

Chapter 11 (First Set of Exercises)

11.1. $\sqrt{11}$. **11.5.** $x - 2y + 3z = 0$. **11.9.** $2x - y - 3z - 3 = 0$. **11.13.** $x - 2y - z = 0$. **11.17.** $2\pi/3$. **11.21.** $(2 + \sqrt{2})x + (\sqrt{2} - 1)y + (1 - \sqrt{2})z = 1$.

Chapter 11 (Second Set of Exercises)

11.22. (a) Yes; (b) No. **11.24.** $(\frac{9}{5}, \ 1\frac{7}{5}, \ 1\frac{6}{5})$. **11.28.** $3x + 2z - 14 = 0$; $y - 2 = 0$. **11.32.** $6x + 3y + 2z - 31 = 0$. **11.36.** $(x-1)/119 = -(y-2)/25$ $= (z-1)/14$. **11.40.** arc cos $(\sqrt{3}/9)$, $(\frac{9}{10}, \ -\frac{1}{10}, \ 1\frac{1}{10})$. **11.44.** $x = 0$, $y = 0$; distance $= 3$. **11.48.** $\sqrt{58}/3$. **11.52.** A point.

Chapter 12 (First Set of Exercises)

12.1. $(g \cdot f)(n) = 1/n^3$.   **12.3.** $(-1)^k$.   **12.5.** *Hint:* Use definition by induction to define f_k for a fixed k. Use definition by induction again to define a function $N \to \mathfrak{F}(N,N)$.   **12.8.** $f(2) = \sqrt{2 + \sqrt{2}}$, $f(3) = \sqrt{2 + \sqrt{2 + \sqrt{2}}}$.   **12.13.** *Hint:* Show that the sequence is increasing and that 2 is an upper bound.   **12.15.** Bounded but not monotone.   **12.17.** 6.   **12.20.** lub = 1, glb = -1.   **12.32.** (a) 1; (b) 8.

Chapter 12 (Second Set of Exercises)

12.40. $\frac{1}{2}$, $\frac{3}{4}$, $\frac{7}{8}$, $\frac{15}{16}$, $(2^k - 1)/2^k$.   **12.42.** No.   **12.46.** No.   **12.49.** Converges absolutely.   **12.53.** No. (Compare with $1/\sqrt{2n}$.)   **12.58.** $|x| < 1$. **12.60.** They both converge absolutely.   **12.62.** No.

Chapter 13

13.3. Any $\varepsilon < 1$.   **13.7.** Continuous only at $x = 0$.   **13.9.** Not continuous for $x = 0, \pm 1, \pm 2, \pm 3$.   **13.11.** Only the function in Exercise 13.6 is bounded. **13.16.** (a) The function g is not defined if $f(x) = 0$ for some x; if g is defined it need not be bounded. (b) glb $|f(x)| \neq 0$.   **13.20.** (b) Yes.   **13.22.** No, $\frac{2}{3}$.   **13.26.** Discontinuous if mx is an integer.   **13.28.** (a) k^2, (b) $k(k - 1)$; (c) 0; (d) 1. **13.30.** (a) Has a limit. (b) No limit. (c) No limit.   **13.36.** $1\frac{1}{100}$.   **13.41.** (a) 0; (b) i; (c) does not exist.   **13.43.** (a) $+\infty$; (b) Does not exist.

Chapter 14 (First Set of Exercises)

14.1. (a) $\sqrt{t}$; (b) $t \sin t$; (c) $\cos t$.   **14.4.** (a) 0; (b) $-\frac{8}{9}$; (c) 1.   **14.11.** No, it does not preserve products.   **14.19.** (a) $(\sin 2t)/t$; 2; (b) $f(t) = 0$; 0; (c) $(\sin^2 t)/t + i(1 - \cos^2 t)/t$; 0.   **14.28.** The equilateral triangle.   **14.30.** Relative and absolute maximum at $x = 1$, relative and absolute minimum at $x = -1$. **14.35.** (a) $c = \frac{1}{2}$; (b) $c = (2/\pi)$ arc cos $(2/\pi)$.

Chapter 14 (Second Set of Exercises)

14.39. (b) $\frac{1}{90}$.   **14.43.** (a) $\frac{1}{6}$; (b) $\frac{45}{8}$; (c) $-\frac{24}{25}$.   **14.46.** (a) 2; (b) $1 - \sqrt{2}$; (c) 0; (d) 4.   **14.48.** (a) $+\infty$; (b) $-\infty$.   **14.57.** $1/x$.

Notations

Index